Ready® *Common Core*

Mathematics **Teacher Resource Book** ❶

Curriculum Associates®

Teacher Advisors

Rachel Adelstein, Assistant Principal, Briggs Avenue Academy, Bronx, NY

Crystal Bailey, Math Impact Teacher, Eastern Guilford Middle School, Guilford County Schools, Gibsonville, NC

Max Brand, Reading Specialist, Indian Run Elementary, Dublin City School District, Dublin, OH

Dinah Chancellor, Professional Development Mathematics Consultant, Southlake, TX

Helen Comba, Supervisor of Basic Skills & Language Arts, School District of the Chathams, Chatham, NJ

Cindy Dean, Classroom Teacher, Mt. Diablo Unified School District, Concord, CA

Leah Flynn, Classroom Teacher, Brockton Public Schools, Brockton, MA

Randall E. Groth, Ph.D, Associate Professor of Mathematics Education, Salisbury University, Salisbury, MD

Bill Laraway, Classroom Teacher, Silver Oak Elementary, Evergreen School District, San Jose, CA

Jennifer Lerner, Classroom Teacher, PS 57, New York City Public Schools, New York, NY

Susie Legg, Elementary Curriculum Coordinator, Kansas City Public Schools, Kansas City, KS

Sarah Levine, Classroom Teacher, Springhurst Elementary School, Dobbs Ferry School District, Dobbs Ferry, NY

Nicole Peirce, Classroom Teacher, Eleanor Roosevelt Elementary, Pennsbury School District, Morrisville, PA

Donna Phillips, Classroom Teacher, Farmington R-7 School District, Farmington, MO

Maria Rosati, Classroom Teacher, Harwood Elementary School, Warren Consolidated Schools, Warren, MI

Kari Ross, Reading Specialist, MN

Sunita Sangari, Math Coach, PS/MS 29, New York City Public Schools, New York, NY

Eileen Seybuck, Classroom Teacher, PS 57, New York City Public Schools, New York, NY

Mark Hoover Thames, Research Scientist, University of Michigan, Ann Arbor, MI

Shannon Tsuruda, Classroom Teacher, Mt. Diablo Unified School District, Concord, CA

Acknowledgments

Project Manager: Cynthia Tripp
Cover Designers, Illustrators: Julia Bourque, Matt Pollock
Book Designer: Scott Hoffman

Executive Editor: Kathy Kellman
Supervising Editor: Pamela Halloran
Director–Product Development: Daniel J. Smith
Vice President–Product Development: Adam Berkin

Table of Contents

M = Lessons that have a major emphasis in the Common Core Standards
S/A = Lessons that have supporting/additional emphasis in the Common Core Standards

M = Lessons that have a major emphasis in the Common Core Standards
S/A = Lessons that have supporting/additional emphasis in the Common Core Standards

M = Lessons that have a major emphasis in the Common Core Standards
S/A = Lessons that have supporting/additional emphasis in the Common Core Standards

Ready® Common Core is an integrated program of assessment and data-driven instruction designed to teach your students the Common Core State Standards (CCSS) for Mathematics. The program also teaches and assesses the Standards for Mathematical Practice. You can use the program in a supplemental way to address specific standards where your students need instruction and practice, or in a more comprehensive way to engage students in all the CCSS.

Built for the Common Core. Not just aligned.

Ready Common Core Instruction and Activity Book

Ready Common Core Instruction provides differentiated instruction and independent practice of key concepts and skills that builds student confidence. Unit assessments give frequent opportunities to monitor progress.

Ready Common Core Activity Book provides extensive opportunities for students to develop understanding and fluency with key skills and concepts through practice activities and games.

Teacher Resource Book and Teacher Toolbox

Ready Common Core Teacher Resource Books support teachers with strong professional development, step-by-step lesson plans, and best practices for implementing the CCSS.

Ready Common Core Teacher Toolbox provides online lessons, prerequisite lessons from previous grades, and targeted best-practice teaching strategies.

i-Ready® Diagnostic

Built to support the Common Core and integrated with the **Ready** program, the **i-Ready Diagnostic** helps teachers track student growth and identify areas that need more work, pointing teachers to **Ready** lessons to use for remediation. See page A18 for details. (**i-Ready** sold separately.)

Features

 Built with all-new content written specifically for the Common Core

 Uses a research-based, gradual-release instructional model

 Requires higher-order thinking and complex reasoning to solve problems

 Integrates Standards for Mathematical Practice throughout every lesson

 Embeds thoughtful professional development

 Encourages students to develop deeper understanding of concepts and to understand and use a variety of mathematical strategies and models

 Promotes fluency and connects hands-on learning with clearly articulated models throughout

 Forms the foundation to meet expectations in upcoming grades

Supporting the Implementation of the Common Core

The Common Core State Standards (CCSS) were developed to make sure that by the time students graduate from high school, they are college- and career-ready. Therefore, the creators of the standards started with the expectations they had for students at the end of 12th grade and worked down to kindergarten. As a result of this backward design approach, the CCSS are more rigorous than most current standards. The creators of the standards want students at every grade to develop a deep mastery of fundamental math concepts; learn the coherence among seemingly different math concepts; demonstrate complex, higher-order thinking by solving more rigorous problems; and learn the mathematical practices that allow them to become confident, successful math students. *Ready® Common Core* is here to help.

Because every Common Core mathematics standard has been addressed with a clear, thoughtful pedagogy, you can use the *Ready* program as the main structure of a year-long program. Any other materials aligned to the CCSS can be easily woven into the curriculum.

Each *Ready* lesson covers the entirety of a particular skill, so classrooms can work through any lesson independently from the rest of the book. This gives teachers transitioning to the CCSS enormous flexibility, knowing that *Ready* lessons can be pulled out and applied to any implementation plan.

Keep Up to Date with the *Ready® Teacher Toolbox*

The online *Ready Teacher Toolbox* gives you access to a host of multilevel resources, such as instructional support, online lessons, and lessons for prerequisite skills. (See pages A16 and A17 for more.) You can access the latest version of *Ready Practice* there, as well.

You can ensure you have access to the latest updates by visiting the *Ready Teacher Toolbox* (*www.teacher-toolbox.com*).

Helpful Resources for the Transition to the Common Core

http://www.corestandards.org/
The main website for the Common Core. Here you'll find the full text of the standards, plus frequently asked questions and resources.

http://www.smarterbalanced.org/ and *http://www.parcconline.org/*
The testing consortia creating Common Core assessments for future implementation.

http://www.ascd.org/common-core-state-standards/common-core.aspx
A helpful list of all of ASCD's Common Core resources. A repository of evidence-based strategies, videos, and supporting documents that help educators transition to the Common Core.

http://commoncoretools.me/category/progressions/

http://www.nea.org/assets/docs/14047-CommonCore_Toolkit_14.pdf

http://www.sharemylesson.com/article.aspx?storyCode=50003209

http://illustrativemathematics.org/

http://www.utdanacenter.org/ccss/index.php

http://www.hepg.org/hel/article/543#home

Answering the Demands of the Common Core with *Ready*®

THE DEMANDS OF THE COMMON CORE	HOW *READY*® DELIVERS
Focus: The Common Core Standards for Mathematics focus on fewer topics each year, allowing more time to truly learn a topic. Lessons need to go into more depth to help students to build better foundations and understanding.	*Ready* lessons reflect the same focus as the Common Core standards. In fact, the majority of the lessons in each grade directly address the major focus of the year. Furthermore, each lesson was newly-written specifically to address the Common Core Standards. There is at least one lesson for each standard and only lessons that address the Common Core Standards are included.
Coherent Connections (Building on Prior Knowledge): Instruction needs to provide logical ways for students to make connections between topics within a grade as well as across multiple grades. Instruction must **build on prior knowledge** and be organized to take advantage of the natural connections among standards within each cluster as well as connections across clusters or domains. This coherence is required for students to make sense of mathematics.	*Ready* units are organized by domains following the cluster headings of the Common Core standards. Each lesson starts with a hands-on activity drawing on prior knowledge and making connections to what students already know, particularly reinforcing algebraic thinking and problem-solving. These connections are highlighted for teachers in the Learning Progressions of the Teachers Resource Book so teachers can see at a glance how the lesson connects to previous and future learning.
Rigor and Higher-Order Thinking: To meet the Common Core standards, equal attention must be given to conceptual understanding, procedural skill and fluency, and applications in each grade. Students need to use **strategic thinking** to answer questions of varying difficulty requiring different cognitive strategies and higher-order thinking skills.	*Ready* lessons balance conceptual understanding, skill and procedural fluency, and applications. Students are asked higher-order thinking questions throughout the lessons. They are asked to understand, interpret, or explain concepts, applications, skills and strategies. Practice questions match the diversity and rigor of the Common Core standards.
Conceptual Understanding: In the past, a major emphasis in mathematics was on procedural knowledge with less attention paid to understanding math concepts. The Common Core explicitly identifies standards that focus on conceptual understanding. Conceptual understanding allows students to see math as more than just a set of rules and isolated procedures and develop a deeper knowledge of mathematics.	*Ready* includes conceptual understanding in every lesson through questions that ask students to explain models, strategies, and their mathematical thinking. In addition, a "Focus on Math Concepts" lesson is included for every Common Core standard that focuses on conceptual development—those standards that begin with the word "understand."
Mathematical Practices: The Standards for Mathematical Practice (SMP) must support content standards and be integrated into instruction. The content standards must be taught through intentional, appropriate use of the practice standards.	The Standards for Mathematical Practice are fully integrated in an age-appropriate way throughout each lesson. The Teachers Resource Book includes SMP Tips that provide more in-depth information for select practice standards addressed in the lesson. See pages A9 and A28 for more details.
Mathematical Reasoning: Mathematical reasoning must play a major role in student learning. Students must be able to analyze problems, determine effective strategies to use to solve them, and evaluate the reasonableness of their solutions. They must be able to explain their thinking, critique the reasoning of others, and generalize their results.	*Ready* lessons build on problem-solving as a main component of instruction. Students work through a problem, discuss it, draw conclusions, and make generalizations. Guided Practice problems ask students to critique arguments presented by fictional characters and justify their own solutions.

The Standards for Mathematical Practice

Mastery of the Standards for Mathematical Practice (SMP) is vital for educating students who can recognize and be proficient in the mathematics they will encounter in college and careers. As the chart below shows, the SMPs are built into the foundation of *Ready® Instruction*.

1. Make sense of problems and persevere in solving them:

Try more than one approach, think strategically, and succeed in solving problems that seem very difficult.

Each *Ready* lesson leads students through new problems by using what they already know, demonstrates multiple approaches and access points, and gives encouraging tips and opportunities for cooperative dialogue.

2. Reason abstractly and quantitatively:

Represent a word problem with an equation, or other symbols, solve the math, and then interpret the solution to answer the question posed.

Ready lessons lead students to see mathematical relationships connecting equations, visual representations, and problem situations. Each lesson challenges students to analyze the connection between an abstract representation and pictorial or real-world situations.

3. Construct viable arguments and critique the reasoning of others:

Discuss, communicate reasoning, create explanations, and critique the reasoning of others.

In *Ready*, the teacher-led Mathematical Discourse feature guides students through collaborative reasoning and the exchange of ideas and mathematical arguments. *Ready* lessons also provide error-analysis problems that ask students to examine a fictional student's wrong answer, as well as multiple opportunities to explain and communicate reasoning.

4. Model with mathematics:

Use math to solve actual problems.

Students work with a mathematical model using pictures, diagrams, tables, or equations to solve problems in each *Ready* lesson. In the Teacher Resource Book, the Hands-On Activity feature adds another dimension to understanding of a skill.

5. Use appropriate tools strategically:

Make choices about which tools, if any, to use to solve a problem.

Ready lessons model the use of a variety of tools, including diagrams, tables, or number paths; Guided Practice problems may be solved with a variety of strategies.

6. Attend to precision:

Explain and argue, draw, label, and compute carefully and accurately.

Ready lessons guide students to focus on precision in both procedures *and* communication, including special error-analysis tasks and group discussion questions that motivate students to employ precise, convincing arguments.

7. Look for and make use of structure:

Build mathematical understanding by recognizing structures such as place value and the decomposition of numbers.

Each *Ready* Focus on Math Concepts lesson builds understanding of new concepts by explicitly reviewing prior knowledge of mathematical structure.

8. Look for and express regularity in repeated reasoning:

Recognize regularity in repeated reasoning and make generalizations or conjectures about other situations.

Each *Ready* lesson leads students to focus attention on patterns that reflect regularity. Where appropriate, students draw a conclusion or make a generalization and explain their reasoning by referencing the observed pattern.

Use *Ready®* as Your Primary Instructional Program

Because every Common Core Standard is addressed with clear, thoughtful instruction and practice, you can use *Ready® Common Core* as your primary instructional program for a year-long mathematics course. The lesson sequence is based on the learning progressions of the Common Core to help students build upon earlier learning, develop conceptual understanding, use mathematical practices, and make connections among concepts.

Instruct

Teach one *Ready® Common Core Instruction* lesson per week, using the Pacing Guides on pages A12 and A13, for planning.

Use the web-based, electronic resources found in the *Teacher Toolbox* to review prerequisite skills and access on-level lessons as well as lessons from previous grades. See pages A16 and A17 for more information.

Assess and Monitor Progress

Use the informal assessment opportunities provided in the Step by Step to monitor student progress throughout the lesson. Assess student understanding using the Unit Reviews in *Ready Common Core Instruction*. See page A38 for more information.

Differentiate Instruction

Identify struggling students and differentiate using the Assessment and Remediation page at the end of each skill lesson in the *Teacher Resource Book*. See page A21 for a sample.

Access activities and prerequisite lessons (including lessons from other grades) in the *Teacher Toolbox* to reteach and support students who are still struggling. See pages A16 and A17 for more details.

Use *Ready®* with the *i-Ready® Diagnostic*

You can add the *i-Ready Diagnostic* as part of your *Ready* solution.

- Administer the *i-Ready Diagnostic* as a cross-grade-level assessment to pinpoint what students know and what they need to learn.

- Use the detailed individual and classroom diagnostic reports to address individual and classroom instructional needs using the lessons in *Ready Common Core Instruction* and the *Teacher Toolbox*.

See pages A18 and A19 for more information.

Using *Ready®* to Supplement Your Current Math Program

If your instructional program was not written specifically to address the Common Core Standards, then your textbook likely does not include the concepts, skills, and strategies your students need to be successful. By supplementing with **Ready® Common Core Instruction**, you'll be able to address these concerns:

- Filling gaps in mathematics content that has shifted from another grade

- Incorporating Common Core models and strategies into instruction

- Integrating the habits of mind that are in the Standards for Mathematical Practice

- Asking questions requiring students to engage in higher-level thinking, such as questions that ask students to explain effective strategies used to solve problems, critique the reasoning of others, and generalize their results

- Including lessons and questions that develop conceptual understanding

The implementation plan below details one approach you can use to immediately begin supplementing your current math program with **Ready® Common Core Instruction**.

Step-by-Step Implementation Plan

STEP 1

IDENTIFY CONTENT NEEDS

How do I know what to teach?

- Identify the **Ready** lessons you need to include in your instructional plan.

  – First identify the **Ready** lessons that address standards that are a major emphasis in the Common Core. See page A14 or the Table of Contents to easily identify these **Ready** lessons.

  – Next, identify the Common Core standards in the table on page A15 that are not addressed in your current math program.

- Identify the place in your scope and sequence to insert the **Ready** lessons. "Focus on Math Concepts" lessons should come before the lesson in your current book.

STEP 2

INTEGRATE READY

How do I make time to teach the *Ready* lessons?

- Remove lessons or units from your current instructional plan that are no longer covered in the Common Core standards at that grade level.

- Replace lessons or units that do not teach topics using the models, strategies, and rigor of the Common Core with the appropriate **Ready** lessons.

STEP 3

MEASURE STUDENT PROGRESS

How can I address gaps in student knowledge?

- Use the Unit Reviews in **Ready** to make sure your students are successfully able to meet the rigorous demands of the Common Core.

- Use the **Ready® Teacher Toolbox** to access activities, on-level lessons, and lessons from other grades to address gaps in students' background and learning. See pages A16 and A17 for more on the **Teacher Toolbox**.

A11

Ready Instruction Year-Long Pacing Guide

Week	*Ready® Common Core Instruction* Lesson	Days	Minutes/day
1	*i-Ready* Baseline Diagnostic	3	60
2	L1: Count On to Add	5	30–45
3	L2: Count On to Subtract	5	30–45
4	L3: Add and Subtract in Word Problems	5	30–45
5	L4: *Understand* Missing Addends	5	30–45
6	L5: Subtract to Compare in Word Problems	5	30–45
	Unit 1 Review	**1**	**30–45**
7	L6: Doubles and Doubles Plus 1	5	30–45
8	L7: Number Partners for 6 and 7	5	30–45
9	L8: Number Partners for 8 and 9	5	30–45
10	L9: Number Partners for 10	5	30–45
11	L10: *Understand* the Equal Sign	5	30–45
12	L11: Facts I Know	5	30–45
	Unit 2 Review	**1**	**30–45**
13	L12: *Understand* Teen Numbers	5	30–45
14	L13: *Understand* Sums Greater than 10	5	30–45
15	L14: Make a Ten to Add	5	30–45
16	L15: Add Three Numbers	5	30–45
17	L16: Make a Ten to Subtract	5	30–45
	Unit 3 Review	**1**	**30–45**
18	L17: *Understand* Tens	5	30–45
19	L18: The 120 Chart	5	30–45
20	L19: *Understand* 10 More and 10 Less	5	30–45
21	L20: Add and Subtract Tens	5	30–45
	Unit 4 Review	**1**	**30–45**
22	L21: *Understand* Tens and Ones	5	30–45
23	L22: Compare Numbers	5	30–45
24	L23: Add Tens to Any Number	5	30–45
25	L24: Add Tens and Add Ones	5	30–45
26	L25: Add and Regroup	5	30–45
	Unit 5 Review	**1**	**30–45**
27	L26: *Understand* Shapes	5	30–45
28	L27: *Understand* Putting Shapes Together	5	30–45
29	L28: *Understand* Breaking Shapes Into Parts	5	30–45
	Unit 6 Review	**1**	**30–45**
30	L29: Sort and Count	5	30–45
31	L30: Compare Data	5	30–45
32	L31: Order Objects by Length	5	30–45
33	L32: Compare Lengths	5	30–45
34	L33: *Understand* Length Measurement	5	30–45
35	L34: Tell Time	5	30–45
	Unit 7 Review	**1**	**30–45**
36	*i-Ready* Year-End Diagnostic	3	60

Teaching a *Ready*® Lesson

The ***Ready Common Core Instruction*** introduces each lesson with an engaging opening activity, followed by a gradual release of responsibility. Each lesson closes with targeted differentiated instruction activities.

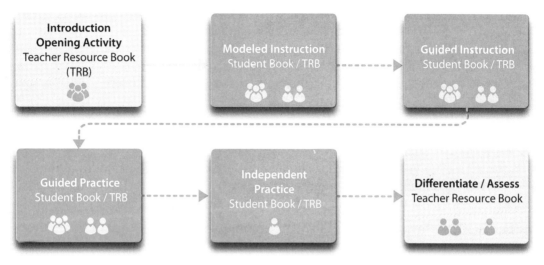

Ready® Instruction Weekly Pacing (One Lesson a Week)

Use ***Ready Common Core Instruction*** as the foundation of a year-long mathematics program. The Year-Long Sample Week (below) shows a recommended schedule for teaching one lesson per week. Each day is divided into periods of direct instruction, independent work, and assessment. Use the Year-Long Pacing Guide on page A12 for a specific week-to-week schedule.

	Day 1 Introduction	Day 2 Modeled Instruction	Day 3 Guided Instruction	Day 4 Guided Practice	Day 5 Independent Practice
Whole Class	**Opening Activity** in the Teacher Resource Book. (30 minutes) **Vocabulary** (10 minutes)	Discuss graphic and verbal representations of the problem in the Student Book. (10 minutes) **Mathematical Discourse** (5 minutes)	Discuss graphic and verbal representations of the problem in the Student Book. (10 minutes) **Concept Extension** (5 minutes)	Discuss the sample problem in the Student Book. (5 minutes) **Visual Support** (5 minutes)	
Small Group/ Independent		Work the math with a modeled representation and practice with **Model It** in the Student Book. (10 minutes) **Hands-On Activity** (10 minutes)	Work the math with a symbolic representation and practice with **Model It** in the Student Book. (10 minutes) **Fluency Activity** (10 minutes)	Work two problems in the Student Book independently. (15 minutes)	Solve problems. (30 minutes)
Assessment	Discuss answer to the **Check for Understanding** problem in the Teacher Resource Book. (5 minutes)	Discuss solutions to the problem. (10 minutes)	Discuss solutions to the **Talk About It** problem in the Student Book. (10 minutes)	Check solutions and discuss. (20 minutes)	Review solutions and explanations. (15 minutes) **Assessment and Remediation** (time will vary)

Content Emphasis in the Common Core Standards

Major Areas of Emphasis

Not all of the content in a given grade is emphasized equally in the Common Core Standards. Some clusters of the standards require greater emphasis than others. This greater emphasis may be based on the depth of the ideas, the time that students need to master the concepts, the content's importance to future mathematics topics, or a combination of some or all of these. A greater focus on the most critical material at each grade allows for lessons to go more in-depth and for students to have more time to master concepts and mathematical practices.

The tables on these two pages identify the Major Clusters emphasized by the Common Core Standards and assessments and those that are Supporting and Additional Clusters. In addition, the **Ready®** lessons that correspond to these clusters are also identified.

Use the tables on these pages to help inform instructional decisions regarding the amount of time spent on clusters of varying degrees of emphasis. If you are using **Ready** as a supplement with another program, you may want to spend more time with the **Ready** lessons connected to clusters with a major emphasis.

The table below indicates the clusters of Major Emphasis in the Common Core Standards.

Standard Clusters with Major Emphasis	Standards	*Ready* Lessons
OPERATIONS AND ALGEBRAIC THINKING		
Represent and solve problems involving addition and subtraction.	1.OA.A.1, 1.OA.A.2	3, 5, 15
Understand and apply properties of operations and the relationship between addition and subtraction.	1.OA.B.3, 1.OA.B.4	4, 8
Add and subtract within 20.	1.OA.C.5, 1.OA.C.6	1, 2, 6, 9, 11, 13, 14, 16
Work with addition and subtraction equations.	1.OA.D.7, 1.OA.D.8	7, 10
NUMBER AND OPERATIONS IN BASE TEN		
Extend the counting sequence.	1.NBT.A.1	18
Understand place value.	1.NBT.B.2, 1.NBT.B.3	12, 17, 21, 22
Use place value understanding and properties of operations to add and subtract.	1.NBT.C.4, 1.NBT.C.5, 1.NBT.C.6	19, 20, 23, 24, 25
MEASUREMENT AND DATA		
Measure lengths indirectly and by iterating length units.	1.MD.A.1, 1.MD.A.2	31, 32, 33

Supporting and Additional Areas of Emphasis

Although some clusters have greater emphasis in the Common Core Standards, this does not mean that standards within the clusters identified as Supporting or Additional can be neglected during instruction. Neglecting material will leave gaps in students' skills and understanding and may leave students unprepared for the challenges of a later grade. Standards for topics that are not major emphases are written in such a way as to support and strengthen the areas of major emphasis. This allows for valuable connections that add coherence to the grade.

In addition, the Supporting and Additional clusters provide students with understanding that is essential for success on the Common Core assessments, though they are not a major focus of the assessments. The Common Core assessments will mirror the emphasis developed by the Common Core and highlighted here. Major clusters will represent the majority of the questions on the Common Core assessments, but it is important to note that items identified as being Supporting or Additional will also be included.

The table below indicates the clusters with Supporting or Additional Emphasis in the Common Core Standards.

Standard Clusters with Supporting or Additional Emphasis	Standards	*Ready* Lessons
MEASUREMENT AND DATA		
Tell and write time.	1.MD.B.3	34
Represent and interpret data.	1.MD.C.4	29, 30
GEOMETRY		
Reason with shapes and their attributes.	1.G.A.1, 1.G.A.2, 1.G.A.3	26, 27, 28

Additional Resources

For more information on Content Emphases, see these helpful resources.

media.doe.in.gov/commoncore/docs/math_shifts_and_major_work_of_grade.pdf

www.parcconline.org/parcc-model-content-frameworks

www.smarterbalanced.org/wordpress/wp-content/uploads/2011/12/Math-Content-Specifications.pdf

engageny.org/resource/math-content-emphases/

Connecting with the *Ready® Teacher Toolbox*

Designed for use with the **Ready® Common Core Instruction**, the Teacher Toolbox provides a host of multilevel resources teachers can use to differentiate instruction. If you purchased the Teacher Toolbox, you should have received an insert with access codes and information. Please contact Customer Service at (800) 225-0248 if you need this information. Visit *www.teacher-toolbox.com* to get started.

The Common Core builds on skills covered in the previous year's standards. Of course, many students will not have mastered those standards, and most students could use a review. **Ready Common Core** allows you to access lessons from previous **Ready** grades through the Teacher Toolbox.

How Do I Use the Teacher Toolbox?

Lessons are conveniently organized to match your print materials, making it easy to find additional resources for teaching the skills and standards associated with each lesson. All of these resources are perfect for use with any interactive whiteboard or other computer projection screen.

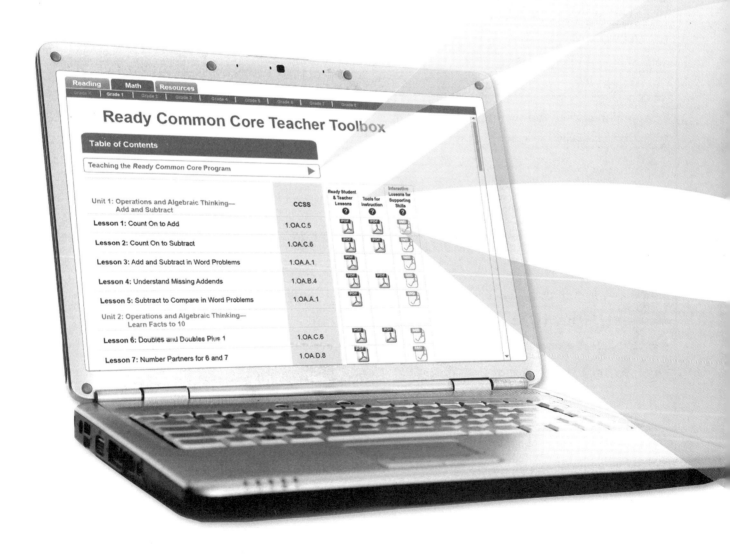

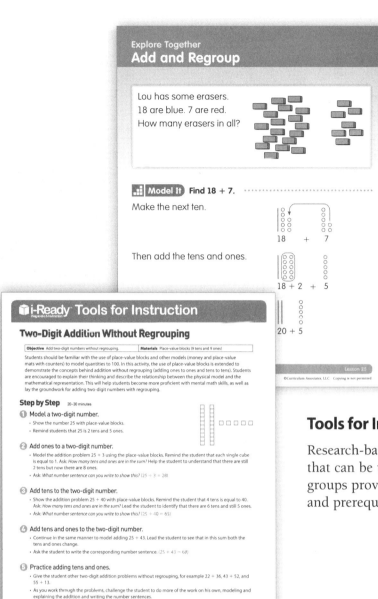

Downloadable *Ready®* Lessons

Downloadable *Ready®* lessons make it easy for teachers to focus on particular skills, or even reteach skills that students may not have mastered at earlier grade levels. What you get:

- Every lesson in this book is available online as an individual PDF file, which you can project for whole-class and small-group use and access from any internet connection.

- Prerequisite student and teacher lessons are available from prior grades to address gaps in content coverage or strengthen prerequisite skills.

Tools for Instruction

Research-based, best-practice routines and activities that can be used with the whole class or small groups provide ways to teach or review standards and prerequisite skills.

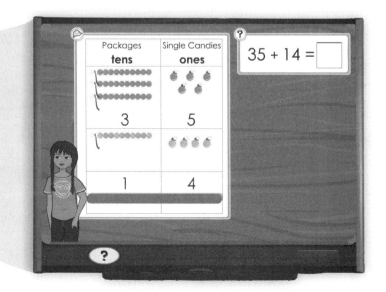

Guided Interactive Tutorials

Guided interactive tutorials give teachers another engaging way to provide whole-class or small-group instruction. Lessons follow a consistent structure of explicit instruction and guided practice. Immediate corrective feedback continuously supports students.

A17

Using *i-Ready® Diagnostic* with *Ready® Common Core*

If you have already purchased *i-Ready® Diagnostic*, you can use its robust reporting to monitor students' overall and domain-specific mathematics proficiency as they move through **Ready® Instruction**. Specifically, use the Student Profile report and the Instructional Grouping report to identify Next Step skills for student instruction.

i-Ready Diagnostic available for Grades K–12

Student Profile Report

The **Student Profile** report shows teachers students' performance levels for each domain and shows where they are struggling. Plus, it provides detailed recommendations and resources to support teacher-led instruction.

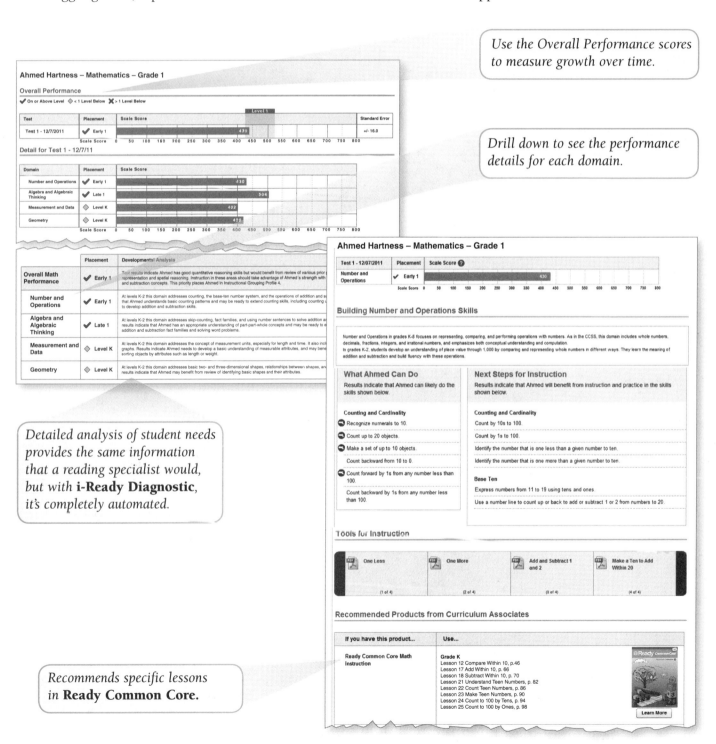

Use the Overall Performance scores to measure growth over time.

Drill down to see the performance details for each domain.

Detailed analysis of student needs provides the same information that a reading specialist would, but with **i-Ready Diagnostic**, *it's completely automated.*

Recommends specific lessons in **Ready Common Core**.

Instructional Grouping Profile

The **Instructional Grouping Profile** report shows teachers exactly how to group students so that students who are struggling with the same skills get the most out of small-group instruction. The report also gives effective instructional recommendations and resources for each group profile.

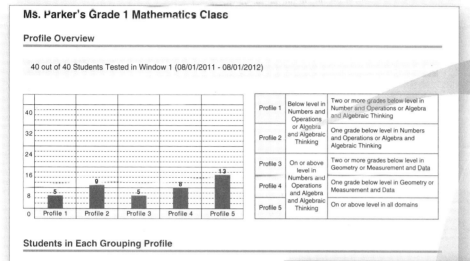

Ms. Parker's Grade 1 Mathematics Class

Profile Overview

40 out of 40 Students Tested in Window 1 (08/01/2011 - 08/01/2012)

Profile 1	Below level in Numbers and Operations or Algebra and Algebraic Thinking	Two or more grades below level in Number and Operations or Algebra and Algebraic Thinking
Profile 2		One grade below level in Numbers and Operations or Algebra and Algebraic Thinking
Profile 3	On or above level in Numbers and Operations and Algebra and Algebraic Thinking	Two or more grades below level in Geometry or Measurement and Data
Profile 4		One grade below level in Geometry or Measurement and Data
Profile 5		On or above level in all domains

Bar graph values: Profile 1 = 5, Profile 2 = 9, Profile 3 = 5, Profile 4 = 8, Profile 5 = 13

Students in Each Grouping Profile

Profile 1	Profile 2	Profile 3	
Iman, Michael	Afridi, Tia	Mach, Avis	Ha
Kapanadze, Leigh	Agarwal, Angeline	Marciano, Blaine	Ha
Labrecque, Benny	Bailey, Diedre	Martin, Lakisha	Ha
Lee, Cary	Batie, Jorge	Mclucas, Brent	He
Leth, Yash	DeCruz, Glen	Montgomery, Maggie	Hill

Drill down to see instructional priorities and tools for profiles.

Downloadable instructional PDFs based on every student's unique needs allow teachers to pinpoint remediation for students.

Priorities for Profile 1

Children in this profile are still developing their understanding of number and concepts of quantity, either in areas related to number recognition and counting or in areas related to the part-part-whole concepts behind addition and subtraction, or both.

Those children with a low score in Number and Operations may have gaps in connecting written numerals with quantities of objects, in rote counting, or in counting with one-to-one correspondence. Those children with a low score in Algebra and Algebraic Thinking likely need work with the ideas of joining, separating, or comparing sets using manipulatives or in word problem contexts to develop addition and subtraction concepts. They will particularly benefit from instruction on the skills described below in the section *Algebraic Thinking*. All children in this profile are also likely to benefit from reinforcement of essential vocabulary.

	2 Levels or More Below	1 Level Below	On or Above Level
Number and Operations and/or Algebra and Algebraic Thinking		•	

Students in Profile 1

	Overall Scale Score	Overall Placement	Needs Analysis	
			Number and Operations	Algebra and Algebraic Thinking
Iman, Michael	367	Level K	Level K	Level K
Kapanadze, Leigh	328	Level K	Level K	Level K
Labrecque, Benny	289	Level K	Level K	Level K
Lee, Cary	262	Level K	Level K	Level K
Leth, Yash	323	Level K	Level K	Level K

Counting
- Recognize the number symbols (numerals) for 1-20.
- Recognize sets of up to 5 objects without counting.
- Count a collection of objects by ones up to 20 objects and tell how many there are.
- Rote count to 100 by ones.

Children should master rote counting to 100 with special attention spent on change numbers 19, 29, 39, and so on, and the number that comes next starting the next group of ten. Using five-frames or groups of five connecting cubes, assist children in visualizing sets of 5 and number combinations to 5. This is the building block to grouping in tens, the foundation for place value. Have children count objects, giving each one its proper number name. Then have children add one more object to the group to practice counting on. They should understand that the last number named in counting is the number of objects in the collection (cardinality).

Algebraic Thinking
- Relate addition and subtraction to part-part-whole concepts.
- Find the combinations for 5 and 10 and identify missing addends.
- Solve addition problems using "counting on" with addends less than 10.
- Solve subtraction problems in "taking from" or "taking apart" situations with numbers less than 10.

Use five-frames, ten-frames, connecting cubes, and so forth to assist children in visualizing the number combinations for five and ten, and in solving part-part-whole problems. Fluency in these combinations is the foundation for the children's future work with base-ten numbers and operations. Giving children multiple daily "real world" opportunities to solve word problems is essential to development of their understanding of addition and subtraction.

Tools for Instruction

Algebra and Algebraic Thinking

Number Pairs for Sums to 10	Find Missing Addends for Sums to 10	Count On to Add	Subtraction Number Sentences
(1 of 4)	(2 of 4)	(3 of 4)	(4 of 4)

Quickly see how your class breaks down by skill and level of instructional need.

i-Ready® Instruction

i-Ready also has an automated online **Instruction** program. Engaging interactive modules provide differentiated online instruction, and built-in progress monitoring allows you to assess student performance. Learn more at *www.i-Ready.com.*

Features of *Ready® Common Core Instruction*

This section guides teachers to the key features of the Student Book and Teacher Resource Book. Numbered boxes call out and describe the key features. Use this section to familiarize yourself with the overall structure of a **Ready® Instruction** lesson. There are two types of lessons in **Ready: Develop Skills and Strategies** lessons and **Focus on Math Concepts** lessons.

Develop Skills and Strategies lessons teach a skill, procedure, or strategy using models to connect to understanding. Students apply and practice the skill in first guided, then independent problem sets. These lessons emphasize flexible, appropriate, and efficient procedures for calculation and symbolic representation. As students build an understanding of the meaning behind procedures, they can apply what they have learned to new situations.

Focus on Math Concept lessons emphasize number sense and the conceptual understanding of operations and properties. These lessons connect new concepts to familiar ones through activities and/or visual representations. Understanding is developed through questioning, discussing, drawing or writing, and open-ended problem solving.

Pages A22–A25 show a **Develop Skills and Strategies** lesson and pages A26–A31 show a **Focus on Math Concepts** lesson.

Develop Skills and Strategies Lessons

In the Teacher Resource Book, each lesson begins with a full page of orientation on the standards addressed in that lesson.

Teacher Resource Book

1 **Lesson Objectives** identify specific mathematical goals of the lesson. **Prerequisite Skills** list key concepts and skills required for success with the lesson.

2 **The Learning Progression** helps teachers see the standard in context, how the standard builds on prior knowledge, particularly from the previous grade, and how it leads to the expectations for the next year.

3 **Vocabulary** that is new as well as terms for review are provided with clear definitions. New vocabulary can be taught as it occurs within the lesson.

4 *Ready Teacher Toolbox* identifies on-level and prerequisite lessons, activities, and tutorials that are connected to the lesson and available online in the Teacher Toolbox.

5 **CCSS Focus** identifies the Common Core State Standards featured in the lesson, Additional Standards covered in activities in the Teacher Resource Book, and the Standards for Mathematical Practice integrated into the lesson.

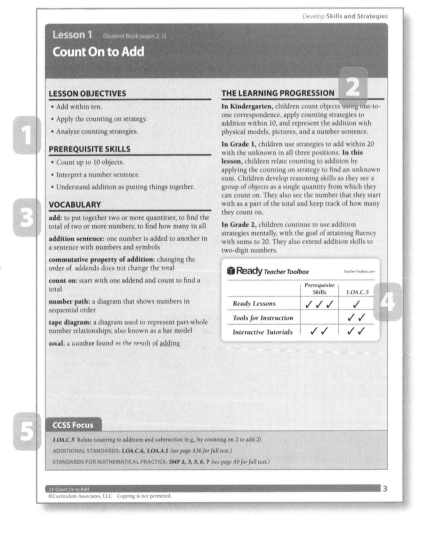

A20

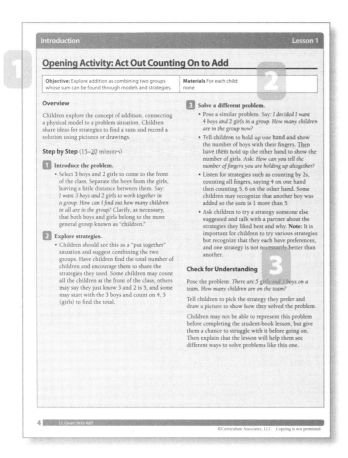

Teacher Resource Book

Opening Activities introduce the concepts of the lesson through engaging hands-on explorations that activate prior knowledge. Use these open-ended activities to review and build on prerequisite skills that connect to the visual representations of the lesson.

Materials suggested to complete the activity are listed, including, as needed, **Activity Sheets** found on page 270 of this Teacher Resource Book.

Check for Understanding is an informal assessment situation that allows teachers to observe students' level of understanding. Depending on how students complete the task, teachers can form small groups to provide additional support before beginning the lesson.

Differentiated Instruction in *Develop Skills and Strategies* Lessons

Each **Develop Skills and Strategies** lesson concludes with Differentiated Instruction activities, giving you opportunities to extend and reinforce learning with all types of students. In addition to providing alternate methods of teaching, this portion of the lesson provides opportunities for informal assessment and reteaching suggestions for students who need extra support.

Teacher Resource Book

In the **Assessment and Remediation**, a closure question is given with a chart that provides teachers with a list of incorrect answers based on common errors and gives specific remediation suggestions for each incorrect answer.

A **Hands-On Activity** extends the concepts and skills of the standard using manipulatives and group collaboration.

A **Challenge Activity** gives students who have mastered the skills and concepts of the lesson a chance to apply their understanding to a more sophisticated problem-solving challenge.

Modeled Instruction in *Develop Skills and Strategies* Lessons

The teacher supports students as they explore different ways of solving a mathematical problem. The teacher begins by reading the problem aloud, and then, using the Step by Step support in the Teacher Resource Book, models a way to apply the standard to solve the problem.

Student Book

1 A problem is posed that can be solved efficiently by using the lesson's new skills and strategies.

2 The **Model It** shows children one way they might think about solving the problem. Information children need to find a solution is restated to make a clear connection to a visual representation. Making this connection helps children develop strategies and number sense. New vocabulary terms are in bold face in the lessons in which they are introduced.

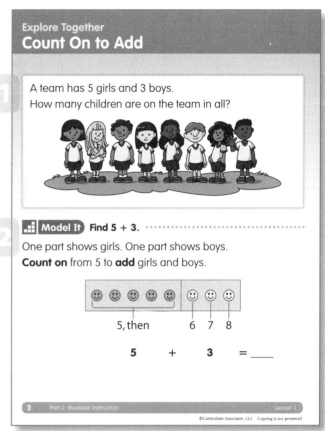

Teacher Resource Book

1 **Step by Step** support provides opportunities for monitoring student understanding and suggested next steps for instruction based on demonstrated needs.

2 Point-of-use **Hands-On Activities** provide a concrete way of representing the problem, creating another access point to develop understanding.

3 The **Mathematical Discourse** questions help teachers lead rich classroom discussions and include answers as well as key topics to listen for in student responses.

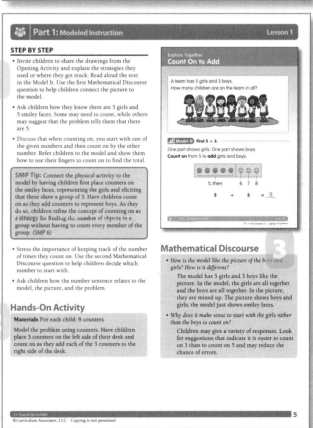

Guided Instruction in *Develop Skills and Strategies* Lessons

The teacher continues to guide students in how to apply the standard to solve a problem. On this page, instead of explicit modeling, the teacher uses prompts to encourage and support learning.

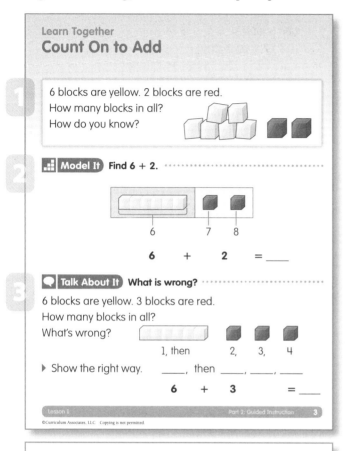

Student Book

1 A second problem is posed that connects the representations on the previous page to a more pictorial representation of the mathematics.

2 Scaffolded support in the **Model It** guides students to extend their thinking as they work through the pictorial representation of a problem similar to the one on the previous page.

3 In **Talk About It**, students apply what they learned to analyze and explain a student error based on common misconceptions. Teachers can use this to engage students in a discussion about the math concepts of the lesson.

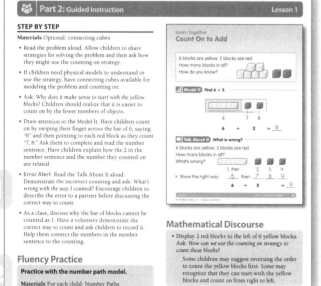

Teacher Resource Book

1 **Error Alerts** explain a typical computational error, the wrong answer it might produce, and explanations to help students avoid those errors in the future.

2 **Fluency Practice** activities help students build and maintain procedural fluency throughout the year.

3 **SMP Tips** highlight a particular Standard for Mathematical Practice that is one of many practice standards integrated in the lesson. SMP tips also provide helpful insights for teachers as they form small groups and provide methods of differentiation.

Guided Practice in *Develop Skills and Strategies* Lessons

As part of a gradual release model, the teacher guides students through this page, offering support and targeted questions that help students apply their learning.

Student Book

1 The Study Buddy models self-questioning and the habits of mind of proficient mathematics students. Teachers use this example to connect what students have learned on the previous pages to the new problems they will be solving below.

2 Problems provide students with the opportunity to integrate and extend concepts and skills. Visual models continue to guide student learning.

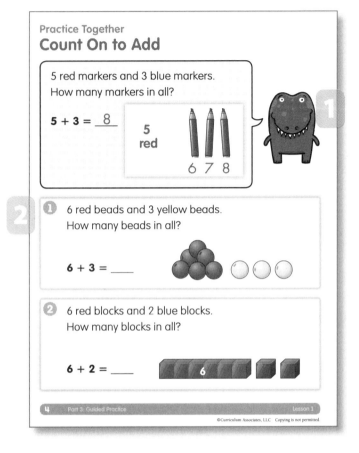

Teacher Resource Book

1 **Step by Step** support provides information and useful tips the teacher can use to build students' understanding of how to think about the problems.

2 **Concept Extensions** reinforce the concept on the page by going deeper into a core aspect of the concept, or by connecting that concept to related understandings.

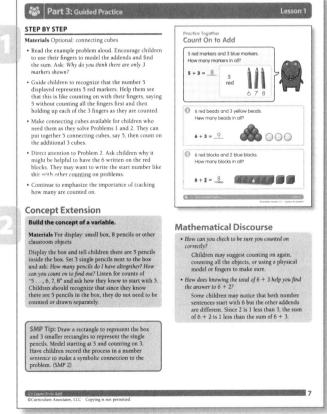

A24

Independent Practice in *Develop Skills and Strategies* Lessons

Students work independently to solve problems, then conclude by discussing their work and sharing solution strategies. The two practice pages use a similar structure, giving students the confidence to complete the page on their own.

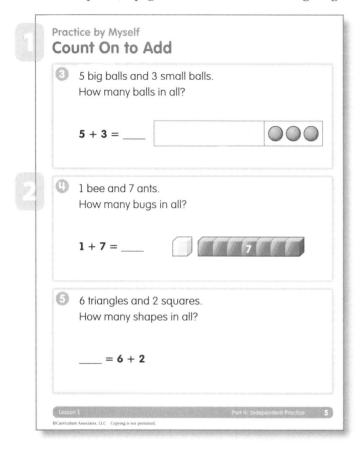

Student Book

Independent Practice provides students with problems that integrate and extend concepts and skills.

Students are encouraged to show their work as they apply what they have learned.

Teacher Resource Book

Step by Step support provides information and useful tips the teacher can use to assess students' understanding as they work independently.

ELL Support activities provide teachers with suggestions for making the text more accessible to English Language Learners. Activities provide background on concepts, content, or words that might confuse children.

Mathematical Discourse questions promote thoughtful dialogue and exchange of ideas and are specific to each page. By responding to questions that require higher level thinking, students develop a deeper understanding of skills and concepts.

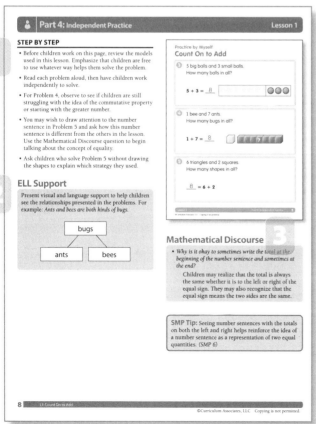

Focus on Math Concepts Lessons

The Common Core State Standards demand a balance between conceptual understanding, procedural skills and fluency, and application. **Ready® Focus on Math Concepts** lessons, develop understanding through questioning, discussing, and problem-solving. These lessons build a solid conceptual understanding of topics so students know why a strategy or procedure works or when it is appropriate to use it—not just how to use it. This understanding empowers students to apply what they have learned to new situations.

Intensive Teacher Support

In the Teacher Resource Book, each lesson begins with a full page of orientation on the standards addressed in that lesson.

Teacher Resource Book

1 **Lesson Objectives** identify specific mathematical goals of the lesson.

2 **The Learning Progression** helps teachers see the standard in context, how the standard build on prior knowledge, particularly from the previous grade, and how it leads to the expectations for the next year.

3 **Prerequisite Skills** list key concepts and skills required for success with the lesson.

4 **Vocabulary** that is new as well as terms for review are provided with clear definitions. New vocabulary can be taught as it occurs within the lesson.

5 *Ready Teacher Toolbox* identifies on-level and prerequisite lessons, activities, and animated videos that are connected to the lesson and available online in the Teacher Toolbox.

6 **CCSS Focus** identifies the Common Core State Standards featured in the lesson, Additional Standards covered in activities in the Teacher Resource Book, and the Standards for Mathematical Practice integrated into the lesson.

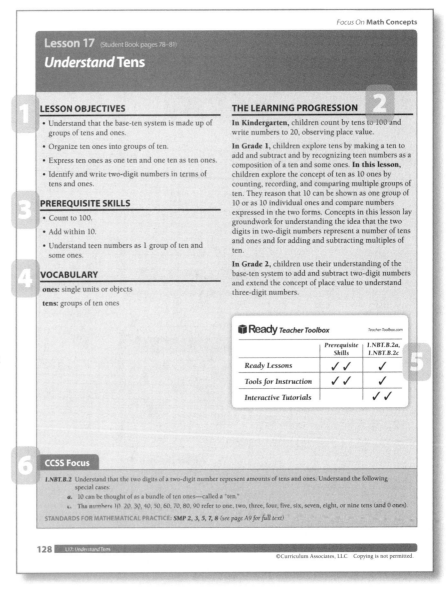

Focus On **Math Concepts**

Lesson 17 (Student Book pages 78–81)
Understand Tens

1 LESSON OBJECTIVES

- Understand that the base-ten system is made up of groups of tens and ones.
- Organize ten ones into groups of ten.
- Express ten ones as one ten and one ten as ten ones.
- Identify and write two-digit numbers in terms of tens and ones.

3 PREREQUISITE SKILLS

- Count to 100.
- Add within 10.
- Understand teen numbers as 1 group of ten and some ones.

4 VOCABULARY

ones: single units or objects

tens: groups of ten ones

2 THE LEARNING PROGRESSION

In Kindergarten, children count by tens to 100 and write numbers to 20, observing place value.

In Grade 1, children explore tens by making a ten to add and subtract and by recognizing teen numbers as a composition of a ten and some ones. **In this lesson,** children explore the concept of ten as 10 ones by counting, recording, and comparing multiple groups of ten. They reason that 10 can be shown as one group of 10 or as 10 individual ones and compare numbers expressed in the two forms. Concepts in this lesson lay groundwork for understanding the idea that the two digits in two-digit numbers represent a number of tens and ones and for adding and subtracting multiples of ten.

In Grade 2, children use their understanding of the base-ten system to add and subtract two-digit numbers and extend the concept of place value to understand three-digit numbers.

Ready *Teacher Toolbox* Teacher-Toolbox.com

	Prerequisite Skills	1.NBT.B.2a, 1.NBT.B.2c
Ready Lessons	✓ ✓	✓
Tools for Instruction	✓ ✓	✓
Interactive Tutorials		✓ ✓

6 CCSS Focus

1.NBT.B.2 Understand that the two digits of a two-digit number represent amounts of tens and ones. Understand the following special cases:
 a. 10 can be thought of as a bundle of ten ones—called a "ten."
 b. The numbers 10, 20, 30, 40, 50, 60, 70, 80, 90 refer to one, two, three, four, five, six, seven, eight, or nine tens (and 0 ones).

STANDARDS FOR MATHEMATICAL PRACTICE: **SMP 2, 3, 5, 7, 8** *(see page A9 for full text)*

128 L17: *Understand Tens*

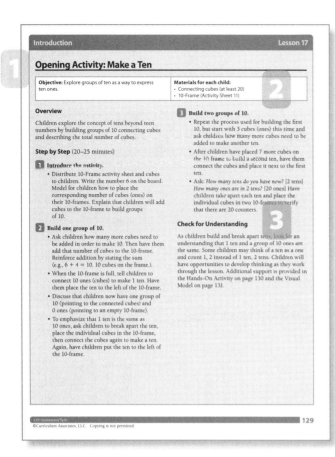

Teacher Resource Book

Opening Activities introduce the concepts of the lesson through engaging hands-on explorations that activate prior knowledge. Use these open-ended activities to review and build on prerequisite skills that connect to key question of the lesson.

Materials suggested to complete the activity are listed, including, as needed, **Activity Sheets** found starting on page 270 of this Teacher Resource Book.

Check for Understanding is an informal assessment situation that allows teachers to observe students' level of understanding. Depending on how students complete the task, teachers can form small groups to provide additional support before beginning the lesson.

Differentiated Instruction in *Focus on Math Concepts* Lessons

Each concept lesson concludes with Differentiated Instruction activities, giving you opportunities to extend and reinforce learning with all types of students. In addition to providing alternate methods of teaching, this portion of the lesson is an opportunity for informal assessment, and includes suggestions on ways to monitor understanding in small groups.

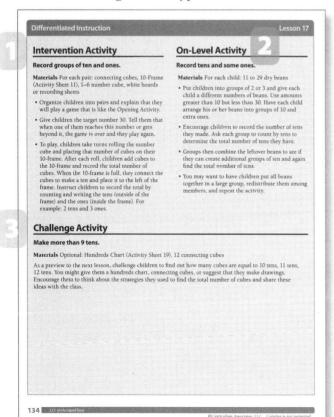

Teacher Resource Book

Intervention Activity provides an opportunity to reteach the concepts and skills of the current lesson.

On-Level Activity has students apply the concepts of the lesson to new situations.

Challenge Activity gives students who have mastered the skills and concepts of the lesson a chance to extend their learning.

Modeled Instruction in *Focus on Math Concepts* Lessons

The teacher supports students as they make connections between what they did in the opening activity and what they are about to learn. By making these connections, students develop a deeper understanding and see the relationship between mathematical concepts, rather than seeing everything as a separate, unrelated idea.

Student Book

1 Each **Focus on Math Concepts** lesson begins with a key question that gets students thinking about the new concept.

2 Students develop deeper understanding by connecting new concepts to prior knowledge and skills.

3 The **Talk About It** is an opportunity for students to discuss the math concept and share their reasoning.

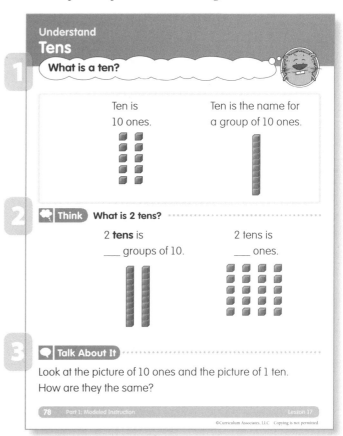

Teacher Resource Book

1 **Step by Step** gives suggestions for leading class discussions for each section of the lesson.

2 **SMP Tips** help teachers recognize a specific opportunity to reinforce one of the Standards for Mathematical Practice.

3 **Mathematical Discourse** questions promote thoughtful dialogue and exchange of ideas and are specific to each page. They can be used for a variety of purposes, including as a launch to or wrap up of the lesson, partner talk, or individual student reflection.

4 **Hands-On Activities** provide a concrete way of representing the problem, creating another access point to develop understanding. The activities include a clear set of directions for use of classroom materials and are flexible enough for whole class work or as small group instruction for students who are not meeting the lesson objective.

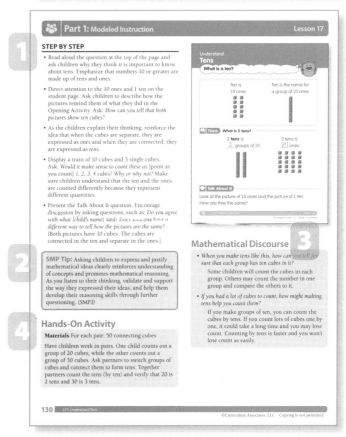

A28

Guided Instruction in *Focus on Math Concepts* Lessons

Teachers ask supporting questions as they guide students through a hands-on activity that makes a concrete connection to the representation on the previous page. By helping students apply mathematical practices such as seeing and using patterns, structure, and/or models as tools, students build on what they already know to gain further understanding of the concept.

Student Book

1. Students use common classroom manipulatives to build understanding of the concept concretely.

2. Students apply what they have learned to new problems.

3. In the **Talk About It** students answer questions about a specific problem using the concepts of the lesson. This critical thinking question can be used to informally assess students' understanding and to engage students in mathematical discourse.

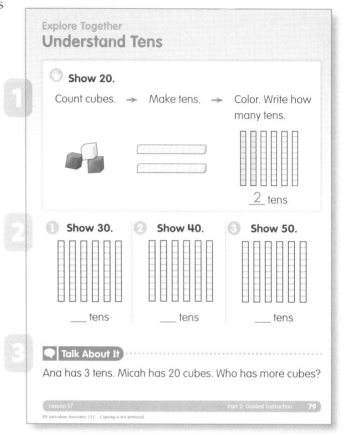

Teacher Resource Book

1. **Step by Step** gives teaching suggestions and questions for leading class discussions for each page.

2. Use the **Visual Model** to encourage interactivity, engage visual learners, and give ELL students a new perspective on the concept.

3. **Mathematical Discourse** questions provide authentic opportunities for meaningful discussions to validate student thinking. These open-ended questions promote reasoning and challenge students to have a conversation.

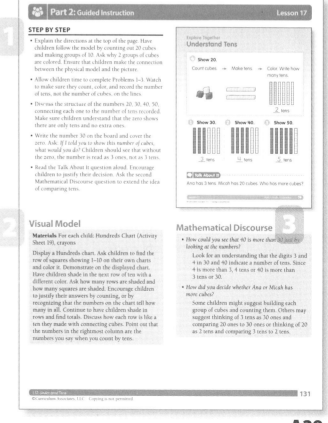

Guided Practice in *Focus on Math Concepts* Lessons

As part of a gradual release model, the teacher guides students through this page, offering support and targeted questions that help them show, reason about, and explain their thinking.

Student Book

1 Students develop deeper understanding by connecting to prior knowledge and skills. They use the Standards for Mathematical Practice to solve problems designed to promote higher-order thinking.

2 Students analyze and explain a student error based on common misconceptions.

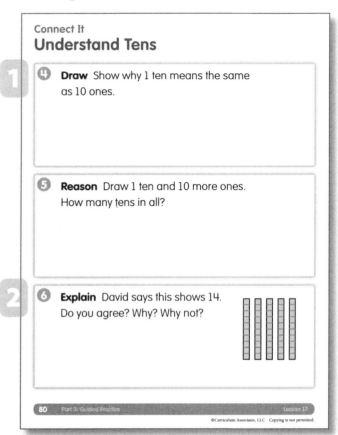

Teacher Resource Book

1 **Step by Step** gives teacher support and suggestions for leading class discussions for each page.

2 **SMP Tips** help teachers recognize a specific opportunity to reinforce one of the Standards for Mathematical Practice.

3 **Misconception Alert** describes common habits of thinking that may interfere with proper understanding of the underlying concepts, and provides handy ways of overcoming them.

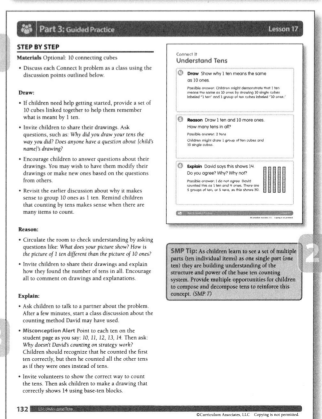

Independent Practice in *Focus on Math Concepts* Lessons

On this page, students work independently on a task with multiple components that, collectively, requires them to engage in both specific as well as generalized thinking about the concepts covered in the lesson. Teachers observe students as they work, asking probing questions that encourage critical thinking and problem-solving strategies.

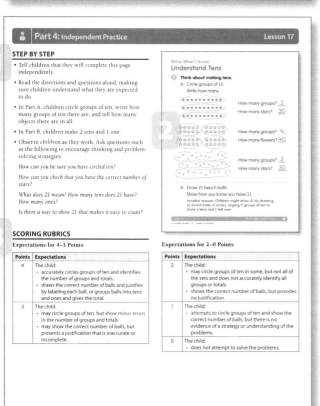

Student Book

In **Show What I Know**, students are asked to think through a critical-thinking problem that often has multiple points of entry and/or more than one correct answer.

The tasks are scaffolded, with each step building on previous steps.

Teacher Resource Book

Step by Step provides suggestions and prompts that help students consolidate their learning.

Sample responses and worked-out solutions are provided for the performance task.

Scoring Rubrics offer guidance for evaluating students' responses.

Supporting Research

Overview

Ready® Common Core Mathematics is founded on research from a variety of federal initiatives, national literacy organizations, and literacy experts. As a result, this program may be used in support of several instructional models.

Ready® Uses . . .	Examples	Research Says . . .
Instructional Strategies		
Scaffolded Instruction is the gradual withdrawal of support through modeled, guided, and independent instruction.	*Ready* lessons follow the pattern of modeled and guided instruction, modeled and guided practice, and independent practice.	"Successful teachers help to create independent learners . . . . Contingent scaffolded instruction . . . is a powerful tool for achieving this goal." (Beed et al., 1991)
Mathematical Discourse in instruction uses questioning, listening, writing, and reflection to encourage conversation about mathematics.	*Ready* lessons include regular verbal exchange of ideas and sharing of understanding in whole group, small group, and pair settings. **Talk About It** leads students through discussions of key ideas and prompts students to compare answers and reasoning to identify misconceptions. **Mathematical Discourse** in the Teacher Resource Book suggests thoughtful question prompts.	"The process of encouraging students to verbalize their thinking—by talking, writing, or drawing the steps they used in solving a problem—was consistently effective." (NCTM, 2007)
Applying Prior Knowledge These are experiences and knowledge that a student brings with himself or herself to learn about a topic.	In each lesson, an **Opening Activity** introduces a new skill by guiding students to solve a new problem by applying prior knowledge.	"What and how students are taught should reflect not only the topics that fall within a certain academic discipline, but also the key ideas that determine how knowledge is organized and generated within that discipline." (Schmidt, Houang, & Cogan, 2002)
Collaborative Learning Students work together in pairs or small groups to attain their individual goals.	**Talk About It** leads students through discussions of key ideas and prompts students to compare answers and reasoning to identify misconceptions.	Collaborative learning improves computational skills. Use of cooperative or collaborative learning has been advocated in various mathematics education reports and in state curricular frameworks, policies, and instructional guidelines. (National Math Advisory Panel, 2008)
Visual Representation is using an image to help describe or define a mathematical problem or relationship, or to depict a real-life problem situation.	*Ready* routinely uses pictorial and other visual models such as number bonds (**Model It**) to illustrate mathematical concepts. **Visual Support** in the Teacher Resource Books suggests additional visual representations.	"Graphic representations of mathematical concepts and problems . . . are crucial components of programs used in nations that perform well on international comparisons, such as Singapore, Korea, or the Netherlands." (NCTM, 2007)

Ready® Uses . . .	Examples	Research Says . . .
Instructional Strategies (continued)		
Multiple Representations are the ways in which a teacher or student represents a math idea, including spoken, written, symbolic, and concrete formats.	*Ready* routinely uses pictorial and visual models (**Model It**) to illustrate mathematical concepts. **Connect It** develops the symbolic representation. **Hands-On Activities** and **Visual Support** in the Teacher Resource Book offer suggestions for additional representations.	"The usefulness of numerical ideas is enhanced when students encounter and use multiple representations for the same concept." (National Research Council, 2001)
Formative Assessment (or **Progress Monitoring**) is a strategy that involves frequent, in-classroom progress checks of students' understanding and mastery of math concepts and skills.	**Talk About Its** with **Error Alerts** in the Teacher Resource Books create ongoing formative assessment opportunities, with support for correcting misconceptions throughout each lesson. **Assessment and Remediation** charts at the end of the lesson help the teacher assess mastery of the skill, identify specific misconceptions, and remediate on the spot as necessary.	Teachers' regular use of formative assessment improves their students' learning, especially if teachers have additional guidance on using the assessment to design and to individualize instruction. (National Mathematics Advisory Panel, 2008)
Differentiated Instruction is an approach to teaching that gives students multiple ways to access and make sense of mathematical ideas.	*Ready* student books provide verbal, visual, and symbolic representations of each new skill and concept. **Hands-On Activities**, **Visual Support**, **Concept Extension**, and **Challenge Activities** in the Teacher Resource Books provide additional differentiation options.	Many teachers and teacher educators have recently identified differentiated instruction as a method of helping more students in diverse classroom settings experience success. (Hall et al., 2003)
Hands-On Activities are any activities in which the student is handling manipulatives used to explore mathematical quantities, relationships, or operations.	Found throughout the Teacher Resource Book.	"The benefit of this [hands-on, manipulative] approach may be that its intensity and concreteness help students maintain a framework in their working memory for solving problems of this type." (NCTM, 2007)
ELL Support consists of tips to provide teachers the content knowledge and pedagogy to minimize obstacles to learning math due to language or cultural issues.	The *Ready* student book uses pictorial and visual representations combined with direct simple text to clearly present concepts. Point-of-use **ELL Support** tips for teachers are found throughout the Teacher Resource Book as appropriate.	Expanded opportunities should be available to English language learners (ELL students) who need them to develop mathematical understanding and proficiency. (NCTM, 2008)

Ready® Uses . . .	Examples	Research Says . . .
Instructional Features		
Standards for Mathematical Practice (SMPs) identify habits of mind and everyday ways of approaching math that are hallmarks of successful math students.	Throughout **Ready** Student Book, SMPs are built into the instruction and problems. Teacher Resource Books feature **SMP Tips** in every lesson to alert teachers to particular instances of each SMP.	"These practices rest on important 'processes and proficiencies' with longstanding importance in mathematics education." (CCSS, 2010)
Computational Fluency is having quick recall of number facts and knowledge and ability to apply multiple computational methods involving whole numbers, decimals, fractions, and other numbers as appropriate to the grade level.	**Ready** lessons all directly address computation skills, develop the conceptual understanding to support computation, or provide applications of computation skills.	"Basic skills with numbers continue to be vitally important for a variety of everyday uses. They also provide a crucial foundation for the higher-level mathematics essential for success in the workplace, which must now also be part of a basic education." (Ball et al., 2005)
Conceptual Understanding is the knowledge of why math processes and rules work.	All **Ready** lessons begin by laying a foundation of conceptual understanding of the mathematical principles underlying the skill being addressed. Special **Focus on Math Concepts** lessons put a special emphasis on these principles. **Concept Extension** features in the Teacher's Resource Book further support conceptual understanding.	"To prepare students for Algebra, the curriculum must simultaneously develop conceptual understanding, computational fluency, and problem-solving skills." (National Mathematics Advisory Panel, 2008)
Problem Solving (or **Application**) is the process of formulating a real-life problem as a mathematical problem, then performing the calculations necessary, and interpreting the result to find the solution to the problem.	**Ready** presents new math problems in real-world contexts and models finding the solution. Students then practice with similar problems.	". . . An important part of our conception of mathematical proficiency involves the ability to formulate and solve problems coming from daily life or other domains, including mathematics itself." (National Research Council, 2001)
Answer Explanations for Students As a part of scaffolded instruction, students receive immediate feedback on their answers and the reasoning behind correct and incorrect answers.	In the **Guided Instruction**, **Guided Practice**, **Independent Practice**, and **Unit Review** sections of the Teacher Resource Book, answers or sample responses are given for each question.	When students receive direct instruction about the reasons why an answer choice is correct or incorrect, they demonstrate long-term retention and understanding of newly learned content. (Pashler et al., 2007)

A34

References

Ball, D. L., Ferrini-Mundy, J., Kilpatrick, J., Milgram, R. J., Schmid, W., & Schaar, R. (2005). Reaching for common ground in K–12 mathematics education. *Notices of the American Mathematical Society*, 52(9).

Beed, P. L., Hawkins, E. M., & Roller, C. M. (1991). Moving learners toward independence: The power of scaffolded instruction. *The Reading Teacher*, 44(9), 648–655.

Eastburn, J. A. (2011). The effects of a concrete, representational, abstract (CRA) instructional model on tier 2 first-grade math students in a response to intervention model: Educational implications for number sense and computational fluency. Dissertation. *ProQuest Information & Learning*, AAI3408708.

Furner, J. M., Yahya, N., & Duffy, M. L. (2005). 20 Ways to teach mathematics: strategies to reach all students. *Intervention in School and Clinic*, 41(1).

Hall, T., Strangman, N., & Meyer, A. (2003). Differentiated instruction and implications for UDL implementation. National Center on Accessing the General Curriculum. Accessed at: *http://aim.cast.org/learn/historyarchive/backgroundpapers/differentiated*

Hess, K. K., Carlock, D., Jones, B., & Walkup, J. R. (2009). *What exactly do "fewer, clearer, and higher standards" really look like in the classroom? Using a cognitive rigor matrix to analyze curriculum, plan lessons, and implement assessments.* Accessed at: *http://www.nciea.org/cgi-bin/pubspage.cgi?sortby=pub_date.*

National Council of Teachers of Mathematics. (2007). Effective strategies for teaching students with difficulties in mathematics. Accessed at: *http://www.nctm.org/news/content.aspx?id=8452.*

———. (2008). Teaching mathematics to English language learners. Accessed at: *http://www.nctm.org/about/content.aspx?id=16135*

National Governors Association Center for Best Practices and Council of Chief State School Officers. (2010). *Common Core State Standards for Mathematics.* Accessed at: *http://www.corestandards.org/the-standards.*

———. (2012). *Publisher's Criteria for the Common Core State Standards in Mathematics, K–8.* Accessed at: *http://www.corestandards.org/resources.*

National Mathematics Advisory Panel. (2008). Foundations for success: The final report of the National Mathematics Advisory Panel. Accessed at: *http://www2.ed.gov/about/bdscomm/list/mathpanel/index.html.*

National Research Council. (2001). *Adding it Up: Helping Children Learn Mathematics.* Mathematics Learning Study Committee: Kilpatrick, J., Swafford, J., & Findell, B. (eds.). Washington, D.C.: National Academy Press.

Partnership for Assessment of Readiness for College and Careers. (2011). *PARCC model content frameworks: English language arts/literacy grades 3–11.* Accessed at: *http://www.parconline.org/parcc-model-content-frameworks.*

Pashler, H., Bain, P., Bottge, B., Graesser, A., Koedinger, K., McDaniel, M., & Metcalfe, J. (2007). *Organizing instruction and study to improve student learning* (NCER 2007–2004). Washington, D.C.: National Center for Education Research, Institute of Education Sciences, U.S. Department of Education. Retrieved from *http://ncer.ed.gov.*

Robertson, K. (2009). Math instruction for English language learners. *Colorìn Colorado!* Accessed at: *http://www.colorincolorado.org/article/30570/.*

Schmidt,W., Houang, R., & Cogan, L. (2002). A coherent curriculum, *American Educator*, Summer, 2002.

Seethaler, P. M., Fuchs, L. S., Fuchs, D., & Compton, D. L. (2012). Predicting first graders' development of calculation versus word-problem performance: the role of dynamic assessment. *Journal of Educational Psychology* 104(1), 224–234.

Smarter Balanced Assessment Consortium. (2012). *General Item Specifications.* Accessed at: *http://www.smarterbalanced.org/wordpress/wp-content/uploads/2012/05/TaskItemSpecifications/ItemSpecifications/GeneralItemSpecifications.pdf.*

Common Core State Standards Coverage by *Ready® Instruction*

The table below correlates each Common Core State Standard to the **Ready® Common Core Instruction** lesson(s) that offer(s) comprehensive instruction on that standard. Use this table to determine which lessons your students should complete based on their mastery of each standard.

Common Core State Standards for Grade 1 — Mathematics Standards		Content Emphasis	Ready® Common Core Instruction Lesson(s)
Operations and Algebraic Thinking			
Represent and solve problems involving addition and subtraction.			
1.OA.A.1	Use addition and subtraction within 20 to solve word problems involving situations of adding to, taking from, putting together, taking apart, and comparing, with unknowns in all positions, e.g., by using objects, drawings, and equations with a symbol for the unknown number to represent the problem.	Major	3, 5
1.OA.A.2	Solve word problems that call for addition of three whole numbers whose sum is less than or equal to 20, e.g., by using objects, drawings, and equations with a symbol for the unknown number to represent the problem.	Major	15
Understand and apply properties of operations and the relationship between addition and subtraction.			
1.OA.B.3	Apply properties of operations as strategies to add and subtract. Examples: If $8 + 3 = 11$ is known, then $3 + 8 = 11$ is also known. (Commutative property of addition.) To add $2 + 6 + 4$, the second two numbers can be added to make a ten, so $2 + 6 + 4 = 2 + 10 = 12$. (Associative property of addition.)	Major	8
1.OA.B.4	Understand subtraction as an unknown-addend problem. For example, subtract $10 - 8$ by finding the number that makes 10 when added to 8.	Major	4
Add and subtract within 20.			
1.OA.C.5	Relate counting to addition and subtraction (e.g., by counting on 2 to add 2).	Major	1
1.OA.C.6	Add and subtract within 20, demonstrating fluency for addition and subtraction within 10. Use strategies such as counting on; making ten (e.g., $8 + 6 = 8 + 2 + 4 = 10 + 4 = 14$); decomposing a number leading to a ten (e.g., $13 - 4 = 13 - 3 - 1 = 10 - 1 = 9$); using the relationship between addition and subtraction (e.g., knowing that $8 + 4 = 12$, one knows $12 - 8 = 4$); and creating equivalent but easier or known sums (e.g., adding $6 + 7$ by creating the known equivalent $6 + 6 + 1 = 12 + 1 = 13$).	Major	2, 6, 9, 11, 13, 14, 16
Work with addition and subtraction equations.			
1.OA.D.7	Understand the meaning of the equal sign, and determine if equations involving addition and subtraction are true or false. For example, which of the following equations are true and which are false? $6 = 6$, $7 = 8 - 1$, $5 + 2 = 2 + 5$, $4 + 1 = 5 + 2$.	Major	10
1.OA.D.8	Determine the unknown whole number in an addition or subtraction equation relating three whole numbers. For example, determine the unknown number that makes the equation true in each of the equations $8 + ? = 11$, $5 = \_\_ - 3$, $6 + 6 = \_\_$.	Major	7

The Standards for Mathematical Practice are integrated throughout the instructional lessons.

Common Core State Standards © 2010. National Governors Association Center for Best Practices and Council of Chief State School Officers. All rights reserved.

Common Core State Standards for Grade 1 — Mathematics Standards	Content Emphasis	Ready® Common Core Instruction Lesson(s)
Number and Operations in Base Ten		
Extend the counting sequence.		
1.NBT.A.1 Count to 120, starting at any number less than 120. In this range, read and write numerals and represent a number of objects with a written numeral.	Major	18
Understand place value.		
1.NBT.B.2 Understand that the two digits of a two-digit number represent amounts of tens and ones. Understand the following as special cases:	Major	12, 17, 21
1.NBT.B.2a 10 can be thought of as a bundle of ten ones—called a "ten."		
1.NBT.B.2b The numbers from 11 to 19 are composed of a ten and one, two, three, four, five, six, seven, eight, or nine ones.		
1.NBT.B.2c The numbers 10, 20, 30, 40, 50, 60, 70, 80, 90 refer to one, two, three, four, five, six, seven, eight, or nine tens (and 0 ones).		
1.NBT.B.3 Compare two two-digit numbers based on meanings of the tens and ones digits, recording the results of comparisons with the symbols >, =, and <.	Major	22
Use place value understanding and properties of operations to add and subtract.		
1.MD.A.1 Order three objects by length; compare the lengths of two objects indirectly by using a third object.	Major	31, 32
1.MD.A.2 Express the length of an object as a whole number of length units, by laying multiple copies of a shorter object (the length unit) end to end; understand that the length measurement of an object is the number of same-size length units that span it with no gaps or overlaps. *Limit to contexts where the object being measured is spanned by a whole number of length units with no gaps or overlaps.*	Major	33
Tell and write time.		
1.MD.B.3 Tell and write time in hours and half-hours using analog and digital clocks.	Supporting/ Additional	34
Represent and interpret data.		
1.MD.C.4 Organize, represent, and interpret data with up to three categories; ask and answer questions about the total number of data points, how many in each category, and how many more or less are in one category than in another.	Supporting/ Additional	29, 30
Geometry		
Reason with shapes and their attributes.		
1.G.A.1 Distinguish between defining attributes (e.g., triangles are closed and three-sided) versus non-defining attributes (e.g., color, orientation, overall size); build and draw shapes to possess defining attributes.	Supporting/ Additional	26
1.G.A.2 Compose two-dimensional shapes (rectangles, squares, trapezoids, triangles, half-circles, and quarter-circles) or three-dimensional shapes (cubes, right rectangular prisms, right circular cones, and right circular cylinders) to create a composite shape, and compose new shapes from the composite shape.	Supporting/ Additional	27
1.G.A.3 Partition circles and rectangles into two and four equal shares, describe the shares using the words *halves, fourths,* and *quarters,* and use the phrases *half of, fourth of,* and *quarter of.* Describe the whole as two of, or four of the shares. Understand for these examples that decomposing into more equal shares creates smaller shares.	Supporting/ Additional	28

Unit Review Correlations

The tables below show the standards addressed for the items in the Unit Reviews and the corresponding *Ready® Instruction* lesson(s) being assessed by each item. Use this information to adjust lesson plans and focus remediation.

Ready® Common Core Unit Review Correlations

Unit 1: Operations and Algebraic Thinking—Add and Subtract

Question	Standard(s)	Ready® Common Core Student Lesson(s)
1	1.OA.A.1, 1.OA.C.5, 1.OA.C.6	2, 3
2	1.OA.A.1, 1.OA.C.5, 1.OA.C.6	1, 3
3	1.OA.C.5, 1.OA.C.6, 1.OA.D.8	2
4	1.OA.C.5, 1.OA.C.6, 1.OA.D.8	1
5	1.OA.C.5, 1.OA.C.6, 1.OA.D.8	2
6	1.OA.C.5, 1.OA.C.6, 1.OA.D.8	1
7	1.OA.A.1, 1.OA.C.6, 1.OA.D.8	3, 5
8	1.OA.A.1, 1.OA.B.4, 1.OA.C.6, 1.OA.D.8	3, 4
9	1.OA.A.1, 1.OA.C.6	3

Unit 2: Operations and Algebraic Thinking—Learn Facts to 10

Question	Standard(s)	Ready® Common Core Student Lesson(s)
1	1.OA.C.6, 1.OA.D.8	6, 9, 11
2	1.OA.C.6, 1.OA.D.8	7, 11
3	1.OA.C.6, 1.OA.D.7	8, 10, 11
4	1.OA.C.6, 1.OA.D.8	9, 11
5	1.OA.C.6, 1.OA.D.8	7, 11
6	1.OA.B.3, 1.OA.C.6, 1.OA.D.7	8, 10, 11
7	1.OA.B.3, 1.OA.C.6, 1.OA.D.7, 1.OA.D.8	7, 10, 11
8	1.OA.B.3, 1.OA.C.6, 1.OA.D.8	9, 11
9	1.OA.C.6, 1.OA.D.7, 1.OA.D.8	8, 10, 11

Unit 3: Operations and Algebraic Thinking and Number and Operations in Base Ten—Add and Subtract to 20

Question	Standard(s)	Ready® Common Core Student Lesson(s)
1	1.OA.B.3, 1.OA.C.6, 1.NBT.B.2a, 1.NBT.B.2b	12, 13, 14
2	1.OA.B.3, 1.OA.C.6	16
3	1.OA.A.2, 1.OA.B.3, 1.OA.C.6	15
4	1.OA.B.3, 1.OA.C.6	16
5	1.NBT.B.2a, 1.NBT.B.2b	12
6	1.OA.B.3, 1.OA.C.6, 1.NBT.B.2a, 1.NBT.B.2b	13, 14
7	1.OA.A.2, 1.OA.B.3, 1.OA.C.6, 1.NBT.B.2a, 1.NBT.B.2b	12, 13, 14, 15
8	1.OA.C.6, 1.NBT.B.2a, 1.NBT.B.2b	12, 13
9	1.OA.C.6, 1.NBT.B.2a, 1.NBT.B.2b	12, 16

Unit 4: Number and Operations in Base Ten—Tens

Question	Standard(s)	Ready® Common Core Student Lesson(s)
1	1.OA.C.5, 1.NBT.A.1, 1.NBT.C.4	18
2	1.OA.C.5, 1.NBT.A.1, 1.NBT.C.5	18, 19
3	1.OA.C.5, 1.NBT.C.5	19
4	1.OA.C.5, 1.NBT.C.6	19, 20
5	1.OA.C.5, 1.NBT.C.6, 1.NBT.C.4	20
6	1.OA.C.5, 1.NBT.A.1	18
7	1.NBT.B.2a, 1.NBT.B.2c	17
8	1.OA.C.5, 1.NBT.C.4, 1.NBT.C.6	19
9	1.NBT.B.2a, 1.NBT.B.2c, 1.NBT.C.4, 1.NBT.C.6	17, 20

Unit 5: Number and Operations in Base Ten—Tens and Ones

Question	Standard(s)	Ready® Common Core Student Lesson(s)
1	1.NBT.B.2a, 1.NBT.B.2c, 1.NBT.B.3	22
2	1.NBT.B.2a, 1.NBT.C.4	21, 23, 24
3	1.NBT.B.2a, 1.NBT.B.2c	21
4	1.NBT.B.2a, 1.NBT.B.2c, 1.NBT.C.4	21, 23
5	1.NBT.B.2a, 1.NBT.B.2c, 1.NBT.B.3	22
6	1.NBT.B.2a, 1.NBT.B.2c, 1.NBT.C.4	24
7	1.NBT.B.2a, 1.NBT.B.2c, 1.NBT.B.3	22
8	1.NBT.B.2a, 1.NBT.B.2c, 1.NBT.C.4	25
9	1.NBT.B.2a, 1.NBT.B.2c, 1.NBT.C.4	21, 23, 24, 25

Unit 6: Geometry—Shapes

Question	Standard(s)	Ready® Common Core Student Lesson(s)
1	1.G.A.3	28
2	1.G.A.3	28
3	1.G.A.1	26
4	1.G.A.2	27
5	1.G.A.1	26
6	1.G.A.2	27
7	1.G.A.1, 1.G.A.2	26, 27
8	1.G.A.1	26
9	1.G.A.1, 1.G.A.2, 1.G.A.3	26, 27, 28

Unit 7: Measurement and Data—How Many? How Much? How Long?

Question	Standard(s)	Ready® Common Core Student Lesson(s)
1	1.MD.A.1	31
2	1.MD.B.3	34
3	1.MD.C.4, 1.OA.A.1, 1.OA.C.6	29, 30
4	1.MD.A.1	31, 32
5	1.MD.B.3	34
6	1.MD.A.1, 1.MD.A.2	31, 32, 33

Unit 1: Operations and Algebraic Thinking— Add and Subtract

Which lessons are students building upon?

Kindergarten, Lesson 11
Count 10
K.CC.A.3, K.CC.B.4a, K.CC.B.4b, K.CC.B.4c, K.CC.B.5

Kindergarten, Lesson 14
Understand Addition
K.OA.A.1, K.OA.A.3, K.OA.A.5

Kindergarten, Lesson 18
Add Within 10
K.OA.A.1, K.OA.A.3, K.OA.A.5

Kindergarten, Lesson 11
Count 10
K.CC.A.3, K.CC.B.4a, K.CC.B.4b, K.CC.B.4c, K.CC.B.5

Kindergarten, Lesson 16
Understand Subtraction
K.OA.A.1, K.OA.A.3, K.OA.A.5

Kindergarten, Lesson 19
Subtract Within 10
K.OA.A.1, K.OA.A.3, K.OA.A.5

Kindergarten, Lesson 18
Add Within 10
K.OA.A.1, K.OA.A.3, K.OA.A.5

Kindergarten, Lesson 19
Subtract Within 10
K.OA.A.1, K.OA.A.3, K.OA.A.5

Kindergarten, Lesson 18
Add Within 10
K.OA.A.1, K.OA.A.3, K.OA.A.5

Kindergarten, Lesson 19
Subtract Within 10
K.OA.A.1, K.OA.A.3, K.OA.A.5

Kindergarten, Lesson 20
Practice Facts to 5
K.OA.A.3, K.OA.A.5

Kindergarten, Lesson 18
Add Within 10
K.OA.A.1, K.OA.A.3, K.OA.A.5

Kindergarten, Lesson 19
Subtract Within 10
K.OA.A.1, K.OA.A.3, K.OA.A.5

Kindergarten, Lesson 20
Practice Facts to 5
K.OA.A.3, K.OA.A.5

Which lessons are students preparing for?

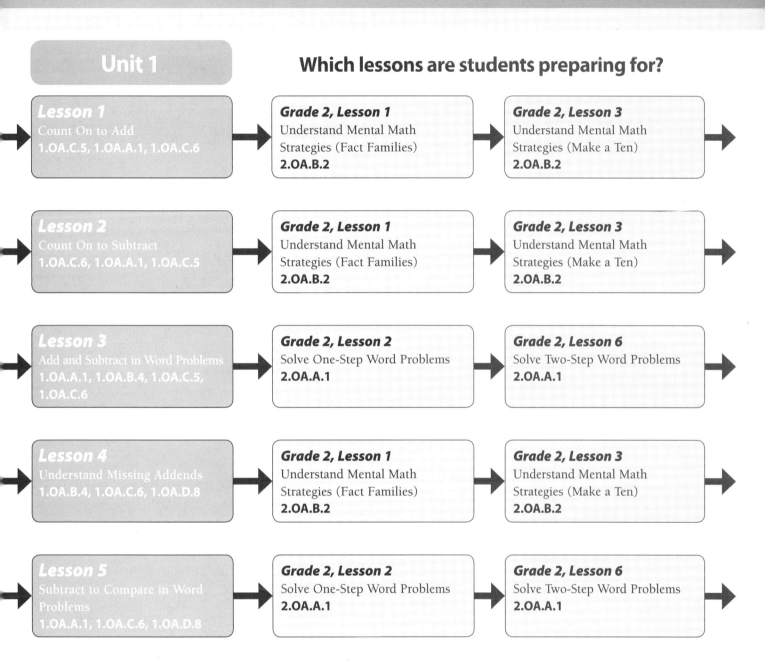

Lesson 1
Count On to Add
1.OA.C.5, 1.OA.A.1, 1.OA.C.6

Grade 2, Lesson 1
Understand Mental Math
Strategies (Fact Families)
2.OA.B.2

Grade 2, Lesson 3
Understand Mental Math
Strategies (Make a Ten)
2.OA.B.2

Lesson 2
Count On to Subtract
1.OA.C.6, 1.OA.A.1, 1.OA.C.5

Grade 2, Lesson 1
Understand Mental Math
Strategies (Fact Families)
2.OA.B.2

Grade 2, Lesson 3
Understand Mental Math
Strategies (Make a Ten)
2.OA.B.2

Lesson 3
Add and Subtract in Word Problems
1.OA.A.1, 1.OA.B.4, 1.OA.C.5,
1.OA.C.6

Grade 2, Lesson 2
Solve One-Step Word Problems
2.OA.A.1

Grade 2, Lesson 6
Solve Two-Step Word Problems
2.OA.A.1

Lesson 4
Understand Missing Addends
1.OA.B.4, 1.OA.C.6, 1.OA.D.8

Grade 2, Lesson 1
Understand Mental Math
Strategies (Fact Families)
2.OA.B.2

Grade 2, Lesson 3
Understand Mental Math
Strategies (Make a Ten)
2.OA.B.2

Lesson 5
Subtract to Compare in Word
Problems
1.OA.A.1, 1.OA.C.6, 1.OA.D.8

Grade 2, Lesson 2
Solve One-Step Word Problems
2.OA.A.1

Grade 2, Lesson 6
Solve Two-Step Word Problems
2.OA.A.1

Lesson 1 (Student Book pages 2–5)

Count On to Add

LESSON OBJECTIVES

- Add within ten.
- Apply the counting on strategy.
- Analyze counting strategies.

PREREQUISITE SKILLS

- Count up to 10 objects.
- Interpret a number sentence.
- Understand addition as putting things together.

VOCABULARY

add: to put together two or more quantities; to find the total of two or more numbers; to find how many in all

addition sentence: one number is added to another in a sentence with numbers and symbols

commutative property of addition: changing the order of addends does not change the total

count on: start with one addend and count to find a total

number path: a diagram that shows numbers in sequential order

tape diagram: a diagram used to represent part-whole number relationships; also known as a bar model

total: a number found as the result of adding

THE LEARNING PROGRESSION

In Kindergarten, children count objects using one-to-one correspondence, apply counting strategies to addition within 10, and represent the addition with physical models, pictures, and a number sentence.

In Grade 1, children use strategies to add within 20 with the unknown in all three positions. **In this lesson,** children relate counting to addition by applying the counting on strategy to find an unknown sum. Children develop reasoning skills as they see a group of objects as a single quantity from which they can count on. They also see the number that they start with as a part of the total and keep track of how many they count on.

In Grade 2, children continue to use addition strategies mentally, with the goal of attaining fluency with sums to 20. They also extend addition skills to two-digit numbers.

Ready *Teacher Toolbox*   *Teacher-Toolbox.com*

	Prerequisite Skills	*1.OA.C.5*
Ready Lessons	✓ ✓ ✓	✓
Tools for Instruction		✓ ✓
Interactive Tutorials	✓ ✓	✓ ✓

CCSS Focus

1.OA.C.5 Relate counting to addition and subtraction (e.g., by counting on 2 to add 2).

ADDITIONAL STANDARDS: **1.OA.C.6, 1.OA.A.1** (see page A36 for full text.)

STANDARDS FOR MATHEMATICAL PRACTICE: **SMP 2, 3, 5, 6, 7** (see page A9 for full text.)

Opening Activity: Act Out Counting On to Add

Objective: Explore addition as combining two groups whose sum can be found through models and strategies.	**Materials** For each child: none

Overview

Children explore the concept of addition, connecting a physical model to a problem situation. Children share ideas for strategies to find a sum and record a solution using pictures or drawings.

Step by Step (15–20 minutes)

1 Introduce the problem.

- Select 3 boys and 2 girls to come to the front of the class. Separate the boys from the girls, leaving a little distance between them. Say: *I want 3 boys and 2 girls to work together in a group. How can I find out how many children in all are in the group?* Clarify, as necessary, that both boys and girls belong to the more general group known as "children."

2 Explore strategies.

- Children should see this as a "put together" situation and suggest combining the two groups. Have children find the total number of children and encourage them to share the strategies they used. Some children may count all the children at the front of the class, others may say they just know 3 and 2 is 5, and some may start with the 3 boys and count on 4, 5 (girls) to find the total.

3 Solve a different problem.

- Pose a similar problem. Say: *I decided I want 4 boys and 2 girls in a group. How many children are in the group now?*

- Tell children to hold up one hand and show the number of boys with their fingers. Then have them hold up the other hand to show the number of girls. Ask: *How can you tell the number of fingers you are holding up altogether?*

- Listen for strategies such as counting by 2s, counting all fingers, saying 4 on one hand then counting 5, 6 on the other hand. Some children may recognize that another boy was added so the sum is 1 more than 5.

- Ask children to try a strategy someone else suggested and talk with a partner about the strategies they liked best and why. **Note:** It is important for children to try various strategies but recognize that they each have preferences, and one strategy is not necessarily better than another.

Check for Understanding

Pose the problem: *There are 5 girls and 3 boys on a team. How many children are on the team?*

Tell children to pick the strategy they prefer and draw a picture to show how they solved the problem.

Children may not be able to represent this problem before completing the student-book lesson, but give them a chance to struggle with it before going on. Then explain that the lesson will help them see different ways to solve problems like this one.

STEP BY STEP

- Invite children to share the drawings from the Opening Activity and explain the strategies they used or where they got stuck. Read aloud the text in the Model It. Use the first Mathematical Discourse question to help children connect the picture to the model.

- Ask children how they know there are 5 girls and 5 smiley faces. Some may need to count, while others may suggest that the problem tells them that there are 5.

- Discuss that when counting on, you start with one of the given numbers and then count on by the other number. Refer children to the model and show them how to use their fingers to count on to find the total.

> **SMP Tip:** Connect the physical activity to the model by having children first place counters on the smiley faces, representing the girls and eliciting that these show a group of 5. Have children count on as they add counters to represent boys. As they do so, children refine the concept of counting on as a strategy for finding the number of objects in a group without having to count every member of the group. (SMP 6)

- Stress the importance of keeping track of the number of times they count on. Use the second Mathematical Discourse question to help children decide which number to start with.

- Ask children how the number sentence relates to the model, the picture, and the problem.

Hands-On Activity

Materials For each child: 8 counters

Model the problem using counters. Have children place 5 counters on the left side of their desk and count on as they add each of the 3 counters to the right side of the desk.

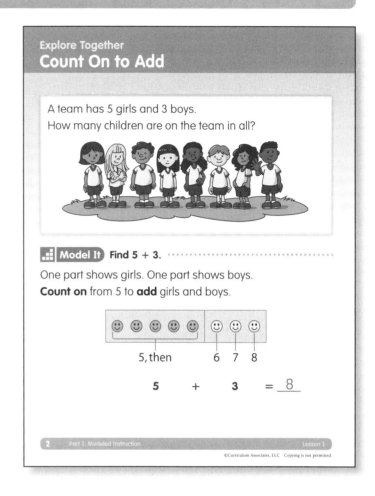

Mathematical Discourse

- *How is the model like the picture of the boys and girls? How is it different?*

  The model has 5 girls and 3 boys like the picture. In the model, the girls are all together and the boys are all together. In the picture, they are mixed up. The picture shows boys and girls; the model just shows smiley faces.

- *Why does it make sense to start with the girls rather than the boys to count on?*

  Children may give a variety of responses. Look for suggestions that indicate it is easier to count on 3 than to count on 5 and may reduce the chance of errors.

STEP BY STEP

Materials Optional: connecting cubes

- Read the problem aloud. Allow children to share strategies for solving the problem and then ask how they might use the counting on strategy.

- If children need physical models to understand or use the strategy, have connecting cubes available for modeling the problem and counting on.

- Ask: *Why does it make sense to start with the yellow blocks?* Children should realize that it is easier to count on by the fewer numbers of objects.

- Draw attention to the Model It. Have children count on by swiping their finger across the bar of 6, saying "6" and then pointing to each red block as they count "7, 8." Ask them to complete and read the number sentence. Have children explain how the 2 in the number sentence and the number they counted on are related.

- **Error Alert** Read the Talk About It aloud. Demonstrate the incorrect counting and ask: *What's wrong with the way I counted?* Encourage children to describe the error to a partner before discussing the correct way to count.

- As a class, discuss why the bar of blocks cannot be counted as 1. Have a volunteer demonstrate the correct way to count and ask children to record it. Help them connect the numbers in the number sentence to the counting.

Fluency Practice

Practice with the number path model.

Materials For each child: Number Paths (Activity Sheet 1)

Distribute the Number Paths worksheet. Have children shade the squares 1–6. Then have them circle the 6 and draw a curved arrow from 6 to 7 and from 7 to 8. Make sure children notice that the two jumps represent counting on two. Write several different number sentences on the board. Ask children to model the addition on number paths.

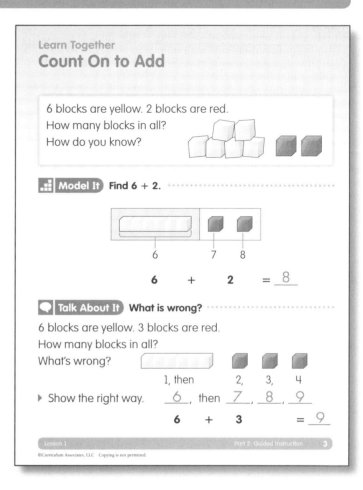

Mathematical Discourse

- Display 2 red blocks to the left of 6 yellow blocks. Ask: *How can we use the counting on strategy to count these blocks?*

  Some children may suggest reversing the order to count the yellow blocks first. Some may recognize that they can start with the yellow blocks and count on from right to left.

SMP Tip: The Mathematical Discourse is a concrete demonstration of the commutative property. Asking children to describe the sets using two different number sentences (e.g., $4 + 3 = 7$ and $3 + 4 = 7$) allows them to make a symbolic connection. Emphasize that the sum has not changed even though the order of the addends has. (SMP 7)

STEP BY STEP

Materials Optional: connecting cubes

- Read the example problem aloud. Encourage children to use their fingers to model the addends and find the sum. Ask: *Why do you think there are only 3 markers shown?*

- Guide children to recognize that the number 5 displayed represents 5 red markers. Help them see that this is like counting on with their fingers, saying 5 without counting all the fingers first and then holding up each of the 3 fingers as they are counted.

- Make connecting cubes available for children who need them as they solve Problems 1 and 2. They can put together 5 connecting cubes, say 5, then count on the additional 3 cubes.

- Direct attention to Problem 2. Ask children why it might be helpful to have the 6 written on the red blocks. They may want to write the start number like this with other counting on problems.

- Continue to emphasize the importance of tracking how many are counted on.

Concept Extension

Build the concept of a variable.

Materials For display: small box, 8 pencils or other classroom objects

Display the box and tell children there are 5 pencils inside the box. Set 3 single pencils next to the box and ask: *How many pencils do I have altogether? How can you count on to find out?* Listen for counts of "5 . . ., 6, 7, 8" and ask how they knew to start with 5. Children should recognize that since they know there are 5 pencils in the box, they do not need to be counted or drawn separately.

> **SMP Tip:** Draw a rectangle to represent the box and 3 smaller rectangles to represent the single pencils. Model starting at 5 and counting on 3. Have children record the process in a number sentence to make a symbolic connection to the problem. *(SMP 2)*

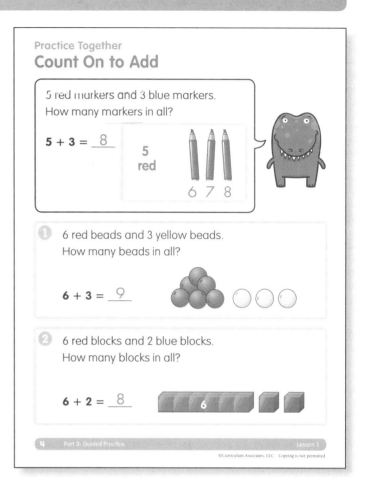

Mathematical Discourse

- *How can you check to be sure you counted on correctly?*

  Children may suggest counting on again, counting all the objects, or using a physical model or fingers to make sure.

- *How does knowing the total of 6 + 3 help you find the answer to 6 + 2?*

  Some children may notice that both number sentences start with 6 but the other addends are different. Since 2 is 1 less than 3, the sum of 6 + 2 is 1 less than the sum of 6 + 3.

STEP BY STEP

- Before children work on this page, review the models used in this lesson. Emphasize that children are free to use whatever way helps them solve the problem.

- Read each problem aloud, then have children work independently to solve.

- For Problem 4, observe to see if children are still struggling with the idea of the commutative property or starting with the greater number.

- You may wish to draw attention to the number sentence in Problem 5 and ask how this number sentence is different from the others in the lesson. Use the Mathematical Discourse question to begin talking about the concept of equality.

- Ask children who solve Problem 5 without drawing the shapes to explain which strategy they used.

ELL Support

Present visual and language support to help children see the relationships presented in the problems. For example: *Ants and bees are both kinds of bugs.*

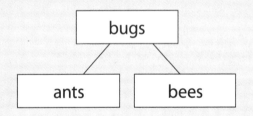

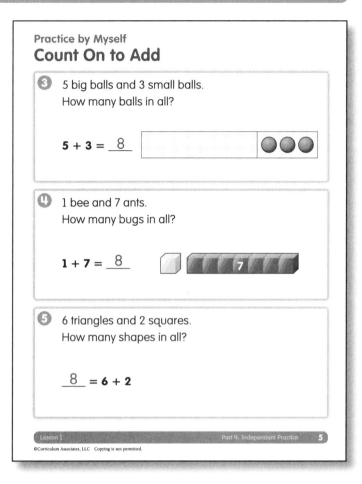

Practice by Myself
Count On to Add

3   5 big balls and 3 small balls.
How many balls in all?

5 + 3 = __8__

4   1 bee and 7 ants.
How many bugs in all?

1 + 7 = __8__

5   6 triangles and 2 squares.
How many shapes in all?

__8__ **= 6 + 2**

Mathematical Discourse

- *Why is it okay to sometimes write the total at the beginning of the number sentence and sometimes at the end?*

  Children may realize that the total is always the same whether it is to the left or right of the equal sign. They may also recognize that the equal sign means the two sides are the same.

SMP Tip: Seeing number sentences with the totals on both the left and right helps reinforce the idea of a number sentence as a representation of two equal quantities. *(SMP 6)*

Assessment and Remediation

- Ask children to count on to find the answer to the following problem: 7 children and 2 adults are at the park. How many people are at the park? [9 people at the park]

- For children who are still struggling, use the chart below to guide remediation.

- After providing remediation, check children's understanding using the following problem: There are 6 blue hats and 2 red hats. How many hats? [8 hats]

If the error is . . .	Children may . . .	To remediate . . .
8	have counted on using 7 as the first count.	Have children model the addends with counters, each in a different color. Ask what group of counters shows the 7 children. Move one of the 2 counters next to the group of 7 and ask: *How many are there now?* Repeat for the remaining counter. Separate the counters and have the child demonstrate the counting on action. Repeat again using other models such as fingers and a number path.
any other number	have miscounted.	Give children counters and a strip of paper divided into ten sections. Help them model the problem using two-color counters. First have them place 7 counters of one color on the strip, counting each one. Then ask them to count on from 7 as they add 2 counters of a different color.

Hands-On Activity

Model number sentences.

Materials For each pair: two-color counters, number sentence cards

- Make number sentence cards for sums to 10. Each includes one addend that is a 1, 2, or 3. Distribute the cards and counters to pairs.

- Have children place the cards face down. One partner picks a card. The other models the addends with two groups of counters. The child who picked the card counts on to find the total. If they both agree it is correct, they write the total on the card.

- Partners alternate roles and repeat until all cards are completed.

Challenge Activity

Find counting patterns.

Materials Optional: counters

Write these number sentences on the board:

$6 + 3 = 9$
$6 + 2 = 8$
$6 + 1 = ?$

- Ask children if they can think of an easy way to find the missing total. Listen for responses that indicate that as one addend goes down by 1, the total goes down by 1.

- Challenge children to write similar groups of number sentences. Suggest that they draw pictures or use counters to help. Lead them to also explore what happens when the second addend stays the same and the first addend changes.

Lesson 2 (Student Book pages 6–9)
Count On to Subtract

LESSON OBJECTIVES

- Apply the counting on strategy to subtract within 10.
- Model the counting on strategy using physical and visual models.
- Connect the counting on strategy to a number sentence.

PREREQUISITE SKILLS

- Add/subtract within 5.
- Represent addition and subtraction situations using physical models and number sentences.
- Count on to add.

VOCABULARY

subtract: to take objects away from a group or to compare groups

subtraction sentence: one number is subtracted from another in a sentence with symbols and numbers

During the lesson you will review the key term:

count on: start with one addend and count to find a total

THE LEARNING PROGRESSION

In Kindergarten, children explore addition and subtraction within 10, using physical models and by acting out situations. Fluency within 5 is expected and is represented in drawings and with number sentences.

In Grade 1, children gain fluency for addition and subtraction within 10 by developing the use of strategies. **In this lesson,** the familiar strategy of counting on is extended to subtraction in the context of "take from" and "take apart" situations. Children analyze the situations to identify the number being subtracted and then count on from that number to find the difference. The strategy of counting on to subtract is a building block for understanding the relationship between addition and subtraction.

In Grade 2, children fluently add and subtract within 20 using mental strategies, articulating why the strategy works and recognizing the relationship between addition and subtraction.

Ready *Teacher Toolbox*   *Teacher-Toolbox.com*

	Prerequisite Skills	1.OA.C.6
Ready Lessons	✓ ✓ ✓	✓
Tools for Instruction	✓ ✓	
Interactive Tutorials	✓ ✓	✓ ✓

CCSS Focus

1.OA.C.6 Add and subtract within 20, demonstrating fluency for addition and subtraction within 10. Use strategies such as counting on; making ten (e.g., $8 + 6 = 8 + 2 + 4 = 10 + 4 = 14$); decomposing a number leading to a ten (e.g., $13 - 4 = 13 - 3 - 1 = 10 - 1 = 9$); using the relationship between addition and subtraction (e.g., knowing that $8 + 4 = 12$, one knows $12 - 8 = 4$); and creating equivalent but easier or known sums (e.g., adding $6 + 7$ by creating the known equivalent $6 + 6 + 1 = 12 + 1 = 13$).

ADDITIONAL STANDARDS: ***1.OA.A.1, 1.OA.C.5*** *(see page A36 for full text)*

STANDARDS FOR MATHEMATICAL PRACTICE: ***SMP 2, 3, 6, 7*** *(see page A9 for full text)*

Opening Activity: Relate Subtraction, Addition, and Counting On

Objective: Explore the relationship between addition and subtraction.	**Materials** For each child: • connecting cubes (optional)

Overview

Children act out a subtraction situation and use results to reinforce the concept of embedded numbers. They then apply the concept to counting on to subtract.

Step by Step (20–30 minutes)

1 **Pose the problem.**

- Say: *Five children are playing ball. Three children leave. How many children are still playing ball?*

2 **Act it out.**

- Select a group of 5 children to come to the front of the class and stand in a line. As you repeat the problem, have 3 of the children turn and take a couple of steps away from the others.

- Ask: *How many children are still playing ball? How do you know?* Children will likely count the remaining players to find that 2 are still playing ball.

- Ask children how this problem can be represented as a subtraction sentence. Listen to a few responses, then write on the board 5 − 3 = 2.

3 **Introduce counting on to subtract.**

- Have 5 different children stand in a line, and then again ask 3 children to turn and take a couple of steps away. Point out that the 3 children who leave are part of the original group of 5 playing ball.

- Tell children that you are going to start with the 3 children who leave and count on to 5. Say "three" and then hold up two fingers one at a time as you count "four, five."

- Ask: *How many did I count on?* [2] Elicit that this action can be represented by the addition sentence 3 + 2 = 5. Write this on the board next to the related subtraction problem.

- Encourage children to describe how the addition and subtraction sentences are alike.

4 **Apply counting on to other subtraction problems.**

- Pose a similar problem, saying that 6 children are playing ball and 4 children leave. Invite children to suggest ways to determine how many children are still playing ball. Discuss their recommendations. You may want to give children connecting cubes and ask them to demonstrate how they might use these to solve the problem.

- Make sure that counting on is one of the strategies you discuss and demonstrate. Continue to make the connection between the subtraction sentence and the related addition sentence.

- Present other subtraction problems as needed to observe whether children are able to make the connection between subtraction and counting on.

Check for Understanding

Look for children who start at 1 and count all instead of counting on. The Visual Model on page 13 will help reinforce the idea of starting at a number other than 1 and counting on.

STEP BY STEP

- Tell children that this page shows a model they can use to solve problems like the one from the Opening Activity. Read aloud the problem at the top of the page.

- Ask children to discuss what is happening in the problem—what they know and what they need to find out. Remind them that there are many ways to find the answer.

- Ask the first Mathematical Discourse question. Encourage children to share mental strategies and compare them to the strategies they used in the Introduction.

- Draw attention to Model It. Ask children to describe how this model is similar to counting on using their fingers.

SMP Tip: Ask children to describe how the number sentence tells what is happening in the problem. In order to contextualize and decontextualize the information in this problem, children need to make a clear connection between the problem situation, the illustration, and the number sentence. (SMP 2)

Fluency Practice

Subtract with the number path model.

Materials For each child: Number Paths (Activity Sheet 1), counters

Write on the board 6 − 4 = ___ and 4 + ___ = 6. Have children put a counter on 4 on the number path. Ask them to count on to 6 and tell how many they counted. Complete the number sentences as they respond. Write several different subtraction sentences on the board. Ask children to write the corresponding addition sentence, use the number path to model the problem, then complete the number sentences.

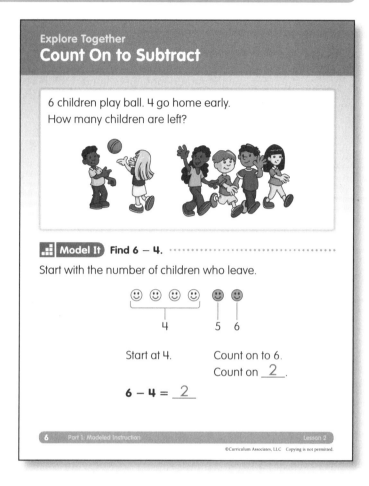

Mathematical Discourse

- Say: *Close your eyes and think about the problem. (read the problem).* Ask: *How can you tell in your head how many children are left after 4 go home?*

    Children may respond that they can use fingers to count on. Some may say they can see the 2 children that are left. Be sure children can justify their responses.

- *How can you make sure you found the right answer to this problem?*

    Some children may return to the original problem and act it out to check. Others may add 4 and 2 to get 6, recognizing that 4 and 2 are parts of the 6 children who are playing.

STEP BY STEP

- Read the problem aloud. Ask: *How is this like the problem about the children playing ball? How is it different?* Help children see that this is a subtraction problem, but it is not a "take away" situation.

- Some children may not understand how this problem can be modeled with subtraction since nothing is being "taken away." Ask the class to describe why subtraction makes sense for this problem. Use the illustration as necessary to help them recognize that there are 7 bikes in all; some are red and some are black. They can subtract the number of red bikes from all the bikes to find the number of black bikes.

- Discuss the number path with children. Point out that the entire block of 4 boxes represents the red bikes, and that is why you start at 4. Ask: *Why do you stop at 7 when counting on in this problem?* [There are 7 bikes in all.]

- Help children see that the addition sentence for this problem models the counting on process they used.

> **SMP Tip:** Seeing pairs of related number sentences in this problem (7 − 4 = ___ and 4 + ___ = 7) and throughout the lesson helps reinforce the idea of inverse operations and prepare children for work with number bonds and fact families. *(SMP 7)*

- **Error Alert** Read the Talk About It problem aloud. Tell children to think about the ways that Buzz and Boom counted on. Encourage children to share ideas and justify using blocks or drawings. Use the Mathematical Discourse question to discuss the error.

Mathematical Discourse

- *What did Buzz do wrong?*

    Children should respond that Buzz counted the 5 as one of the girls. They should recognize that 5 is the number of boys, so 5 is not included in the count for the number of girls.

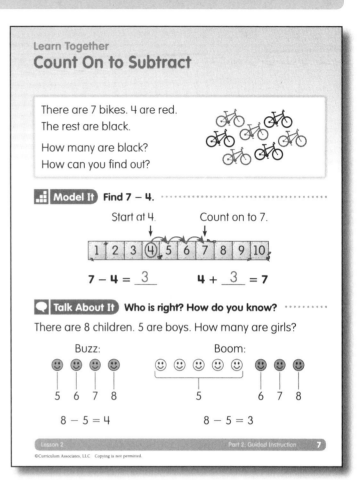

Visual Model

Write $4 + \boxed{} = 7$ on the board and ask children what they think the box means. Since the box represents how many more are needed to get to 7, show children how they can make tally marks or dots in the box as they count on:

$$4 + \boxed{\bullet\ \bullet\ \bullet} = 7 \text{ so } 4 + 3 = 7$$
$$5\ 6\ 7$$

STEP BY STEP

Materials Optional: blocks

- Read the example problem aloud. Ask children to explain why the subtraction sentence $7 - 5 = ?$ can be used to model this problem. Then guide children to make the connection between this subtraction sentence and the addition sentence $5 + 2 = 7$.

- Read Problem 1. Give children time to think about the problem and then invite volunteers to demonstrate strategies for solving it. Have children describe how the number sentences given with the problem model the situation and/or strategy used.

> **SMP Tip:** Draw attention to the addition sentence $8 = \_\_\_ + 5$ and ask why it can also be written $5 + \_\_\_ = 8$. Help children recognize that in addition, the order of the addends doesn't affect the total because of the commutative property of addition. Also emphasize that either the addends or the total can be placed to the left or right of the equal sign. (*SMP 7*)

- Tell children to look at Problem 2. Ask why the 6 is circled. Make sure children understand that the 6 represents the number of balloons that popped. Support children who need help by encouraging them to model the problem with blocks and/or by coloring or outlining the block of squares 1–6 on the page.

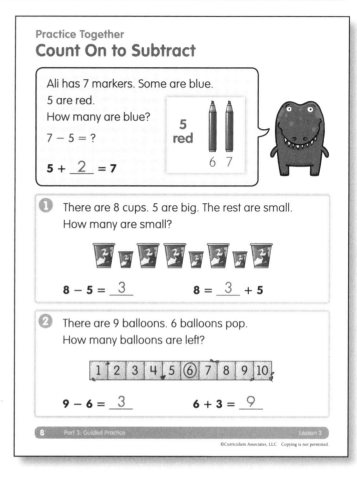

Practice Together
Count On to Subtract

Ali has 7 markers. Some are blue.
5 are red.
How many are blue?
$7 - 5 = ?$

5 red

$5 + \underline{2} = 7$

① There are 8 cups. 5 are big. The rest are small. How many are small?

$8 - 5 = \underline{3}$ $8 = \underline{3} + 5$

② There are 9 balloons. 6 balloons pop. How many balloons are left?

| 1 | 2 | 3 | 4 | 5 | ⑥ | 7 | 8 | 9 | 10 |

$9 - 6 = \underline{3}$ $6 + 3 = \underline{9}$

8   Part 3: Guided Practice   Lesson 2
©Curriculum Associates, LLC   Copying is not permitted.

Mathematical Discourse

- *How does adding help you make sense of a subtraction problem?*

    Children should see that addition models the process of counting on, and some may say it is easier to think of counting on than counting back.

ELL Support

In Problem 2, some children may interpret the word "left" as a directional term. Tell them that in problems like Problem 2, the word "left" means "left over" and refers to the balloons that did not pop.

STEP BY STEP

- Before children work on this page, review the models used in this lesson. Children may complete the models given with the problem and then write the answers in the number sentences. Emphasize that children are free to use whatever way helps them solve the problem.

- Read each problem aloud, then have children work independently to solve.

- You may wish to point out that each problem is modeled by a subtraction sentence and that the related addition sentence gives them a clue about how to count on to solve the subtraction sentence.

- For those who struggle to start Problem 5, ask questions such as: *What do you know about the flowers? How many might you draw first? Why? How many more do you need to draw?* Ask the first Mathematical Discourse question to promote algebraic thinking—any shape or symbol can be used to represent the flowers.

- The second Mathematical Discourse question can be used to check understanding of the counting on strategy.

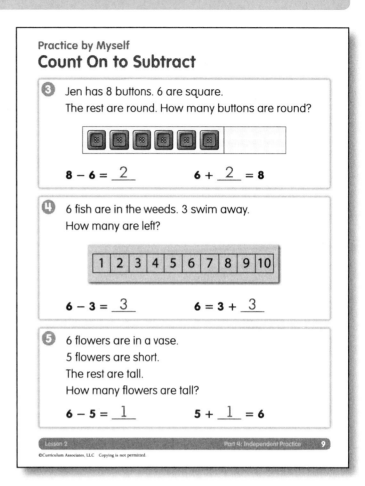

Mathematical Discourse

- *If you don't want to draw flowers, how might you show tall flowers and short flowers?*

    Children may suggest drawing long lines to show tall flowers and short lines to show short flowers. Some may suggest using a tape diagram or other shapes.

- *How is counting on to subtract like counting on to add? How are they different?*

    Children should recognize that the process and the numbers used to start are the same, but counting on to subtract involves finding one addend and not the total.

Assessment and Remediation

- Ask children to find the answer to the following problem: 9 leaves are on a tree. 7 leaves fall off. How many leaves are still on the tree? [2]

- For children who are still struggling, use the chart below to guide remediation.

- After providing remediation, check children's understanding using the following problem: There are 8 apples in a bowl. Some apples are red and some are yellow. 5 are red. How many apples are yellow? [3]

If the error is . . .	Children may . . .	To remediate . . .
3	have counted on 7, 8, 9 including 7 in the counts.	Ask children to show with counters how many leaves fell off the tree and then set these aside. Have them count on more counters to get to 9. Encourage children to compare the result with their original answer. Check answers by putting 2 counters and then 3 counters with the group of 7 and counting to find the total.
16	have counted on 7 from 9.	Have children draw a picture of the problem to see that when 7 leaves are taken from 9, only a portion of the original 9 remain.
any other answer	have miscounted.	Repeat the first remediation to check for accuracy.

Hands-On Activity

Find the number of hidden counters.

Materials For each pair: bowls, counters, whiteboards

- Distribute the materials to pairs of children.

- Use a partner to model the activity. Place a number of counters (5–10) on the desk, count them, and then cover them with the bowl. Have your partner record the number of counters under the bowl.

- Lift one side of the bowl and remove some of the counters so your partner doesn't see how many are left under the bowl. The partner writes a missing addend number sentence, uses the counting on strategy to determine the number of counters under the bowl, and then completes the number sentence.

- After children complete several rounds, talk about what numbers were easy to count on (1, 2, 3), what numbers were not so easy, and why.

Challenge Activity

Write subtraction word problems.

Materials For each child: picture books

- Give each child two or three picture books. Tell them to read or look at the books, thinking about subtraction problems they could write using the pictures or context of the story.

- Ask children to write/dictate two subtraction word problems. You may want to suggest that one be a "take away" problem and the other be a "take apart" problem.

- After writing the two word problems, have children write an addition number sentence and a subtraction number sentence to go with each word problem. Have children find and justify the solution to each one using pictures, visuals, or physical models.

Lesson 3   (Student Book pages 10–13)

Add and Subtract in Word Problems

LESSON OBJECTIVES

- Use strategies, including counting on, to solve addition and subtraction word problems.

- Complete number sentences to solve addition and subtraction word problems.

PREREQUISITE SKILLS

- Count on to add.

- Count on to subtract.

VOCABULARY

addend: a number being added

number bond: a diagram with a total and two addends

During the lesson you will review the key term:

count on: start with one addend and count to find a total

THE LEARNING PROGRESSION

In Kindergarten, children count objects and count forward from a given number. They use objects or drawings to solve word problems and they count all to find the total.

In Grade 1, children move from counting all to counting on to add and subtract. **In this lesson,** children solve "add to," "take from," and "put together/take apart" word problems. Seeing that the unknown appears in different positions helps children begin to develop an algebraic perspective.

In Grade 2, children continue to solve one-step word problems involving all types of situations. They extend this work to solve two-step word problems and add and subtract within 100.

■ Ready *Teacher Toolbox*   *Teacher-Toolbox.com*

	Prerequisite Skills	*1.OA.A.1*
Ready Lessons	✓ ✓	✓
Tools for Instruction	✓ ✓	
Interactive Tutorials	✓ ✓	✓ ✓

17

Opening Activity: Act Out an "Add To" Word Problem

Objective: Act out an "add to" word problem and draw the associated number bond	**Materials** For each child: • paper or personal white board • marker • 2 small toy animals or 2 pictures of an animal

Overview

Children act out an "add to" word problem that is very similar to the Explore Together problem. They count on to reach the total. Then they use a number bond to illustrate the problem and discover that the number sentence has the unknown in the middle position.

Step by Step (10–15 minutes)

1 Pose the problem.

• Tell children to imagine that it's summertime and they are at a picnic. Say: *There is room for 5 children at a picnic table and 3 children are already sitting down. Some more children sit down and now the table is full.* Explain that they need to figure out how many children just got there by acting it out.

2 Model the problem.

• Invite 5 children to act out the problem. Explain that 3 of them will sit down, and then the rest will come and join them.

• Read the problem again and have the children act it out. Tell the 2 children who are joining the original 3 to come in one at a time, while the class counts on from 3.

3 Write a number bond.

• Draw a number bond on the board. Fill in 5 as the total. Ask children to explain what the 5 means. [The total number of children sitting at the table at the end of the problem.]

• Ask children to describe what else the problem tells. Challenge them to identify what other two numbers are needed to complete the number bond. Finish the number bond with their correct suggestions.

• Have children explain what the 3 means [those who were already seated] and then what the 2 means [those who came after]. Point out that the problem tells how many children in all (point to 5) and how many were already seated (point to 3). But it doesn't say how many came after.

4 Write the number sentence and talk about the meaning of the unknown.

• Write "3 + ___ = 5" on the board.

• Have children relate the number sentence to the number bond. Ask them which number is missing and why. [The 2 is missing because the problem says "some more children"; it doesn't say how many "some" is.] Review the meaning of the other numbers.

Check for Understanding

Provide the children with the following problem: *In the hot, dry desert, 1 animal was drinking from a pool of water. Later, a few more animals came. Now there are 4 animals. How many animals came later?*

Have children act out the story in pairs, using their toy animals or pictures, and write a number sentence. Ask them to explain how they decided where to put the numbers in the number sentences.

Children who are able to solve the problem by acting it out are able to make sense of the problem situation. It's likely that many children will not be able to write a number sentence. Activities and suggestions within the lesson will help them with the next step—representing the situation symbolically.

STEP BY STEP

Materials For each child: two-color counters

- Begin by asking children what they learned or what they remember from the Opening Activity. Elicit that the problem told "how many in all" and asked for the number of children who joined the three who were already sitting at the table. Explain that this page includes a similar problem.

- Read aloud the problem at the top of the page. Have a volunteer describe the situation. Discuss and elicit that in this problem, we don't know how many children came to sit down.

- Discuss the Model It. Have children set up three counters to represent the seated children. Help them see the connection between the counters and the three yellow faces. Invite a volunteer to demonstrate counting on to the total using counters of a different color. Relate this to the green faces and the numbers beneath. Use the Mathematical Discourse question to reinforce the counting on strategy.

- Tell children to count the new counters to find the missing addend and then complete the number sentence. Discuss how the number sentence relates to the visual model.

ELL Support

Discuss the difference between "are sitting" and "sit down." "three children are sitting" means the children are already there and they continue to sit. "More children sit down" means that these children join the ones that are already sitting. Children may be familiar with "sit up," meaning "do not slouch." But "sit down" is not the opposite of "sit up." You may want to provide a demonstration of these terms.

Fluency Practice

Materials For each child: Number Bond Recording Sheet (Activity Sheet 2)

On the board, display a number bond with the numbers 3, 2, and 5. Have children record as many number bonds as they can that have totals of 5 and 6. Remind them that the parts can include different numbers and appear in different orders.

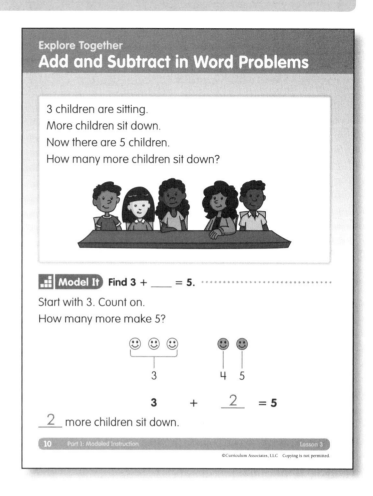

Mathematical Discourse

- *How can you use two-color counters to count on and solve this problem?*

    Children might describe counting from the initial amount (3) until reaching the total (5). Another approach would be to count out 5 red counters and replace 3 of them with yellow counters. Children may come up with other approaches, but the key is to differentiate between the total, the children who are already sitting, and the children who arrive later.

STEP BY STEP

- Read aloud the problem at the top of the page and discuss. Have children relate the illustration and the number sentence to the numbers in the problem.

- Read aloud Model it. Ask children how the addition sentence and the number path can help them count on to solve the problem. Have them draw an arrow on the number path to model the addition and then fill in the blanks.

- To check understanding, ask children how they know that "1" answers the question. Guide them to see that if Jan starts with 6 pencils and gives away 1, she has 5 left. Connect this to the original problem. Use the Mathematical Discourse question to extend this discussion.

- Direct attention to the Talk About It. Read it aloud. Have children explain what the numbers in the problem mean and how the illustration supports the meaning.

- **Error Alert** Point out the two number sentences. Ask: *Who is correct? How do you know?* Listen to responses to ensure children understand that 8 is the total number of pencils and that 4 yellow pencils is one of the addends. Discuss why Boom's number sentence shows this and Buzz's does not.

> **SMP Tip:** Reinforcing the connection between the numbers, the model, and what these represent in the problem helps children contextualize and decontextualize the problem situation. Ask questions to support a focus on the part of the problem and the number sentence they need to find. *(SMP 2)*

Hands-On Activity

Materials For each pair: counters

Have children work in pairs to recreate the Model It with counters. Ask pairs to share and explain what they did. Guide children to consider how their models relate to the visual model and to the number sentence. Ask: *How do counters help you answer the question "How many more to make 6?"* Ask children whether they prefer the visual model or the counters and explain why.

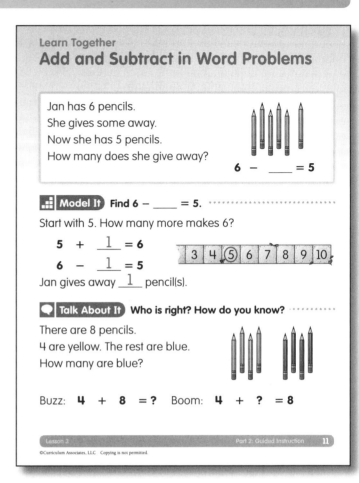

Learn Together
Add and Subtract in Word Problems

Jan has 6 pencils.
She gives some away.
Now she has 5 pencils.
How many does she give away?

$6 - \underline{} = 5$

Model It Find $6 - \underline{} = 5$.

Start with 5. How many more makes 6?

$5 + \underline{1} = 6$

$6 - \underline{1} = 5$

3 4 ⑤ 6 7 8 9 10

Jan gives away $\underline{1}$ pencil(s).

Talk About It Who is right? How do you know?

There are 8 pencils.
4 are yellow. The rest are blue.
How many are blue?

Buzz: $4 + 8 = ?$ Boom: $4 + ? = 8$

Mathematical Discourse

- *How could you check your answer to this problem?*

  Children might suggest using pencils to act it out as an addition problem. Some children may act out the subtraction to verify that the counting on process worked. Encourage children to describe their strategies and tell why their approach makes sense.

STEP BY STEP

- Work through Practice Together. Read the example problem aloud. Ask: *Why is this a subtraction problem?* [The total is given and you need to find the number in one group.] Invite volunteers to describe what the number path model shows, including how many to count on.

- Problem 1 is a "take from" subtraction problem. Have children explain what is happening and tell what the unknown represents. [the toys Greg put away]

- Ask: *How can you use the circles and tape diagram to model this problem?* One way is to put a bracket under 6 circles to represent the toys that are left. Then count on from 6 to 8, making circles to record the counts.

- The number sentence in Problem 2 starts with an unknown quantity. Ask children what strategy they might use to solve this problem. Guide children to discover that they can use a counting on strategy, using the known addend (5), even if it is not the first addend in the number sentence.

> **SMP Tip:** Counting on makes intuitive sense to many children. It also helps them grasp the structure of numbers, such as 6 and 2 within the number 8. You can use number bonds to further reinforce the "hidden" numbers within the numbers in a problem. *(SMP 7)*

Concept Extension

Use the commutative property of addition.

Materials For each pair: a pair of addition expressions written on cards (e.g., 6 + 2 and 2 + 6), one card for each child

After Problem 2, write the completed number sentence 2 + 5 = 7, and draw a model of 2 balls and 5 balls. Write 5 + 2 = 7 under the first number sentence, and draw a model of 5 balls and 2 balls. Ask: *Does it matter which number I start with when I add?* [no] *Why not?* [The total is the same either way.] Give each child a card and have everyone find the child who has the other part of the pair.

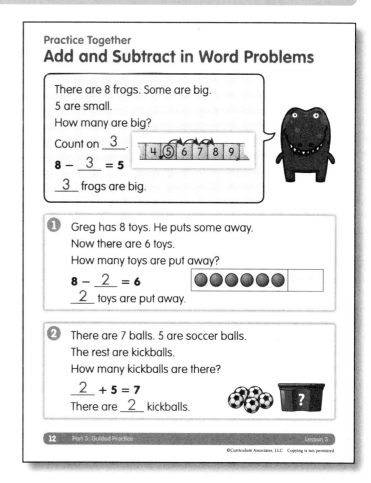

Practice Together
Add and Subtract in Word Problems

There are 8 frogs. Some are big.
5 are small.
How many are big?

Count on __3__.

8 − __3__ = 5

__3__ frogs are big.

1 Greg has 8 toys. He puts some away.
Now there are 6 toys.
How many toys are put away?

8 − __2__ = 6

__2__ toys are put away.

2 There are 7 balls. 5 are soccer balls.
The rest are kickballs.
How many kickballs are there?

__2__ + 5 = 7

There are __2__ kickballs.

Mathematical Discourse

- *When you read a new problem, how would you decide where to put the blank in a number sentence?*

  Children need to understand that the unknown quantity in a number sentence can be in any position and that the location of the "missing number" in a number sentence depends on the meaning of the unknown quantity in the problem context. Discuss the meaning of each quantity, how to construct the associated number sentence, including where the blank goes and why.

STEP BY STEP

- Before children work on this page, review the models used in this lesson. Explain that the models are started for them, and that children can complete them or use some other method they prefer to solve the problem.

- Read each problem aloud, then have children work independently to solve.

- If children have difficulty with the subtraction sentence in Problem 4, guide them to write a related addition sentence.

- Ask volunteers to describe how they solved Problem 5. To check understanding, ask: *What model did you use? Why? How did you know what numbers to write?*

- You may want to take advantage of the opportunity to explore the relationship between addition and subtraction, which is an emphasis of the next lesson. Have children write a related number sentence for each problem: If the given number sentence is addition, they write a subtraction sentence, and vice versa. Use the Mathematical Discourse question to relate addition and subtraction contextually.

Mathematical Discourse

- *Think about what Problem 3 says. What does the addition sentence mean for this problem? What subtraction sentence could be used to solve the problem?*

  The addition sentence is $3 + 3 = 6$. Emma has 3 beads and she gets 3 more beads. Now she has 6 beads. The subtraction sentence that can be used is $6 - 3 = 3$. Emma has 6 beads now. She started with 3 beads, and she got 3 new ones. There are many ways to describe these situations, so allow several children to present their interpretations. Encourage a discussion about each other's ideas.

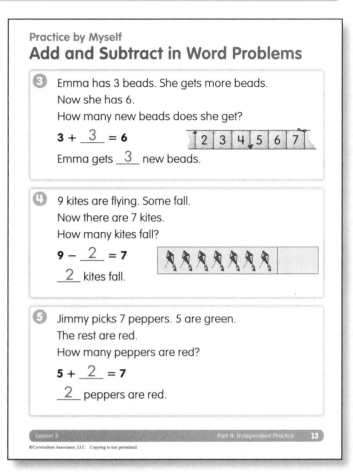

Practice by Myself
Add and Subtract in Word Problems

3 Emma has 3 beads. She gets more beads. Now she has 6. How many new beads does she get?

$3 +$ _3_ $= 6$

Emma gets _3_ new beads.

4 9 kites are flying. Some fall. Now there are 7 kites. How many kites fall?

$9 -$ _2_ $= 7$

_2_ kites fall.

5 Jimmy picks 7 peppers. 5 are green. The rest are red. How many peppers are red?

$5 +$ _2_ $= 7$

_2_ peppers are red.

Assessment and Remediation

- Ask children to draw a model and complete the number sentence to solve the following problem: There are 9 dogs. Some are big. 6 are small. How many are big? 9 − ___ = 6 [9 − 3 = 6]

- For children who are still struggling, use the chart below to guide remediation.

- After providing remediation, check children's understanding using the following problem: There are 7 crackers. Danny eats some. There are 5 left. 7 − ___ = 5. Danny says he ate 3. Is this correct? [No.] Can you correct his mistake? [He ate 2. 7 − 2 = 5]

If the error is . . .	Children may . . .	To remediate . . .
15	not understand the relationship of the numbers to the meaning of the problem, or the part and whole relationship.	Give children 9 counters to represent the 9 dogs. Emphasize that this is the total. Ask them what else they know from the problem. Then guide children to make a group of 6 counters to show the 6 small dogs. Relate the counters to the number sentence. Have children use the counters to count on from 6, then say how many big dogs there are.
9 or 6	not understand the relationship of the numbers to the meaning of the problem.	Ask what each number in the problem and what each number in the number sentence represents. Then have children tell what's missing, or what they need to find. Guide children to answer these questions and have them count on to find the missing number.
a number that is not 9, 6, or 3	not have counted on correctly.	Review the meaning of the numbers in the problem. Ask: *How do you know what number to start with to count on? How do you know when to stop? How do you find how many dogs are big?* Then ask children to try the problem again.

Hands-On Activity

Count on to solve subtraction word problems.

Materials For display: bag, cubes, paper, pencil

- Put some number of cubes in the bag. Invite one child to help you with the activity.

- Tell a story: *This bag has [number] cubes in it. [Child's name] takes some out.* (Child removes and conceals some cubes. Then you dump the bag.) *There are [number] cubes left. How many did [child's name] take?*

- To answer the question, children count on from the visible cubes to reach the total.

- Reveal the hidden cubes. Repeat the story, with different numbers.

Challenge Activity

Retell a subtraction story as addition, then solve.

Materials For each child: index cards, counters (counters are optional)

- Write subtraction stories on cards, with the missing number being subtracted (e.g., 7 puppets: some are people, 5 are animals). Have children retell the story as an addition story, write a number sentence, and solve (e.g., 5 puppets are animals, some are people and there are 7 in all. 5 + ___ = 7, so 2 puppets are people). Children may use counters. Discuss how the stories and the number sentences are related and generalize how addition and subtraction are related.

Lesson 4 (Student Book pages 14–17)

Understand Missing Addends

LESSON OBJECTIVES

- Understand the relationship between addition and subtraction.
- Write a missing addend sentence for a corresponding subtraction sentence.
- Connect addition and subtraction sentences to a number bond.
- Relate subtraction sentences and missing addend sentences to a problem situation.

PREREQUISITE SKILLS

- Add and subtract within 10.
- Model addition and subtraction problems with number sentences.

VOCABULARY

During the lesson you will review the key terms:

addend: a number being added

total: a number found as the result of adding

THE LEARNING PROGRESSION

In Kindergarten, children solve addition and subtraction problems within 10 as well as decompose numbers to 10 using objects or drawings.

In Grade 1, children fluently add and subtract within 10 by applying strategies and by recognizing the relationship between addition and subtraction. **In this lesson,** children explore the concept of missing addends through the visual model of a number bond and by utilizing addition to solve a subtraction problem. Connecting a number bond to its corresponding number sentences is achieved through hands-on exploration and visual models, and by engaging children in open-ended problem solving.

In Grade 2, children continue to use the relationship between addition and subtraction as one strategy for developing fluency with addition and subtraction within 20. They also learn to apply mental strategies and solve problems with the unknown in all positions.

Ready *Teacher Toolbox* — Teacher-Toolbox.com

	Prerequisite Skills	1.OA.B.4
Ready Lessons	✓ ✓ ✓	✓
Tools for Instruction	✓	
Interactive Tutorials		✓ ✓

CCSS Focus

1.OA.B.4 Understand subtraction as an unknown-addend problem. *For example, subtract 10 − 8 by finding the number that makes 10 when added to 8.*

ADDITIONAL STANDARDS: **1.OA.C.6, 1.OA.D.8** *(see page A36 for full text)*

STANDARDS FOR MATHEMATICAL PRACTICE: **SMP 1, 2, 3, 4, 7, 8** *(see page A9 for full text)*

Opening Activity: Show Missing Addends in Number Bonds

Objective: Explore missing addends and number bonds

Materials For each child:
- counters, paper, markers
- Number Bond Mat (Activity Sheet 3)

Overview

Children explore the concept of missing addends by modeling a problem with counters on a number bond mat.

Step by Step (20–25 minutes)

1 Pose the problem.

- Present the problem: *8 rabbits are eating lunch. Some rabbits eat carrots and some eat lettuce. 5 rabbits eat carrots. How many rabbits eat lettuce?*

2 Use familiar strategies to model the problem.

- Encourage children to think of what they would do to solve the problem. Remind them that there are many ways to solve.

- Provide children access to paper, markers, counters, and other available classroom materials and ask them to show how to solve the problem.

- Invite volunteers to share their solution strategies with the class. Ask questions such as: *What does the group of 8 show? Why did you move 5 there?*

- Ask children to identify number sentences that model the problem. Record them on the board. Discuss how each sentence does or does not model the problem. Guide children to identify two addition and two subtraction sentences using the numbers 5, 3, and 8. Erase all but these four number sentences.

3 Use a number bond to model the problem.

- Provide each child with a number bond mat and ask them to place 8 counters in the top section. On the board, display a number bond with 8 circles in the top box and the bottom sections labeled "Carrots" and "Lettuce."

- Ask children to tell how they might show that 5 of the 8 bunnies eat carrots. Guide them to move 5 of the counters from the top portion of the mat to the section labeled "Carrots." Mimic this action on the board by erasing 5 circles in the top box and drawing 5 circles in the "carrots" section.

- Discuss how the number bond can help you find the number of rabbits that eat lettuce. Have children move the 3 counters from the top box to the "lettuce" section. Do the same with the number bond on the board and write the appropriate numbers in each box.

- Help children analyze the structure of the number bond by asking questions such as: *Why is the number 8 in the top box? What can you tell me about the numbers in the bottom boxes?*

- Have children compare the numbers in the number bond to those in the number sentences on the board. Lead them to see that all sentences have the same three numbers in different orders and with addition or subtraction.

Check for Understanding

Use the same problem with different numbers and have children model the new problem on the number bond mats. Ask them to write two addition and two subtraction sentences using the numbers in their number bond.

Look for children who write only one addition and one subtraction sentence and help them see how the parts of the number bond can be arranged in different ways to form four number sentences. The lesson also provides additional exposure to the commutative property.

STEP BY STEP

- Ask children how the number bond used in the Opening Activity helped them think about the problems. Guide them to see that it is a tool that can be used to organize the numbers in both addition and subtraction problems.

- Read the question at the top of the page. Remind children how they used counting on to subtract in Lesson 2. Ask: *Do you think it is easier to add or subtract? Why?* Engage children in a discussion of the similarities and differences between addition and subtraction. Encourage them to suggest answers to the question, "How can adding help me subtract?"

- Read through the Think question. Allow children time to examine the number bonds. It may be helpful for some children to circle the two groups of dots in the top portion of the number bond that correspond to the dots in the two lower portions.

- Ask children to identify the number bond that would help them find 5 − 4. Discuss why or why not each number bond can be used. Use the Hands-On Activity for more support with number bonds.

- Ask the Talk About It question. Have children talk to a partner and decide what addition sentence they could write and explain why. Lead children to recognize that combining the parts at the bottom results in the amount shown at the top.

- Use the Mathematical Discourse question to help clarify the relationship among the numbers in a number bond.

> **SMP Tip:** Asking children to evaluate the ideas of others builds an understanding of reasonableness of strategies and solutions and helps them avoid misconceptions and common errors. (*SMP 3*)

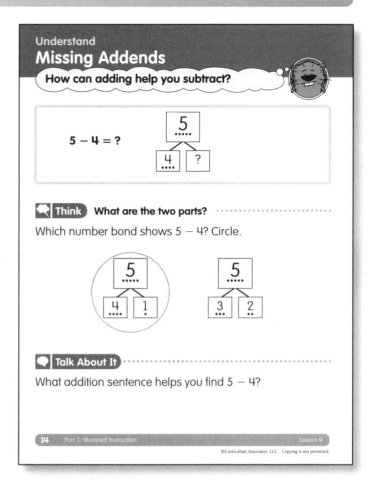

Mathematical Discourse

- *Shawn says that 5 + 1 is an addition sentence for the number bond that includes 5, 4, and 1. What do you think? Why might he think that?*

  Children should notice that this number sentence does not fit with the number bond. Although a 5 and a 1 are both present, 5 represents the whole and 1 represents a part.

Hands-On Activity

Materials For each child: counters, Number Bond Mat (Activity Sheet 3)

Have children use counters and number bond mats to model each of the number bonds on the page by placing 5 counters in the top and moving the correct number of counters into each section. Make sure children recognize that each of the number bonds represents a different way to show 5.

STEP BY STEP

Materials For each child: counters, cup, Number Bond Mat (Activity Sheet 3)

- Provide each child with 7 counters and a cup. Read aloud the directions and have children model this situation with counters.

- Read Problem 1. Ask: *How many counters do you keep? How many do you put in the cup?* [Keep 5 and put 2 in the cup.]

- Connect this problem to a number bond. Allow children to work with counters on number bond mats and then write a number bond with just numbers. Use the Mathematical Discourse question to talk about children's answers and discuss the commutative property.

- Have children work with a partner to complete Problem 2. Compare the results with the example problem. Ask: *How many counters are in and out of the cup in the example problem? What about Problem 2?* Lead children to recognize that in both situations, 7 is broken into groups of 3 and 4 and that when combined, the result is always 7.

> **SMP Tip:** To reinforce the structure of operations, demonstrate that the commutative property applies to addition but not to subtraction. Show a complete fact family.
>
> $7 = 3 + 4$ $7 - 3 = 4$
>
> $7 = 4 + 3$ $7 - 4 = 3$
>
> Guide children to see that with addition, the numbers on each side of the equal sign are the same, but not with subtraction. (*SMP 7*)

- Have children work with a partner to discuss and solve the Talk About It question. Share results and connect to a number bond.

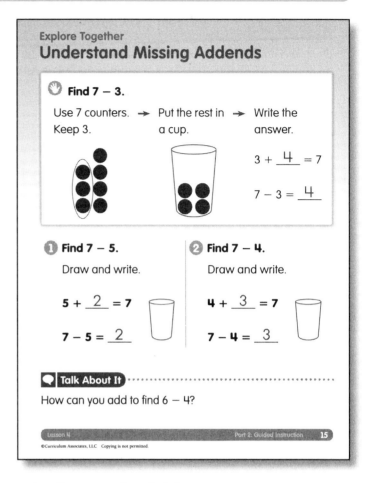

Mathematical Discourse

- *I see that [child's name] wrote 5 + 2 for his number sentence and [child's name] wrote 2 + 5 for her number sentence. How can they both be right?*

  Children should recognize that the order of addends does not affect the sum.

Concept Extension

Record the fact family from the SMP Tip on the board. Show a number bond using the numbers 3, 4, 7. Point out that there are four sentences that can be written for this number bond. Ask: *Do you think there will **always** be four number sentences for a number bond? Can you think of a number bond that has only two number sentences?* Allow children to think about this briefly. If no one suggests an answer, demonstrate how a number bond with 6, 3, 3 only includes two sentences. You may want to challenge children to find other number bonds where only two sentences can be written and explain why.

STEP BY STEP

- Discuss each Connect It problem as a class using the discussion questions outlined below.

Show:

- The number bond in this problem includes only numbers. Some children may still need the visual support of dots and may find it helpful to draw them.

- Have children share the number sentences they wrote. Discuss why there are two possible sentences for each operation.

- If time permits, you may want to draw several number bonds on the board and ask children to think of other numbers that have a total of 8. Record their suggestions.

Reason:

- Read the problem aloud. Encourage children to use a strategy that makes sense to them to solve the problem. You might suggest drawing a picture or diagram and writing a number sentence.

- Have children share their strategies and solutions with the class, emphasizing that there are many ways to approach problems like this.

- If children provide a number sentence solution to the problem, ask: *Why does the number sentence you wrote make sense?* Listen for children to relate the number sentence to the situation. Some may think in terms of subtraction and some in terms of addition. They should be able to justify the sentence they wrote and be confident that it is an accurate representation of the problem.

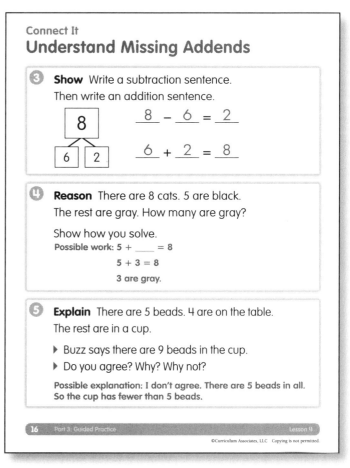

Explain:

- Read the problem aloud and ask children how this problem is like the counters and cup activity they did on the previous page.

- Allow children time to think about the problem and talk about it with a partner. Tell them to make a plan for "proving" their decision by using drawings or counters.

- **Error Alert** Invite volunteer pairs to share their ideas about the error Buzz made. Encourage articulation of mathematical reasoning using questions such as: *Why did you put 5 in the top section of the number bond? How do you think Buzz got 9 as the answer? Why doesn't it make sense to add 5 and 4?*

- Ask children to correct Buzz's answer.

STEP BY STEP

Materials For each child: red and blue crayons

- Tell children that they will complete this page independently.

- Read the directions aloud, making sure children understand what they are expected to do.

- For Part A, provide children with a red and blue crayon or marker. Make sure they understand that there is no one correct way to color the triangles, so their number bonds and number sentences may be different from others in the class.

- In Part B, children color the triangles using a different combination of blue and red.

- Watch to make sure children complete all parts of the problems, including coloring the triangles, completing the number bonds, and writing the number sentences.

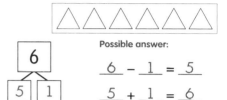

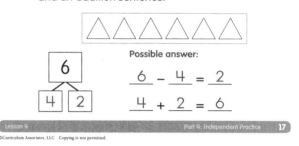

SCORING RUBRICS

Expectations for 4–3 Points

Points	Expectations
4	The child: • colors triangles appropriately to show two different partners of 6. • correctly completes the number bonds and writes an addition and subtraction number sentence that corresponds to each number bond.
3	The child: • colors triangles appropriately to show two different partners of 6. • correctly completes the number bonds but may have one or two minor errors in the number sentences.

Expectations for 2–0 Points

Points	Expectations
2	The child: • colors triangles to show partners of 6 but may not have shown two different partners. • completes the number bonds and number sentences with some errors.
1	The child: • colors the triangles but the number bonds and number sentences are inaccurate and/or incomplete.
0	The child: • colors the triangles but does not attempt to complete the number bonds and number sentences.

Intervention Activity

Connect number bonds to number sentences.

Materials For each child: Number Bond Mat (Activity Sheet 3), Number Bond Recording Sheet (Activity Sheet 2), counters

- Distribute materials to children.

- Provide children with related open number sentences, such as: $6 - 2 =$ ___ and $2 +$ ___ $= 6$, $8 - 5 =$ ___ and $5 +$ ___ $= 8$, $7 +$ ___ $= 9$ and $9 - 7 =$ ___ .

- Have children model the related number sentences using the counters and number bond mat. They then complete the number sentences.

On-Level Activity

Build number bonds.

Materials For each child: 10 counters, cup, Number Bond Recording Sheet (Activity Sheet 2), colored paper

- Children choose a number of counters (5–10) to place in the cup. They write this number in the top of a number bond on the recording sheet.

- Children empty the cup so some counters land on the paper and some land off of the paper.

- In the number bond, they record the numbers on and off the paper.

- Children then write number sentences that correspond with the number bond.

- Repeat until the recording sheet is full. If the result of a "toss" is a duplicate, the child makes the toss again.

Challenge Activity

Make number bonds to find number partners.

Materials For each child: Number Bond Mat (Activity Sheet 3), counters

Challenge children to use counters to find all the ways to create a number bond for the numbers 2–5.

- Have children make a simple table as shown to record their work.

- Ask children to find all the ways to create a number bond for the number 2, then fill in the table as shown.

Number	How many ways?
2	3

Note: The "How many ways?" number in this table includes the following partners: $2 + 0$, $1 + 1$, $0 + 2$. It counts partners with 0 and the same addends in different order as two ways.

Provide children with scratch paper or white boards and demonstrate how they can make a quick draw of number bonds to help them keep track of the different ways to make each number.

When completed, ask children to find a pattern. They should notice that for each consecutive number, one more number bond can be made. Some may notice that the number of ways is one more (if zeros are included) than the number of counters used. Ask children to predict whether this pattern continues with numbers greater than 5. Make sure children justify their conjecture.

Lesson 5 (Student Book pages 18–21)

Subtract to Compare in Word Problems

LESSON OBJECTIVES

- Understand a comparison problem situation as subtraction and/or related addition.

- Compare two amounts, determining which is more or less and identifying how many more or less.

- Write and solve subtraction and addition sentences to solve comparison word problems.

PREREQUISITE SKILLS

- Count on to subtract.

- Add and subtract in word problems.

- Find the missing addend.

VOCABULARY

compare: to decide if amounts or sizes are greater than, less than, or equal to each other

fewer: indicating a lesser quantity or amount

more: indicating a greater quantity or amount

During the lesson you will review the key terms:

subtract: to take objects away from a group or to compare groups

subtraction sentence: one number is subtracted from another in a sentence with symbols and numbers

THE LEARNING PROGRESSION

In Kindergarten, children compare groups of objects and identify which has more or less, without finding the difference between the numbers. They also compare written numerals from 1 to 10. Children understand subtraction as taking away and taking apart.

In Grade 1, children understand subtraction as taking away, taking apart, or comparing. **In this lesson,** children solve comparison word problems. They use models that show one-to-one correspondence to find the difference between two quantities.

In Grade 2, children solve subtraction word problems that involve take away, take apart, or compare situations. They extend subtraction to quantities within 100 and they solve two-step problems.

Ready *Teacher Toolbox*   *Teacher-Toolbox.com*

	Prerequisite Skills	1.OA.A.1
Ready Lessons	✓ ✓ ✓	✓
Tools for Instruction	✓	
Interactive Tutorials	✓ ✓	✓

CCSS Focus

1.OA.A.1 Use addition and subtraction within 20 to solve word problems involving situations of adding to, taking from, putting together, taking apart, and comparing, with unknowns in all positions, e.g., by using objects, drawings, and equations with a symbol for the unknown number to represent the problem.

ADDITIONAL STANDARDS: **1.OA.C.6, 1.OA.D.8** *(see page A36 for full text)*

STANDARDS FOR MATHEMATICAL PRACTICE: **SMP 2, 4** *(see page A9 for full text)*

Opening Activity: Act Out a Comparison Word Problem

Objective: Act out a "subtract to compare" word problem and find the difference.	**Materials** For each child: • 6 two-color counters or connecting cubes

Overview

Children act out a "subtract to compare" word problem that is like the Explore Together problem. They discuss the meaning of the comparison and use a matching strategy to find the difference.

Step by Step (15–20 minutes)

1 **Pose the problem.**

- Say: *Suppose it's raining outside. What could you wear to keep your head dry?* [rain hat] *Imagine that 6 children are getting ready to go outside in the rain. But they have only 4 hats! We can figure out how many children will not have a rain hat.*

2 **Model the problem.**

- Invite 6 children to act out the problem. Set out 4 hats (or pieces of paper that can be used to represent rain hats) in a bunch, on a table in front of the children.

- Restate the problem: *There are 6 children. There are 4 hats. Are there more hats or more children? How many children will not get a hat?* Have the children acting out the problem raise their hands one at a time while the class counts to 6. Ask a volunteer to count the 4 hats.

3 **Match the quantities.**

- Remind children that they know how to compare two quantities to find out which is more and which is less. Explain that you can also find out how many more or how many less one number is than the other.

- Elicit that they can compare the hats and children by matching up 1 hat for each child. Have the 6 children each extend a hand. Give a hat to each of the first 4 children.

4 **Find the difference.**

- Ask: *Are there more hats or more children?* [more children] Ask, *How many children get a hat?* [4]

- Ask the class how they can determine the number of children who do not get a hat. Discuss ways of finding the solution, such as counting on, counting the children without hats, adding (4 and how many more make 6), and subtracting (6 children minus the 4 who have hats). Invite volunteers to demonstrate finding the solution.

Check for Understanding

As children talk about and demonstrate solution strategies, you may find that some can simply add or subtract to find the solution. Allow others to count as necessary to solve the problem. Those children who have difficulty making the connection between comparing and one-to-one correspondence may need the support of concrete materials, such as counters or connecting cubes.

STEP BY STEP

- Begin by asking children what they learned or remember from the Opening Activity. Elicit that the problem asked children to compare the number of children and number of rain hats.

- Read aloud the problem at the top of the page. Ask a volunteer to describe the situation. Have the class count the children and then count the hats.

- Discuss what it means to compare: to see how quantities are alike or different, or in math terms, to see which set has more or which has less. Have children discuss whether there are more hats or more children.

- Read the last question. Ask: *What do we need to find out to answer how many children do not get a hat?* [How many more children there are than hats.] Ask: *How can we find out?* Allow children to suggest a variety of strategies.

- Read Model It. Discuss how this model is like the action of matching the hats and the children. Have children describe what the model shows.

- Use the Mathematical Discourse question to introduce and discuss the subtraction number sentence. Then ask: *How will you solve this subtraction problem?* Children may count on or may use other methods. Have them explain or demonstrate their approaches.

Fluency Practice

What's missing?

Materials For each child: Number Bond Practice to 5 (Activity Sheet 4)

Have children fill in the missing numbers. You may want to review the completed worksheets and ask children to say or write corresponding number sentences.

Mathematical Discourse

- *What number sentence would you use to solve this problem? Why?*

  Children might suggest either subtraction or missing-addend addition to represent comparison. With addition: "4 children with hats, plus how many children who don't get hats, equals 6 children." With subtraction: "6 children, minus 4 who get hats, equals the number who don't get hats." Have children explain their reasoning for preferring one approach or the other.

STEP BY STEP

- Read the problem. Discuss how the illustration represents the meaning of the problem.

- Introduce the word "fewer" and discuss the meaning. Ask: *Which is less, the number of mice or the number of pieces of cheese?* Guide children to understand that "how many fewer" and "how many less" are other ways to compare two quantities.

- Discuss how to solve the problem. Ask how it is like the previous problem and how is it different. Help children recognize that whether the question involves "fewer" or "more," the same solution process can be used.

- Read aloud Model It. Ask how the model is like the one on the first page. Then ask what the numbers in the number sentence mean and how they relate to the problem. Have children work in pairs to solve and then share their solutions with the class.

- **Error Alert** Read Talk About It. Encourage children to discuss with a partner what the illustration shows. Ask: *Who is right, Buzz or Boom? How do you know?* Discuss children's responses.

> **SMP Tip:** Encourage children to model comparisons by aligning numbers of objects to visually show "how many more" and "how many less." Ask: *What does the model show? How does it help you solve the problem?* Have children explain what the modeled objects and the solution mean, in the context of the problem. *(SMP 4)*

ELL Support

Some children may think that "less" and "more" have the same meaning. Explain that "less" and "fewer" mean "not as many as." They are the opposite of "more." Use pictures or objects to provide practice with "less" and "fewer."

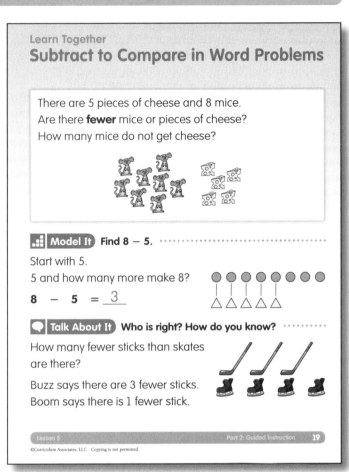

Mathematical Discourse

- *What does the model in Model It show?*

  There are more mice than cheese. There are 3 more mice than cheese. 3 mice don't get a piece of cheese.

- *What is Buzz's mistake in this problem?*

  Children might suggest that Buzz does not understand what "fewer" means. 3 is the number of sticks, not how many fewer sticks there are. The number of sticks is 1 fewer than the number of skates, because 3 is 1 less than 4.

STEP BY STEP

- Work through Practice Together. Read the model problem aloud. Explain that the problem says "which is fewer" (Nan's birds) and asks us to find "how many" fewer. Ask how the number sentence represents the problem situation.

- Direct attention to the tape diagram. Discuss how this is like the previous visual models and how it is different. Ask the class which part shows the birds Nan sees, which shows the birds Cam sees, and how they can tell. Ask what the "?" represents. [how many fewer Nan sees]

- Explain that in Problem 1, children need to complete the diagram. Have some children demonstrate how they did this and how they answered the question.

- Read Problem 2 aloud. Have children work in pairs to fill in the tape diagram. Then have them explain how they got their results.

- Discuss the fact that children must answer "how many more?" in both problems. Challenge children to tell how many fewer red markers and apples there are. Guide them to understand that the "more" and "fewer" numbers are the same.

> **SMP Tip:** Help children understand that they can use a variety of models to show a single situation. Describe a comparison situation and assign different groups a type of model to make for the problem. Discuss what is the same and different about each model, and how the models relate to the subtraction sentence. *(SMP 4)*

Hands-On Activity

Use length to model comparison.

Materials For each child: paper squares or connecting cubes

Have children use paper squares or connecting cubes to model a comparison problem. Children model each quantity by lining up paper squares or making a train of connecting cubes. Then have them line up their models so that the left ends are aligned. Children can compare the lengths to see which quantity is greater or less and by how much. Discuss how this model relates to the tape diagrams shown on the page.

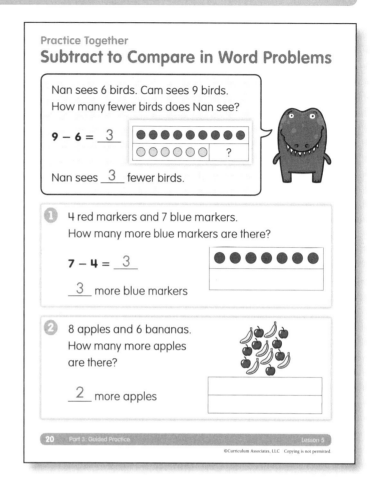

Practice Together

Subtract to Compare in Word Problems

Nan sees 6 birds. Cam sees 9 birds.
How many fewer birds does Nan see?

$9 - 6 = \underline{3}$

Nan sees $\underline{3}$ fewer birds.

① 4 red markers and 7 blue markers.
How many more blue markers are there?

$7 - 4 = \underline{3}$

$\underline{3}$ more blue markers

② 8 apples and 6 bananas.
How many more apples are there?

$\underline{2}$ more apples

Mathematical Discourse

- *How can you check your answer in a comparison problem?*

   One way to check the answer is to add the lesser quantity and the result of the "how many less" or "how many more" comparison and see if this is equal to the greater quantity. Another way would be to use the tape diagram or a visual matching model to see if the quantities match. Children should be able to explain their approach and justify their reasoning.

STEP BY STEP

- Before children work on this page, review the models used in this lesson. Emphasize that children are free to use whatever way helps them solve the problems.

- Read each problem aloud, then have children work independently to solve.

- In Problem 3, challenge children to solve without counting. Ask them why this is easy to do with the numbers in the problem.

- In Problem 4, help children distinguish between comparing size (small vs. big) and comparing number (more vs. fewer). Point out that a model is started. They can complete it to solve the problem.

- Invite volunteers to share the models and solution strategies they used for the problems on this page. Use the Mathematical Discourse question to check children's understanding of comparing quantities.

Visual Model

Make a tape diagram with numbers.

On the board, draw the tape diagram from Problem 3. Copy the size and shape of the diagram, but leave the sections empty. Ask: *What's another way to represent the 7 fish that Jo has?* Guide children to recognize that the 7 circles can be replaced with "7." Do likewise with the 6 circles that represent Pat's fish. Have children discuss the differences between the two visual models and think of advantages for each one. Some children may be ready to use numbers in their tape diagrams.

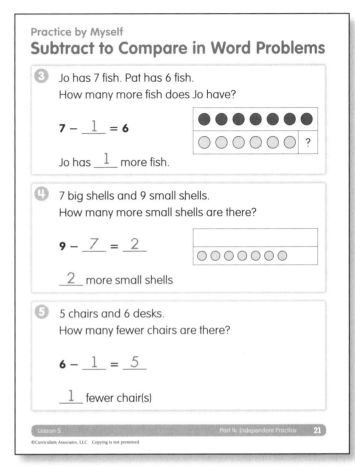

Mathematical Discourse

- *How do you compare two quantities?*

  When comparing two quantities, children must find a way to represent the "how many more" or "how many less" (the difference) conceptually and through representation. They need to understand that there are two parts to a comparison question:

  1. Which quantity is more (or less)?

  2. How much more (or less)?

  Children should also be able to act out the problem, create a visual model, and write an appropriate subtraction sentence to answer both questions.

Assessment and Remediation

- Ask children to use counters to model and answer the following problem: 6 cats and 2 dogs. How many more cats than dogs? [4 more cats than dogs]

- For children who are still struggling, use the chart below to guide remediation.

- After providing remediation, check children's understanding using the following problem: 9 cars and 4 trucks. How many more cars than trucks? [5 more cars than trucks]

If the error is . . .	Children may . . .	To remediate . . .
6 or 2	have only identified the greater (or lesser) number.	Ask children to explain the meaning of the problem. Guide them to consider the question "which is more, cats or dogs?" Then point to the words "How many more." Help children use a model to answer.
8	added the quantities rather than comparing them.	Ask children to explain the meaning of the problem. Have them put their answer in the sentence "There are __ more cats than dogs." Guide children to match the cats and dogs to see that this is a comparison situation and then answer the question.
a number that is not 6, 2, or 8	not understand the comparison relationship.	Reread the problem. Have children use counters to model 6 cats and 2 dogs. Guide them to use counters to match the quantities and then answer the question.

Hands-On Activity

Act out a comparison using a tape diagram.

Materials For display: masking tape

- Make a tape diagram on the classroom floor, large enough for children to stand in.

- Give children a problem from the book or one that you make up, using numbers within 10. Write the problem using simple words.

- Have children act out the problem in the tape diagram, using themselves as counters. Children may count off to check that the right number is in each part of the diagram. To compare quantities, children may count on from the lesser number to the greater number.

Challenge Activity

Use a graph to compare quantities.

Materials For each child: Chart Template (Activity Sheet 35), markers or pencils, up to 9 objects in 3 categories, small sticky notes

- Give children the Chart Template and different numbers of objects for each of three categories. Help children write the names of the objects in the headings of the chart.

- Have children count the objects in each category and represent them on the chart with sticky notes placed end to end with no gaps or overlaps.

- Children use the chart to answer "how many more" and "how many fewer" questions about the objects they classified. Consider having children write subtraction sentences to represent each question and answer.

Unit 1 Review

Solve the problems.

1. 8 blocks in all. 6 are red.
   Some are blue.
   How many are blue?

   8 − _2_ = 6

2. 5 children play. 3 more children come.
   How many children in all?

1	2	3	4	5	6	7	8	9	10

   _8_ = 5 + 3

3. 7 − 2 = _5_

4. 6 + 3 = _9_

5. _7_ = 9 − 2

6. 6 + 1 = _7_

7. 6 birds and 3 ants. How many more
   birds are there than ants?

   Draw a picture that shows the problem.
   Then write a number sentence.

   **Possible answer: Children may draw a row of 3 squares
   above a row of 6 circles to show the comparison of 6 − 3.**

   _6_ − _3_ = _3_

   There are _3_ more birds than ants.

8. 9 buttons in all.
   7 are square. Some are round.
   How many are round?

   Complete the number bond.
   Write an addition sentence.
   Then write a subtraction sentence.

   _7_ + _2_ = 9   _9_ − _7_ = _2_

   There are _2_ round buttons.

STEP BY STEP

- Have children solve the problems independently. Encourage them to show their work. Emphasize that children are free to use whatever way helps them solve the problems.

- **Error Alert** Look for children who seem confused by Problem 2 and Problem 5 where the total is to the left of the equal sign. Some children may think that the equal sign always means "makes" or "results in" rather than always meaning "is the same number as."

- Observe as children work. For Problem 7, children draw to represent a comparison problem, then write a number sentence. You may wish to prompt children who are having difficulty getting started by asking questions such as:

  Which will you draw first, birds or ants?

  How many birds will you draw? How many ants? How do you know?

STEP BY STEP

- On this page, children are given three numbers—7, 5, and 2—and use those numbers to draw and write or tell an addition story. They then record the addition as a number sentence.

- Direct children to complete the Put It Together on their own.

- Read the directions and task aloud. Make sure children understand what they need to do to complete the task.

- As children work on their own, observe their progress and understanding. Respond to their questions and provide additional support as needed.

- If time permits, have children share their addition stories and number sentences with the class.

- Ask children how this question is different from the other questions in this review. Point out that there are lots of ways they can show what they have learned.

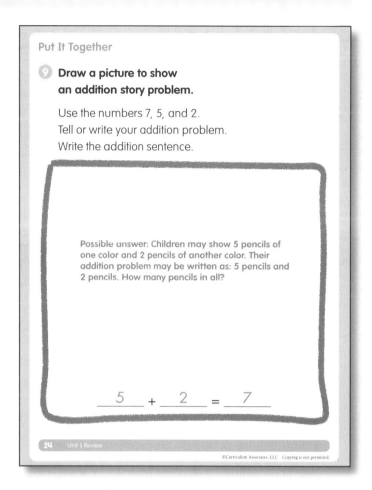

SCORING RUBRICS

Expectations for 4–3 Points

Points	Expectations
4	The child: • represents the given numbers accurately and completely in his or her drawing. • correctly states the total and addends when writing or telling the addition story. • correctly writes the addition sentence.
3	The child: • may represent the given numbers accurately and completely in his or her drawing. • may correctly state the total and addends when writing or telling the addition story. • may incorrectly write the total or one of the addends in the addition sentence.

Expectations for 2–0 Points

Points	Expectations
2	The child: • may inaccurately represent the given numbers in his or her drawing. • may incorrectly state the total or one of the addends when writing or telling the addition story. • may incorrectly write the total of one of the addends in the addition sentence.
1	The child: • may inaccurately represent the given numbers in his or her drawing. • may incorrectly state the total and addends when writing or telling the addition story. • may incorrectly write the total and addends in the addition sentence.
0	The child: • does not attempt to do the task.

Which lessons are students building upon?

Kindergarten, Lesson 18 Add Within 10 **K.OA.A.1, K.OA.A.3, K.OA.A.5**	*Kindergarten, Lesson 19* Subtract Within 10 **K.OA.A.1, K.OA.A.3, K.OA.A.5**	*Kindergarten, Lesson 20* Practice Facts to 5 **K.OA.A.3, K.OA.A.5**
Kindergarten, Lesson 18 Add Within 10 **K.OA.A.1, K.OA.A.3, K.OA.A.5**	*Kindergarten, Lesson 19* Subtract Within 10 **K.OA.A.1, K.OA.A.3, K.OA.A.5**	*Kindergarten, Lesson 20* Practice Facts to 5 **K.OA.A.3, K.OA.A.5**
Kindergarten, Lesson 18 Add Within 10 **K.OA.A.1, K.OA.A.3, K.OA.A.5**	*Kindergarten, Lesson 19* Subtract Within 10 **K.OA.A.1, K.OA.A.3, K.OA.A.5**	*Kindergarten, Lesson 20* Practice Facts to 5 **K.OA.A.3, K.OA.A.5**
Kindergarten, Lesson 18 Add Within 10 **K.OA.A.1, K.OA.A.3, K.OA.A.5**	*Kindergarten, Lesson 19* Subtract Within 10 **K.OA.A.1, K.OA.A.3, K.OA.A.5**	*Kindergarten, Lesson 20* Practice Facts to 5 **K.OA.A.3, K.OA.A.5**
Kindergarten, Lesson 18 Add Within 10 **K.OA.A.1, K.OA.A.3, K.OA.A.5**	*Kindergarten, Lesson 19* Subtract Within 10 **K.OA.A.1, K.OA.A.3, K.OA.A.5**	*Kindergarten, Lesson 20* Practice Facts to 5 **K.OA.A.3, K.OA.A.5**
Kindergarten, Lesson 18 Add Within 10 **K.OA.A.1, K.OA.A.3, K.OA.A.5**	*Kindergarten, Lesson 19* Subtract Within 10 **K.OA.A.1, K.OA.A.3, K.OA.A.5**	*Kindergarten, Lesson 20* Practice Facts to 5 **K.OA.A.3, K.OA.A.5**

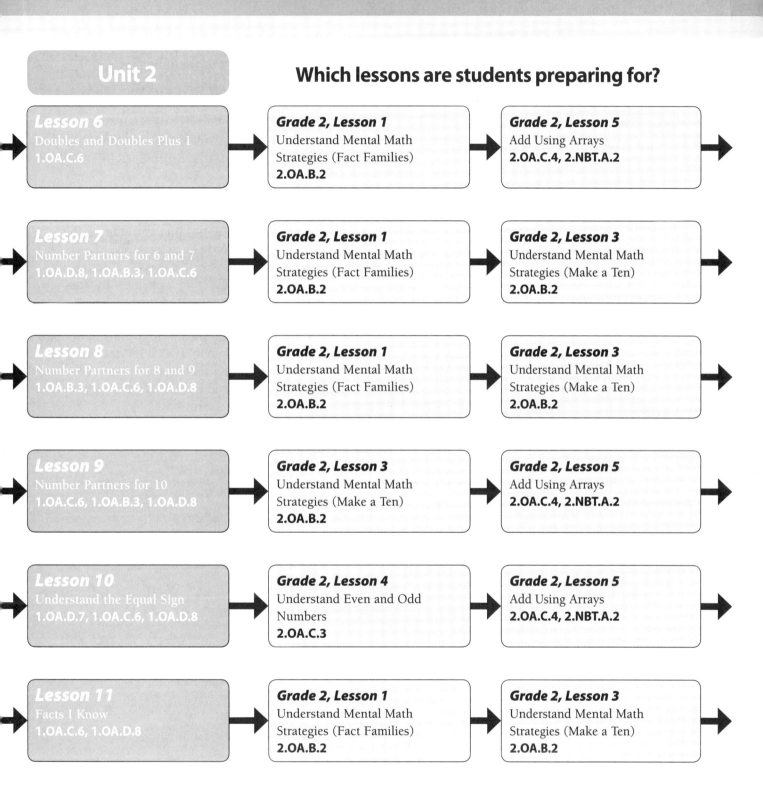

Unit 2

Which lessons are students preparing for?

Lesson 6
Doubles and Doubles Plus 1
1.OA.C.6

→ **Grade 2, Lesson 1**
Understand Mental Math Strategies (Fact Families)
2.OA.B.2

→ **Grade 2, Lesson 5**
Add Using Arrays
2.OA.C.4, 2.NBT.A.2 →

Lesson 7
Number Partners for 6 and 7
1.OA.D.8, 1.OA.B.3, 1.OA.C.6

→ **Grade 2, Lesson 1**
Understand Mental Math Strategies (Fact Families)
2.OA.B.2

→ **Grade 2, Lesson 3**
Understand Mental Math Strategies (Make a Ten)
2.OA.B.2 →

Lesson 8
Number Partners for 8 and 9
1.OA.B.3, 1.OA.C.6, 1.OA.D.8

→ **Grade 2, Lesson 1**
Understand Mental Math Strategies (Fact Families)
2.OA.B.2

→ **Grade 2, Lesson 3**
Understand Mental Math Strategies (Make a Ten)
2.OA.B.2 →

Lesson 9
Number Partners for 10
1.OA.C.6, 1.OA.B.3, 1.OA.D.8

→ **Grade 2, Lesson 3**
Understand Mental Math Strategies (Make a Ten)
2.OA.B.2

→ **Grade 2, Lesson 5**
Add Using Arrays
2.OA.C.4, 2.NBT.A.2 →

Lesson 10
Understand the Equal Sign
1.OA.D.7, 1.OA.C.6, 1.OA.D.8

→ **Grade 2, Lesson 4**
Understand Even and Odd Numbers
2.OA.C.3

→ **Grade 2, Lesson 5**
Add Using Arrays
2.OA.C.4, 2.NBT.A.2 →

Lesson 11
Facts I Know
1.OA.C.6, 1.OA.D.8

→ **Grade 2, Lesson 1**
Understand Mental Math Strategies (Fact Families)
2.OA.B.2

→ **Grade 2, Lesson 3**
Understand Mental Math Strategies (Make a Ten)
2.OA.B.2 →

Lesson 6 (Student Book pages 26–29)

Doubles and Doubles Plus 1

LESSON OBJECTIVES

- Relate an image of two equal groups to doubles.

- Relate an image of two equal groups with one left over as doubles plus one.

- Write addition sentences for doubles and doubles plus one.

- Use properties to write a doubles plus one expression (3 addends) as an expression with 2 addends.

PREREQUISITE SKILLS

- Count on to add.

- Add and subtract in word problems.

- Find the missing addend.

VOCABULARY

doubles: an addition fact that has two addends that are the same, such as $4 + 4$

doubles plus 1: an addition fact that has a double as one addend and the double and one more as the other addend, such as $4 + 5$

THE LEARNING PROGRESSION

In Kindergarten, children solve addition and subtraction word problems, and add and subtract within 10 by using objects or drawings to represent the problem.

In Grade 1, children are expected to fluently add and subtract numbers to 10 and have experience adding and subtracting within 20. Adding and subtracting fluently refers to knowledge of procedures, knowledge of when and how to use them, and skill in performing them flexibly by using different strategies. **In this lesson,** children are introduced to the strategy of doubles and doubles plus one. Children use models to first find sums of doubles, then to find sums of doubles plus one. As they continue to work with doubles and doubles plus one addition sentences, children come to recognize that they can double the smaller number and add 1 more.

In Grade 2, children fluently add and subtract within 20 using mental strategies.

	Prerequisite Skills	1.OA.C.6
Ready Lessons	✓ ✓ ✓	✓
Tools for Instruction	✓ ✓	✓
Interactive Tutorials	✓ ✓	✓ ✓

Ready *Teacher Toolbox* — Teacher-Toolbox.com

CCSS Focus

1.OA.C.6 Add and subtract within 20, demonstrating fluency for addition and subtraction within 10. Use strategies such as counting on; making ten (e.g., $8 + 6 = 8 + 2 + 4 = 10 + 4 = 14$); decomposing a number leading to a ten (e.g., $13 - 4 = 13 - 3 - 1 = 10 - 1 = 9$); using the relationship between addition and subtraction (e.g., knowing that $8 + 4 = 12$, one knows $12 - 8 = 4$); and creating equivalent but easier or known sums (e.g., adding $6 + 7$ by creating the known equivalent $6 + 6 + 1 = 12 + 1 = 13$).

STANDARDS FOR MATHEMATICAL PRACTICE: **SMP 7, 8** *(see page A9 for full text)*

Opening Activity: Doubles and Doubles Plus 1

Objective: Model a doubles and doubles plus one addition problem and identify corresponding addition number sentences.

Materials For each child:
• none

Overview

Children act out a doubles and a doubles plus one addition problem. They identify the addends in the doubles problem as the same and relate adding one more to a double to find another sum.

Step by Step (10–15 minutes)

1 **Pose the problem.**

• Say: *At soccer practice, pairs of players line up on opposite sides of the field to practice passing and trapping the ball. Today there are 8 children. How many pairs of children are at soccer practice?*

2 **Act out the problem.**

• Have eight children line up by twos on opposite sides of the classroom. Count aloud by 2s with the class as each pair lines up.

• Relate counting by 2s to the total of 8 children.

• Ask: *How many children are on the left side of the classroom?* [4] *How many children are on the right side?* [4]

• Have one more child join the group on the left side of the classroom.

• Ask: *Does she (or he) have a partner?* [no]

3 **Write doubles and doubles plus one addition sentences.**

• Write $4 + 4$ on the board. Ask: *What is the total?* [8] Complete the doubles addition sentence $4 + 4 = 8$ on the board.

• Write $4 + 4 + 1$ on the board. Ask: *What is the total?* [9] Complete the doubles plus one addition sentence $4 + 4 + 1 = 9$ on the board.

4 **Talk about the doubles and doubles plus one addition sentences.**

• Point to the addends in the doubles addition sentence $4 + 4 = 8$. Ask: *What do you notice about these numbers?* [They are the same.] Identify the addends as doubles. Ask children why they think the term doubles is used. Children might say that the 4 appears twice or that there are two 4s.

• Ask children how they know the total is 8. Children may respond that they counted on from 4 or that they counted by 2s.

• Identify the addition sentence $4 + 4 + 1 = 9$ as doubles plus one. Ask: *How do you know $4 + 4 + 1 = 9$?* Children may say that they know $4 + 4 = 8$ and $8 + 1 = 9$.

Check for Understanding

Provide the children with the following problem: *Max has 3 red beads and 3 blue beads. How many beads does Max have?* [6] *Then Max finds one more red bead. Now how many beads does Max have in all?* [7]

As children solve the problem, look for an understanding that 7 is one more than 6. Some children may notice that the addends in the first part of the problem match exactly.

STEP BY STEP

Materials For each child: counters

- Begin by asking children what they have learned or remember from the Opening Activity. Help them listen to one another by restating—or having a child restate—key ideas.

- Explain that this page is about doubles, just like the Opening Activity. Read aloud the problem at the top of the page. Tell children they can use counters to model the problem.

- Use the Hands-On Activity to connect adding doubles to the problem on this page.

- Direct children's attention to the Model It. Read aloud the addition fact. Have children discuss what they notice about the addends. [They are the same.] Tell children this addition is a doubles. Then use the Mathematical Discourse question to clarify understanding.

- Read aloud the directive to use doubles to find the total. Have children explain how the counters and 3 + 3 are related. Then have children complete the doubles number sentence.

> **SMP Tip:** Ask children to name some other doubles facts that they know, for example 1 + 1 and 2 + 2. Children use repeated reasoning to conclude that in these doubles facts, the same addend is added twice. *(SMP 8)*

Hands-On Activity

Use models to add doubles.

Materials For each child: 6 counters

Have children make two rows of counters using the number partners 3 and 3. Ask: *Are there the same number of counters in each row?* [Yes] *How do you know?* [Each counter has a partner.] Ask children how they can find the total number of counters. Children may count on from 3 or add 3 + 3 to find the total of 6.

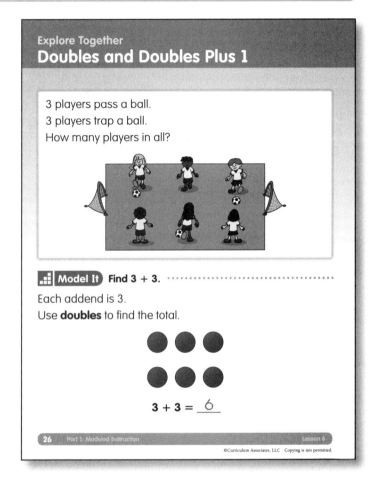

Mathematical Discourse

- *How would you explain in your own words what is a double and what is not a double?*

   Some children may say that addition where the two numbers being added are the same are doubles and addition with two different numbers being added are not doubles. Other children may say that two groups in which each item in one group matches with an item in the other group are doubles and groups in which there is a leftover item are not doubles.

ELL Support

ELL children may not understand the meaning of the term "doubles." Relate doubles to pairs of body parts, such as two eyes, two hands, and two feet. Point out words of similar meaning such as "pairs" and "partners." Provide images that show examples of greater doubles, such as four wheels on a car and four legs on a table.

STEP BY STEP

- Read aloud the problem at the top of the page. Ask children to explain whether they would use addition or subtraction to find the answer.

- Use the Hands-On Activity to connect adding doubles plus one to the problem on this page.

- Direct children' attention to the Model It. Read aloud the directive. Have children look at the model and tell what they think the dashed circle shows. Discuss the labels "3" and "3 and 1 more" with children.

- Ask: *What doubles are in the first number sentence?* [3 + 3] *Why is + 1 in the number sentence?* [After making doubles, there is one more counter.] In using the doubles plus one strategy, children are grouping numbers differently, that is, using three addends, for the first time. Pose the Mathematical Discourse questions to help children make this connection.

- **Error Alert** As children discuss the problem posed in the Talk About It, encourage them to describe how the solutions are alike and how they are different. Listen for children who say that only Boom is correct and ask them to explain their reasoning. Discuss why both strategies are correct and how either strategy can be used to find the total, 9.

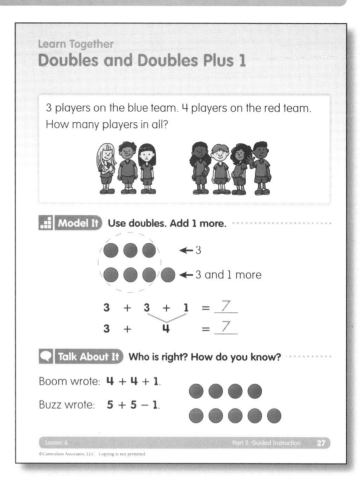

Learn Together
Doubles and Doubles Plus 1

3 players on the blue team. 4 players on the red team. How many players in all?

Model It Use doubles. Add 1 more.

$\leftarrow$ 3
$\leftarrow$ 3 and 1 more

$$3 + 3 + 1 = \underline{7}$$
$$3 + 4 = \underline{7}$$

Talk About It Who is right? How do you know?

Boom wrote: **4 + 4 + 1**.

Buzz wrote: **5 + 5 − 1**.

Hands-On Activity

Use models to add doubles plus one.

Materials For each child: 7 counters

- Have children make two rows of counters using the number partners 3 and 4.

- Ask: *Are there the same number of counters in each row?* [No] *How do you know?* [Pairing the counters in each row leaves one counter left over.]

- Ask children how they can find the total number of counters. Some children may say that they can count on from 3 or 4; others may notice that there are 3 pairs of counters and one left over so they add 3 + 3, then add 1 more for the leftover counter.

- Ask children how many counters there are in all. [7]

Mathematical Discourse

- *How is 3 + 4 related to 3 + 3?*

  Some children may suggest that since they know that 3 + 3 = 6, 3 + 4 is the same as adding a double (3) and a double plus one (4).

- *How is 3 + 3 + 1 like 3 + 4?*

  Some children may say that they are alike because both are a way to show doubles plus one. Other children may suggest they are alike because when added, they have the same total (7).

Concept Extension

Materials For each child: 7 counters

Help children apply the associative property of addition to see how the two number sentences are related. Have children group counters to represent the three addends in 3 + 3 + 1. Then have them regroup the counters to represent the addends in 3 + 4. Discuss whether the total number of counters remains the same.

STEP BY STEP

- Read the problem at the top of the page. Ask: *What do you notice about the number of blue blocks compared to the number of red blocks?* Children may say that there is one more blue block than red blocks.

- Ask children how they can solve the problem. Children may say that they can use the doubles 2 + 2, then add 1 more.

- Ask: *How do you know to add one more?* [Because there are 3 blue blocks and 3 is one more than 2.]

- Connect the first addition sentence, 2 + 2 + 1, to the term doubles plus 1. Then relate the two addition sentences to each other. Ask: *How does finding the total of 2 + 2 + 1 help you find the total of 2 + 3?* Children may say that breaking apart 3 into 2 + 1 helps them use doubles plus one, 2 + 2 + 1, to find the total, 5.

- Read aloud the first problem. Relate the picture to the number bond. Then pose the Mathematical Discourse question.

- Read aloud the second problem. Have children circle the pencils that show the doubles fact and explain how they knew which pencils to circle. [The number of pencils in each group are the same, 3.] Ask: *How many pencils are left over?* [1] Guide children to see how the one leftover pencil relates to the missing addend 1.

> **SMP Tip:** Children may observe patterns and structure as they discover that some numbers make equal groups, but others have one left over. Continue to reinforce these concepts as children use the doubles and doubles plus one strategies. (*SMP 7*)

Mathematical Discourse

- *How can you find the missing addend in* 2 + ___ = 4?

  Children may respond with a variety of suggestions. Look for responses that indicate children see the missing number as a double (2). Since 2 + 2 = 4, the missing number is 2.

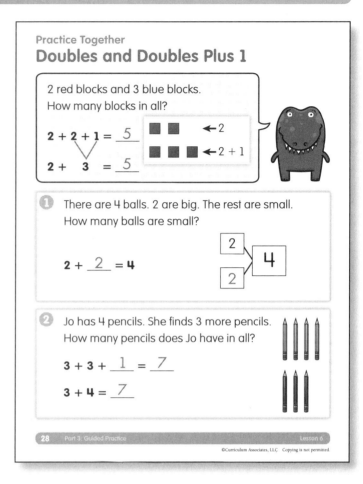

Fluency Practice

Stand and Sit on Even Numbers

Have children sit in a circle and count aloud by ones. Each child says the next consecutive number. Children who say even numbers stand up and do not continue counting: 1, 2 [child stands], 3, 4 [child stands], etc. Continue until all children are standing. Then have children count backward from the last number spoken, continuing in the same direction around the circle. This time children who say even numbers sit and do not count aloud. Continue until all children are sitting.

STEP BY STEP

- Before children work on this page, review the models used in the lesson. Emphasize that children can use whatever way helps them solve the problems.

- Read each problem aloud, then have children work independently to solve.

- For Problem 4, observe to see if children recognize the problem requires them to find an unknown change. Look for children who connect the phrase "how many more" with subtraction and use what they know about doubles and the relationship between addition and subtraction to find the missing addend: $8 - 4 = 4$ and $4 + 4 = 8$.

- Ask children who solve Problem 5 without showing their work to explain which strategy helped them find their solution.

Mathematical Discourse

- *2 + 3 is a doubles plus one. Is 3 + 2 also a doubles plus one? How do you know?*

    Children are not expected to name the commutative property, but some may be familiar enough with it to use it with precision in their explanation: You can draw pictures that show $2 + 3$ and $3 + 2$. The pictures are the same because they each show two equal groups with one left over, so $2 + 3$ and $3 + 2$ are the same. Both are doubles plus 1.

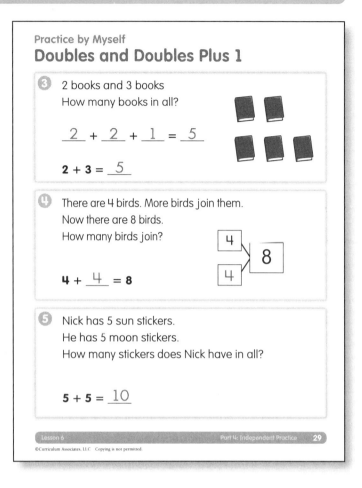

Practice by Myself
Doubles and Doubles Plus 1

③ 2 books and 3 books
How many books in all?

$\underline{2} + \underline{2} + \underline{1} = \underline{5}$

$2 + 3 = \underline{5}$

④ There are 4 birds. More birds join them.
Now there are 8 birds.
How many birds join?

$4 + \underline{4} = 8$

⑤ Nick has 5 sun stickers.
He has 5 moon stickers.
How many stickers does Nick have in all?

$5 + 5 = \underline{10}$

Lesson 6   Part 4: Independent Practice   29
©Curriculum Associates, LLC   Copying is not permitted.

Visual Model

Have children use their fingers to show and name doubles facts.

- Partner A shows two pinkies. Partner B says the number sentence: $1 + 1 = 2$.

- Partner A shows pinkies and ring fingers. Partner B says the number sentence: $2 + 2 = 4$.

- Partners continue showing fingers and naming doubles facts to 10.

- Have partners switch roles and repeat the activity.

- Then have children use their hands to show a doubles fact for 5, 3, 1, 4, and 2.

Assessment and Remediation

- Ask children to tell how many apples Rob has in all if Rob had 2 apples and Tom gave him 2 more. [4]

- For children who are still struggling, use the chart below to guide remediation.

- After providing remediation, check children's understanding using the following problem: Kara puts 3 pencils in a cup. Her teacher puts in 3 more pencils. How many pencils are in the cup? [6]

If the error is . . .	Children may . . .	To remediate . . .
2	have failed to recognize that they need to use addition.	have children draw a picture showing Rob's 2 apples and Tom's 2 apples. Have children count to find the total number of apples.
0	have used subtraction instead of addition.	have children record "2 more" as "+ 2." Then have them use counters to show one group of 2 and another group of 2 and record the doubles fact $2 + 2 = 4$.
3	have failed to recognize $2 + 2$ as a doubles fact.	have children make picture cards for each of the doubles and write the doubles fact on the card. (For example, two eyes for $1 + 1 = 2$, two sets of hands for $5 + 5 = 10$.)

Hands-On Activity

Use connecting cubes to model adding doubles and doubles plus one.

Materials For each pair: 10 connecting cubes, 5 each of two different colors

- One partner uses two different-colored connecting cubes to show the doubles fact $1 + 1$.

- The other partner records the doubles fact on a sheet of paper. [$1 + 1 = 2$]

- The first partner uses cubes of two different colors to continue modeling the doubles facts $2 + 2$, $3 + 3$, $4 + 4$, and $5 + 5$ as the second partner records each doubles fact.

- Partners switch roles and use the cubes to show and record doubles plus one facts: $1 + 2$ and $2 + 1$, $2 + 3$ and $3 + 2$, $3 + 4$ and $4 + 3$, and $4 + 5$ and $5 + 4$.

Challenge Activity

Find doubles, doubles plus one, and doubles minus one patterns on an addition chart.

Materials For each child: Addition Table 1 (Activity Sheet 5), crayons

- Provide children with the Addition Table 1 worksheet.

- Have children write the totals below each addition. Then have them color the doubles facts.

- Ask children to make observations about the doubles facts on the table. [Doubles facts fall on a diagonal line in the chart.]

- Have children look above and below each doubles fact. Ask them what facts they see. [doubles plus 1, doubles minus 1]

Lesson 7 (Student Book pages 30–33)

Number Partners for 6 and 7

LESSON OBJECTIVES

- Develop fluency in addition and subtraction of sums for 6 and 7.
- Model facts for 6 and 7 in a number bond.
- Complete number sentences.

PREREQUISITE SKILLS

- Organize facts in a number bond.
- Read and write number sentences.

VOCABULARY

compose: to combine lesser numbers to make greater numbers

decompose: to break a number into two or more parts

number: tells how much or how many

number partners: two addends that make up a given total

THE LEARNING PROGRESSION

In Kindergarten, children fluently add and subtract within 5. They explore operations on numbers within 10 by decomposing numbers less than 10 through pictures, drawings, and number sentences.

In Grade 1, children gain fluency in addition and subtraction within 10 through physical and visual models, utilization of strategies, and through number sentences. **In this lesson,** children examine the partners for 6 and 7 by first modeling physical and pictorial representations of the partners, and then by completing number bonds and number sentences. Throughout the lesson, children pair visual models with the symbolic representation to help them analyze the structure and reasoning inherent in number partners.

In Grade 2, children extend their knowledge of facts by applying them to fact families and using them to add and subtract two-digit numbers.

▉Ready *Teacher Toolbox*

Teacher-Toolbox.com

	Prerequisite Skills	1.OA.D.8
Ready Lessons	✓ ✓ ✓	✓
Tools for Instruction	✓	
Interactive Tutorials	✓	✓ ✓

CCSS Focus

1.OA.D.8 Determine the unknown whole number in an addition or subtraction equation relating three whole numbers. *For example, determine the unknown number that makes the equation true in each of the equations* $8 + ? = 11$, $5 = \square - 3$, $6 + 6 = \square$.

ADDITIONAL STANDARDS: **1.OA.B.3, 1.OA.C.6** *(see page A36 for full text)*

STANDARDS FOR MATHEMATICAL PRACTICE: **SMP 2, 3, 5, 6, 7, 8** *(see page A9 for full text)*

Opening Activity: Domino Partners

Objective: Explore partners of 6 and 7.	**Materials** For each child: • Two sets of large paper squares containing 　1–6 dots in domino patterns

Overview

Children explore the concept of number partners by finding the other half of a domino with totals of either 6 or 7.

Step by Step (15–20 minutes)

1 Pose the problem.

- Show children a domino piece or display a picture of a domino. Tell children to pretend that they have been given the job of building dominos. Say: *Your first job is to make dominoes that show a total of 6 dots.*

2 Act it out.

- Lay out or place along a chalk rail the paper squares containing 1–5 dots.

- Invite a child to come to the front of the class and choose a square. Ask the child to face the class holding the square so all can see it.

- Ask a volunteer to find a square that would finish the 6-dot domino. Have the children hold their squares next to each other to form a domino and engage the class in determining whether the domino was built correctly and how they know. Listen for children to use previously learned strategies such as counting on.

- Repeat until all the possible domino combinations of 6 have been formed.

3 Explore the concept.

- Stand behind one pair of children and ask one partner to step back a couple of steps. Address the class with the question: *Can anyone find a different partner for [2]?*

- Allow children to wrestle with this question briefly before asking why there are no other partners.

- Repeat for another partner pair before asking children to generalize to all the partner pairs.

4 Apply to partners of 7.

- Display a square containing 4 dots and ask: *If we were making dominoes that show 7 dots, how many partners do you think there are for this square? Why?*

- Have children find the partner for 4 and set the squares next to each other to check.

Check for Understanding

Provide children with a half sheet of paper or white boards. Have them draw a vertical line to divide the space into two sections like a domino. Display the paper squares containing 1–6 dots. Have children draw the dots from one of the squares on one side of their "domino" and then find and draw the partner to make a 7-dot domino.

Look for children who are having difficulty determining how many dots to draw for each pair of partners. The Hands-On Activity on page 51 provides additional support.

STEP BY STEP

- Ask children to share the dominoes they made in the Opening Activity and explain how they know they have found the partner.

- Direct children's attention to the quilt shown and explain that a quilt is made of pieces of cloth sewn together. Tell them that this quilt is made up of small blue and green squares. Ask children how the rows are like the dominoes from the Opening Activity.

- Replicate or project the number bond from the problem at the top of the page. Ask children to tell what numbers belong in the bottom boxes to model the first row of squares. Guide children to recognize that 5 and 1 model the number of blue and green squares in the first row.

> **SMP Tip:** Explore each row of squares in the same way as above, writing number sentences for each one. Help children recognize that the reasoning techniques they use to find the number sentences are used repeatedly. *(SMP 8)*

- Discuss the Model It, explaining that the first addend represents the number of blue squares in the row. Have children fill in the blanks to show the number of green squares in each row.

- Invite volunteers to share their answers. Have children identify 2 addition and 2 subtraction facts for each row of squares. Record the number sentences.

Hands-On Activity

Materials For each child: blue and green connecting cubes

Have children replicate the quilt pattern by connecting sets of 6 blue and green cubes together as shown and then lay each row of cubes together to form the quilt.

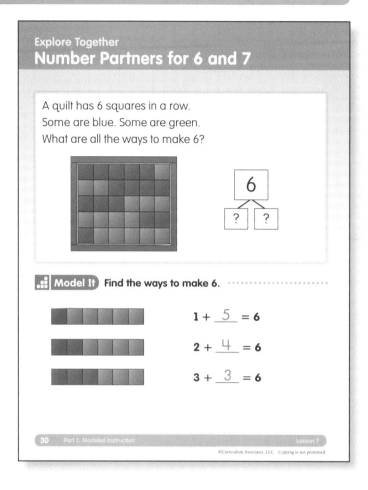

Mathematical Discourse

- *How can you make sure you have found all the partners for 6?*

    Some children may suggest building them; others may think of using a pattern: 1 + 5, 2 + 4, 3 + 3, 4 + 2, 5 + 1.

- *How does knowing number partners help you find the missing number in a number sentence?*

    Children should recognize that by knowing the partners, they can think about the one that is missing in the number sentence.

STEP BY STEP

Materials For each pair: connecting cubes, strip of paper containing 7 open circles

- Draw attention to the painting and engage children in discussing similarities and differences between the painting and the quilt from the previous page.

- Relate the number partners to the domino children created in the Opening Activity. Ask children to find a row of dots that is like their domino and explain how they are alike.

- Provide pairs of children with a set of cubes and a strip of paper with circles. Have children model each row of circles in the picture by placing colored cubes on the open circles. Then have children write corresponding number sentences on white boards.

- Draw children's attention to the Model It and ask: *What can you do to find the missing number in the number sentence?* Allow children to discuss strategies they may use before examining the number bond.

- Guide children to see how the number bond shown relates to the rows of circles. Use the Mathematical Discourse question to reinforce the application of the commutative property.

- As children discuss the Talk About It questions, ask what other number sentences Boom and Buzz could have written.

> **SMP Tip:** Engage children in describing their number sentences, justifying them in words and/or models. Encourage children to articulate clearly using accurate mathematical language and use their justification to check for accuracy. *(SMP 6)*

- **Error Alert** Display a number bond with the 3 and 4 reversed. Ask if Boom and Buzz would still be correct if this was the number bond they used to write their number sentences. Reinforce how the order of the addends in the bond does not affect the corresponding number sentences.

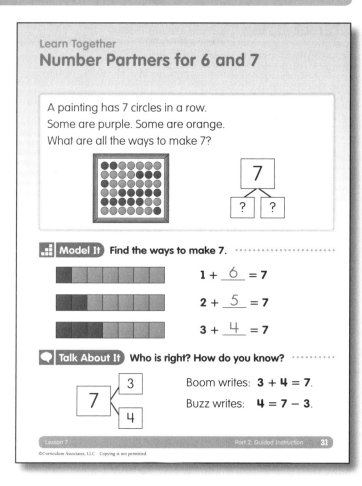

Mathematical Discourse

- *Does it matter where you put the 5 and the 2 in the number bond? Explain.*

  Children may suggest that 5 and 2 are partners for the number 7 so they can go in either of the small boxes. It doesn't matter which box they are in as long as they are not in the big box. That's for the 7.

Concept Extension

Some children may question whether $7 + 0$ and $0 + 7$ could be used in a number bond. If so, engage them in modeling a bar of cubes that would show the number bond and discuss that 0 implies that there are no purple cubes or no orange cubes in that bar. You may extend the concept to subtraction by asking children to model $7 - 0$ and $7 - 7$.

Note: 0 is introduced as a potential partner in a later lesson, so explore the concept without expectation of complete understanding.

STEP BY STEP

Materials For each child: connecting cubes

- Read the sample problem aloud. Revisit how children found the missing addends to number sentences on the previous pages.

SMP Tip: Help children notice the structure of the addends in the sample problem. Emphasize the commutative property by having children model the partners with cubes inverting it to show each addition. *(SMP 7)*

- Ask children to compare the addition sentences in Problem 1 to the sentences in the sample problem. Have physical cubes available for modeling. Use the second Mathematical Discourse question to explore this concept further.

- Direct children's attention to Problem 2. Ask if they can think of another subtraction sentence for the number bond. Show children a bar of 3 blue and 3 yellow cubes. Ask: *If there are 3 left after taking some away, how many do I need to take away?* [3] *Does it matter if I take away the blue cubes or the yellow cubes? Why not?*

- Model why there is only one subtraction sentence as well as only one addition sentence for this number bond.

Concept Extension

Twin Partners

Materials For each child: cubes, dominoes

Ask children if they can find number partners for 7 that only make two number sentences. Allow children to use cubes, dominoes, number bonds, or any strategies they have to explore this idea. Compare the partners of 7 to the partners of 6 and ask: *Why do you think 6 has two identical partners and 7 does not?* Children may or may not recognize odd and even numbers or doubles. These will be introduced in Grade 2. The focus should be on recognizing "twin" partners (a bar with two parts of the same size). Challenge children to find other numbers that have identical partners.

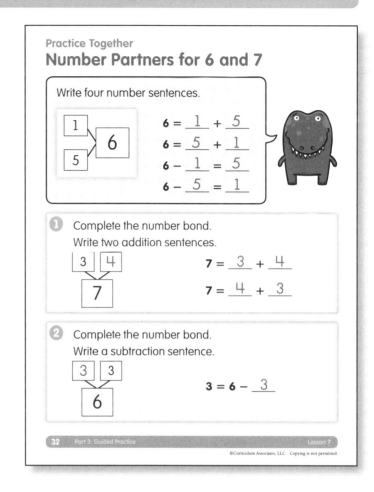

Mathematical Discourse

- *How do you know that you have found all the number sentences?*

   Children may reply that modeling with cubes tells them; others may recognize that each number partner is used in every possible position in the number sentences.

- *Can the number partners for ANY number bond be switched around to make two addition sentences? Explain.*

   Most children will respond that yes they can. Some may justify by inverting bars of cubes; others may explain that since there are only two numbers to add, you can start with one or start with the other. Some children may respond that when 3 + 3 are switched around it is the same number sentence so there is only one addition sentence for it.

STEP BY STEP

- Before children work on this page, review the models used in this lesson. Emphasize that children are free to use whatever way helps them solve the problem.

- Read each problem aloud. Draw attention to the varied positions of the equal sign in the problems on this page as you read. Then have children work independently to solve.

- **Error Alert** Watch for children who randomly place numbers in the blanks without connecting them to the number bond or model shown. Encourage those children to physically model the problem by acting out the additions and subtractions before recording the results.

- You may wish to draw attention to the four number sentences in Problem 5, and use the Mathematical Discourse question to discuss.

Visual Model

Reinforce number partners by having children model them with the fingers on their hands. Demonstrate the partners 1 and 5 for the number 6 by holding up 1 finger on one hand and 5 fingers on the other hand. Have children imitate your representation with their fingers. Have them hold their fingers up to show another set of partners for 6, making sure each partner is represented on separate hands. Then apply the activity to partners of 7.

Fluency Practice

Materials For each child: Partners for 6 Practice (Activity Sheet 6), Partners for 7 Practice (Activity Sheet 7), connecting cubes

Distribute Partners for 6 Practice and Partners for 7 Practice worksheets for practice modeling number partners for 6 and 7 in a number bond. Allow children to model the partners with cubes to help them complete each number bond.

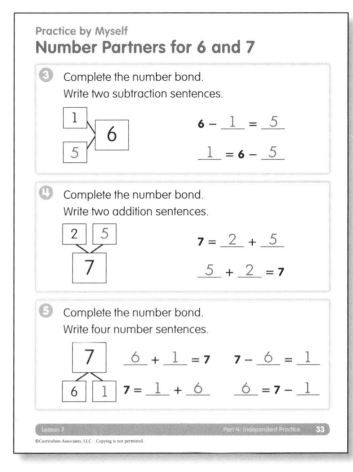

Mathematical Discourse

- *Can you find more than four number sentences for the number bonds? Explain.*

  No. There are only two numbers to add, so there are only two ways to write addition sentences. There are only two numbers to take away, so there are only two ways to write subtraction sentences.

Assessment and Remediation

Ask children to complete the following number sentences: 2 + ___ = 7, 7 − ___ = 2. [5, 5]

- For children who are still struggling, use the chart below to guide remediation.

- After providing remediation, check children's understanding using the following problem: Ask children to find the missing numbers in the following number sentences: 6 = 1 + ___, 1 = 6 − ___. [5, 5]

If the error is . . .	Children may . . .	To remediate . . .
9	have added the 7 and 2.	Model the addition with counters. Help them see that 7 is the sum of 2 and another number. Encourage children to check reasonableness of answers by modeling 2 + 9. They should notice that it does not equal 7. Then model the subtractions in the same way.
4	have recorded the fact for 6.	Show children a domino with 2 and 4 as partners. Ask children what number they are partners for. Ask if it is possible for them to be partners for 7 also. Ask them to find the partner that results in 7 and record it.
any other number	have miscounted.	Provide children with physical and/or visual models representing the number sentence. Have them check the reasonableness of their answer. Encourage children to use strategies such as counting on to help them count accurately.

Hands-On Activity

Counters in a bag

Materials For each pair: paper bag, counters, Number Bond Mat (Activity Sheet 3), set of 1–7 digit cards, white boards or paper

- Have children place 6 counters in a paper bag and the digit card 6 on the Number Bond Mat. One partner removes some, but not all of the counters from the bag and places the corresponding digit card in the number bond.

- The other partner determines the number of counters left in the bag and places the missing digit card in the number bond. They check by counting the counters left in the bag. Children then take turns writing a number sentence for the bond until all are written.

- Repeat until all combinations of 6 are recorded and then complete for partners of 7.

Challenge Activity

Number puzzles

Materials For each child: Grid Paper (Activity Sheet 8), two colors of pencils, crayons, or markers, scissors

- Challenge children to build number puzzles for the numbers 6 and 7 by coloring squares in two colors on grid paper to represent the partners of each number.

- Challenge children to find as many ways to organize the combinations as possible. The only restriction is that each square must be touching another square on a side or corner and each color must be grouped together.

- You may want to give each child a different set of partners to explore, one for 6 and one for 7, to make it more manageable for them.

- Once completed, have the children cut out and display the puzzles.

Lesson 8 (Student Book pages 34–37)

Number Partners for 8 and 9

LESSON OBJECTIVES

- Demonstrate fluency in addition and subtraction for sums 8 and 9.

- Relate the operations of addition and subtraction through number bonds.

- Recognize 0 as a number partner.

PREREQUISITE SKILLS

- Interpret a number bond.

- Write number sentences.

- Add and subtract within 5.

VOCABULARY

zero: a whole number that tells when a set has no objects in it

During the lesson you will review the key terms:

number bond: a diagram with a total and two addends

total: a number found as the result of adding

THE LEARNING PROGRESSION

In Kindergarten, children develop fluency for addition and subtraction within 5 and explore addition involving 0.

In Grade 1, children develop fluency within 10 through visual, tactile, and abstract models as well as through the use of strategies. **In this lesson,** children focus on the partners for 8 and 9 building on previous work with number bonds and the commutative property. They develop strategies for finding partners and extend the concept of partners to include zero, analyzing and defending it as a valid addend.

In Grade 2, children use fact families as a tool to explore sums within 20 and expand their use of strategies to gain fluency in them.

Ready *Teacher Toolbox*   *Teacher-Toolbox.com*

	Prerequisite Skills	1.OA.B.3
Ready Lessons	✓ ✓ ✓	✓
Tools for Instruction	✓	✓
Interactive Tutorials	✓	✓ ✓

CCSS Focus

1.OA.B.3 Apply properties of operations as strategies to add and subtract. *Examples: If 8 + 3 = 11 is known, then 3 + 8 = 11 is also known. (Commutative property of addition.) To add 2 + 6 + 4, the second two numbers can be added to make a ten, so 2 + 6 + 4 = 2 + 10 = 12. (Associative property of addition.)*

ADDITIONAL STANDARDS: *1.OA.C.6, 1.OA.D.8 (see page A36 for full text)*

STANDARDS FOR MATHEMATICAL PRACTICE: *SMP 2, 3, 4, 5, 6, 7, 8 (see page A9 for full text)*

Opening Activity: Explore Partners of 8

Objective: Explore combinations for the number 8.	**Materials** For each child: • counters • paper and pencils

Overview

Children use counters and/or pictures to solve an open-ended problem exploring possible partners for 8.

Step by Step (15–20 minutes)

1 Pose the problem.

- Tell the children that there are 2 vans to carry 8 people to the park. Ask: *How many people are in each van?*

2 Solve the problem.

- Have children solve the problem using counters or pictures, then show with pictures and words how they found their solution.

- Support children in selecting a solution strategy by asking questions such as: *How could counters help you find an answer? What could you use to show the vans? What might you use to show the people?*

- Watch as children solve the problem, making sure they understand the problem and have devised a workable strategy. As they work, guide them with questions such as: *Is it possible for only 1 person to be in a van? Why? If there were 3 people in this van, how many would be in the other van? How do you know?*

- Some children will notice that there is more than one right answer. Encourage them to find additional answers.

3 Share solutions.

- Invite volunteers to share their solutions and strategies in front of the class. Ask questions such as: *How can you be sure there are only 8 people in the vans? Why did you put 6 people in this van?*

- As children share solutions, write a number sentence corresponding to each solution on the board. Ask children if they think there are any other solutions to this problem and how they can be sure.

- Ask children why they think there is more than one correct solution to this problem.

Check for Understanding

Provide children with the following problem: *There are 8 apples. There are 2 apple trees. Show all the ways the apples could be on the two trees.*

Children may not be able to show all the ways to make partners for 8 before completing the lesson, but encourage them to try to find as many combinations as they can. Then explain that the lesson will help them see all the possible ways to solve problems like this one.

STEP BY STEP

- Ask children to share the ways they found to show the people in the vans from the Opening Activity.

- Draw attention to the problem at the top of the page. Ask: *If there is a 3 in the top circle, what number would be in the bottom circle? How do you know?*

- Discuss how the organization of the colored squares in the Model It relates to the number bond and the number sentences. Guide children to see that the number of colored squares in each strip represent the addends in both number sentences on the right.

- Have children describe what is alike and what is different about the paired number sentences. Then ask children to explain which number sentence the strip of squares shows and how they could show the other sentence using the same squares. Encourage children to share how they can be sure that all the ways to make 8 have been found.

- Guide children to notice the pattern shown by the number sentences. [As the first addend increases by 1, the second addend decreases by 1.] Use the Hands-On Activity to reinforce this concept.

> **SMP Tip:** To help children discern the structure within number partners, draw attention to the application of the commutative property by asking questions such as: *Does it matter if the blue square is the first square or the last square? Does it matter if 1 is shown first or last in the number sentence? Explain. (SMP 7)*

Hands-On Activity

Materials For each child: counters, square with "8" on it, Number Bond Mat (Activity Sheet 3)

Have children place the "8" square in the number bond. Have them place one counter in one square and the remaining counters in the second square. Record the number in each square on the board. Ask: *What do you need to do so that there are 2 counters in the circle that has one in it?* Children should see that by taking 1 from the circle containing 7 and placing it in the other circle they have partners of 2 and 6. Record these groups under the first group on the board. Continue until there are 7 counters in the first circle. Children should see that taking a counter from one circle decreases it by one, and adding it to the other, increases it by one.

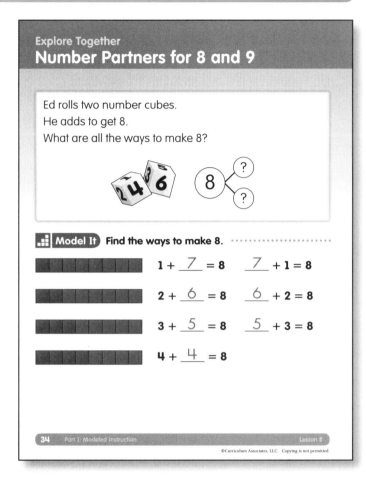

Mathematical Discourse

- *Why isn't there another number sentence for 4 + 4?*

  Children should notice that since both addends are the same, flipping them results in the same number sentence. Some children may recall from the Hands-On Activity that 4 and 4 was listed only once. There is only one way to model it with a number sentence.

Fluency Practice

Materials For each child: Partners for 8 Practice (Activity Sheet 9)

Use the Partners for 8 Practice to help children find and record partners for 8 in a number bond and in number sentences.

STEP BY STEP

Materials For each pair: connecting cubes, Number Bond Mat (Activity Sheet 3)

- Read the problem at the top of the page aloud. Allow children to work in pairs to find all the ways to make 9 using the Number Bond Mat.

- Engage children to share the strategies they used, demonstrating them for the class, if appropriate. Discuss how they knew they found all of the combinations.

- Guide children to see the similarities among the number sentences in the Model It for both 8 and 9. Ask: *If you know one number sentence, how does that help you know another one?* Reinforce that the commutative property allows them to "flip" the addends to make another sentence.

- Read the Talk About It aloud. Allow children to "think out loud" about this question with a partner.

- *Error Alert* Listen to children's ideas, helping those who think Buzz is wrong to articulate and clarify their reasoning by asking: *If there are two groups and 9 children, is it possible for 9 children to be in one group? How many would be in the other group?*

- Model addition with zero using connecting cubes. Show a bar of red cubes and write the number sentence 9 + ___ = 9. Ask: *How many blue cubes can I add so that I have 9 cubes?*

Concept Extension

Use addition patterns to help children make sense of addition with 0. Project the words "red" and "blue" on one side of a paper. Add a large circle with a 9 above it and display red and blue cubes. Ask: *If I put 0 red cubes in the circle, how many blue cubes should I put in to have 9?* Record 0 and 9 below the labels. Continue adding 1 red and 8 blue, etc. until there are 9 red and 0 blue in the circle. Make the numbers in the columns into number sentences, pointing out the partners of 9 and 0.

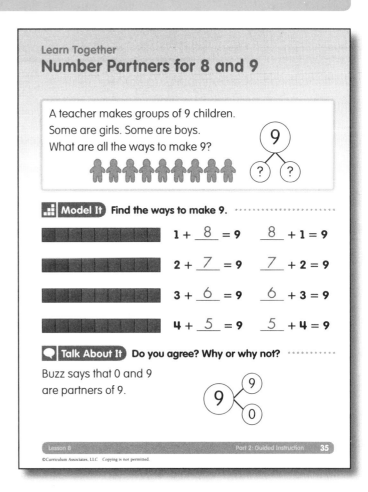

Mathematical Discourse

- *Boom says that 0 means nothing and you cannot have 'nothing' for a partner. What can you tell Boom?*

   Children may respond that 0 means nothing more was added to a group or that it means there are no blue cubes, etc.

- *Can 0 be a partner for any number? Why?*

   Yes. Children may use examples, such as, if there are 8 girls and no boys, there are still 8 people. Some children may also demonstrate their understanding by using greater numbers.

Fluency Activity

Materials For each child: Partners for 9 Practice (Activity Sheet 10)

Use the Partners for 9 Practice to help children find and record partners for 9 in a number bond and in number sentences.

STEP BY STEP

Materials For each child: 8 connecting cubes of two different colors, 9 connecting cubes of two different colors

- Remind children of the previous lesson when they wrote four number sentences for a number bond. Tell them that they can write number sentences for any number bond.

- Have children build a bar of 3 connecting cubes of one color and 5 connecting cubes of another color. Demonstrate how to use the cubes to model each of the number sentences shown.

- Once children have completed each number sentence in the example, ask: *Would 6 + 2 = 8 be a number sentence for this number bond? Why?* Guide children to understand that, although there are many ways to make 8, only the numbers in the number bond can be used in the number sentences.

- Direct children's attention to Problem 1. Ask children to share what they know about the number of addition sentences [2] that can be written for a given number bond. Then pose the first Mathematical Discourse question.

- As children complete the number sentences, point out the addends they have written and ask them to describe what they notice about them. Reinforce the commutative property in the "switched around" arrangement of addends in the number sentence.

- Direct attention to Problem 2. Help children recognize that in this problem, both number sentences begin with 9, but the number that is subtracted is different.

- Have children model the subtraction sentences with connecting cubes, then use the second Mathematical Discourse question to reinforce the relationship between subtraction and addition.

> **SMP Tip:** As children explore four number sentences for a given number bond, they will begin to recognize this as a consistency (regularity in mathematics) that allows them to flexibly add and subtract within any number group. *(SMP 8)*

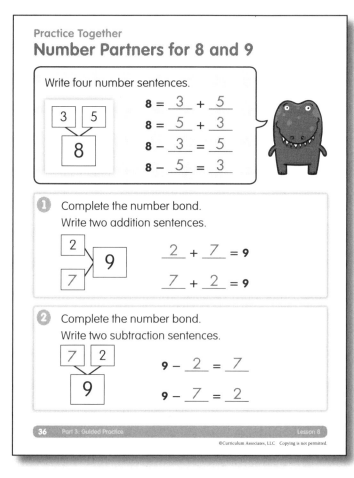

Mathematical Discourse

- *Would it make sense to write the subtraction sentence 2 − 9 = 7? Why?*

  Children may use examples such as: If you had 2 apples you couldn't give 9 away. Others may notice that since 9 is the total in the number bond, it must be the number from which another is subtracted.

- *How does knowing that 2 + 7 is 9 help you know what 9 − 7 equals?*

  Children should relate addition to subtraction by responding that if 2 and 7 are put together to make 9, when you take them apart again and take 7 away, 2 is left.

STEP BY STEP

- Before children work on this page, review the models used in this lesson. Emphasize that children are free to use whatever way helps them solve the problems.

- Read each problem aloud. Then have children work independently to solve.

- **Error Alert** Observe as children work. Look for those who are struggling with the placement of the totals in the number sentences. Use the phrase "is the same as" and the word "equals" interchangeably as you discuss the placement of the equal sign.

- As children complete Problem 3, ask: *How can you be sure you have put the numbers in the correct places?* Discuss how they can check to see that the addends in the addition sentences are "flipped" and that each partner is subtracted in the subtraction sentences.

Concept Extension

Materials For display: Number bonds for 8 and 9 that include a 0

Display the number bonds and write addition sentences for each one. Model and explain each sentence. Draw 9 balloons and color them blue. Relate each number sentence to the balloons. Invite children to write two subtraction sentences from this number bond. To help children understand the subtraction, write the word "blue" under the box in the number bond containing the number 9 and "red" under the box containing the number 0 and model the sentences. For children who still see subtraction as "take away" say: *If I have 9 balloons and 0 balloons pop, how many balloons do I have? If I have 9 balloons and 9 of them pop, how many do I have?* In this way children are using modeling to make sense of an abstract idea.

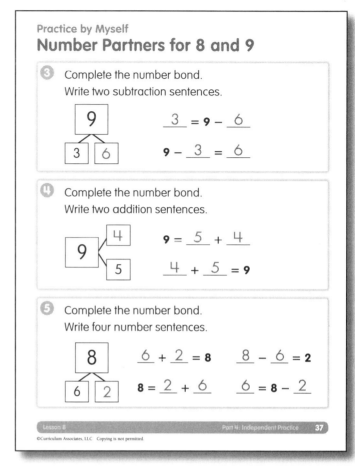

Mathematical Discourse

- *Buzz says he remembers that $5 + 4$ is 9 because he knows $5 + 5$ is 10 and 4 is 1 less than 5 so the answer must be 1 less than 10 or 9. What do you think of his strategy?*

  Children may respond that this strategy makes sense because it uses doubles plus 1. Some may compare it to an addition: Because $5 + 3 = 8$, $5 + 4$ is one more (9). They may suggest that it works backward also.

SMP Tip: Model the situation above to emphasize the regularity within the base-ten number system. This will lead to increased curiosity and application of strategies that make use of this type of reasoning. (*SMP 8*)

Assessment and Remediation

- Ask children to write four number sentences for the number bond that includes the numbers 9, 1, 8. [8 + 1 = 9, 1 + 8 = 9, 9 − 1 = 8, 9 − 8 = 1]

- For children who are still struggling, use the chart below to guide remediation.

- After providing remediation, check children's understanding using the following problem: Write four number sentences for the number bond that includes the numbers 8, 3, 5. [3 + 5 = 8, 5 + 3 = 8, 8 − 3 = 5, 8 − 5 = 3]

If the error is ...	Children may ...	To remediate ...
1 − 9 = 8	be applying the commutative property to subtraction of whole numbers.	Have children read the subtraction sentence and attempt to model it with counters. Invite them to draw 1 counter and attempt to cross out 9. Lead them to recognize the only possible subtraction sentences by modeling with counters or fingers.
9 + 1 = 8	be adding in the order in which the numbers are listed.	Watch children as they model the addition with counters or fingers and ask if it makes sense that 9 and 1 more is 8. Help them model and record accurately.

Hands-On Activity

Play "Break Apart" game with a partner.

Materials For each pair: 9 connecting cubes, Number Bond Mat (Activity Sheet 3), paper circles with the numbers 8 and 9 written on them

- One child connects either 8 or 9 cubes and places the corresponding number circle on the Number Bond Mat.

- The child hides the cubes behind his or her back and breaks the bar into two sections. One section of the cubes is placed on the number bond while the other section remains hidden.

- The partner attempts to figure out how many cubes are hidden. If correct, the partner hiding the cubes reveals them. If not correct, the child tries again until a correct answer is given.

- The child tells either an addition or subtraction sentence that describes the number bond.

- Roles are reversed and play continues. Partners continue reversing roles after each play until allotted time has expired.

Challenge Activity

Write word problems.

Tell children to choose a number bond for 8 or a number bond for 9.

Each child should:

- Write 4 number sentences for the number bond.

- Write a word problem for each number sentence that uses items of interest to their classmates.

- Exchange the set of word problems with a partner.

- Solve each problem, write a number sentence for it, and make the number bond that was used for that set of problems.

- Check to see if the number bond matches the one that was used to write the problems.

- If a problem cannot be solved or the number bonds do not match, return them to the partner to be revised.

- If the number bonds match, post the word problems for classmates to solve.

- Repeat for another number bond, if time permits.

Lesson 9 (Student Book pages 38–41)

Number Partners for 10

LESSON OBJECTIVES

- Fluently add and subtract within 10.
- Apply strategies to addition and subtraction of sums within 10.
- Understand inverse operations as a tool for adding and subtracting.

PREREQUISITE SKILLS

- Add and subtract within 9.
- Interpret a number bond.
- Apply the commutative property of addition.

VOCABULARY

During the lesson you will review the key terms:

doubles: an addition fact that has two addends that are the same, such as $4 + 4$

number bond: a diagram with a total and two addends

total: a number found as the result of adding

THE LEARNING PROGRESSION

In Kindergarten, children explore combinations of numbers whose sum is 10 by decomposing them with physical objects and writing corresponding number sentences.

In Grade 1, children fluently add and subtract within 10 moving beyond the physical representation by developing strategies and utilizing inverse operations. **In this lesson,** children gain fluency in partners for 10 by relating visual models to number sentences and applying properties of addition and inverse operations. They analyze the structure of addends and use the structure as a strategy for developing fluency.

In Grade 2, children utilize facts of 10 as they develop strategies for finding sums within 20. These strategies provide the basis for adding numbers beyond 20 and facts of ten are applied to additions involving multiples of 10.

Ready *Teacher Toolbox*   Teacher-Toolbox.com

	Prerequisite Skills	1.OA.C.6
Ready Lessons	✓ ✓ ✓	✓
Tools for Instruction	✓ ✓	✓
Interactive Tutorials		✓ ✓

CCSS Focus

1.OA.C.6 Add and subtract within 20, demonstrating fluency for addition and subtraction within 10. Use strategies such as counting on; making ten (e.g., $8 + 6 = 8 + 2 + 4 = 10 + 4 = 14$); decomposing a number leading to a ten (e.g., $13 - 4 = 13 - 3 - 1 = 10 - 1 = 9$); using the relationship between addition and subtraction (e.g., knowing that $8 + 4 = 12$, one knows $12 - 8 = 4$); and creating equivalent but easier or known sums (e.g., adding $6 + 7$ by creating the known equivalent $6 + 6 + 1 = 12 + 1 = 13$).

ADDITIONAL STANDARDS: **1.OA.B.3, 1.OA.D.8** *(see page A36 for full text)*

STANDARDS FOR MATHEMATICAL PRACTICE: **SMP 2, 3, 4, 5, 6, 7, 8** *(see page A9 for full text)*

Opening Activity: Ways to Make 10

Objective: Explore combinations of ten.	**Materials** For each child: • 60 connecting cubes • white board

Overview

Children model a situation from literature finding ways to make 10 through the structure of the model.

Step by Step (20–25 minutes)

1 **Pose the problem.**

- Read aloud the literature book *Rooster's Off to See the World* by Eric Carle. After reading, have children model with connecting cubes the structure of one more animal shown on each page until 5 cubes are built. Ask: *If Rooster kept going and meeting more animals, how many do you think he would meet next?* Have children build a bar of 6 and continue to 10. Discuss the "stair case" structure of the cubes and then ask children to find pairs of cube bars that are the same size as the ten bar and record them.

2 **Share strategies.**

- Allow children to find combinations watching to make sure they leave each bar intact.

- Invite volunteers to share the strategy they used to make 10. Listen to all strategies, but focus on the strategy some children may have employed by noticing that 1 goes on 9, 2 goes on 8, etc. Ask them why their strategy made it easy to find combinations and discuss the reason for 5 standing alone.

3 **Extend a strategy.**

- Ask children to hold up both hands showing all their fingers and ask: *How many fingers do you have?* Write 10 on the board and circle it.

- Tell children to fold down a thumb and ask how many fingers are folded down and how many are held up. Write 1 and 9 under the 10. Continue folding down one finger at a time recording the number that are folded down and the number held up to 9 and 1.

4 **Relate the strategy.**

- Discuss how the finger activity was like the cubes and how it was different. Make sure children understand that there are many ways to think about numbers.

- Relate this activity to one the children completed in the previous lesson using cubes and a number bond. As one group was made larger by one, the other group became smaller by one.

Check for Understanding

Pose the following problem: *Mia is playing a math game. Her partner has a card with the number 10. Mia needs to show two cards that make 10. What are all the ways she could show 10?*

Children may not be able to find all the ways to make 10 before completing the student book lesson, but allow time for them to name as many as possible. Look for children who name a limited number of combinations. Additional support is provided in the Visual Model on page 65 and the Hands-On Activity on page 66.

STEP BY STEP

- Begin by allowing children to share their understandings from the Opening Activity. Encourage them to articulate the structure they noticed clearly. Support them by rephrasing or questioning a statement that may not be easily understood.

- Read the problem at the top of the page aloud. Have children draw lines to connect each partner pair for 10 shown by the digit cards. Discuss why 5 does not have a partner shown.

- As children complete the Model It, ask the Mathematical Discourse question. Remind children how they used fingers in the Opening Activity to model additions for 10 and compare that model to the colored cube illustration shown.

- Engage children in finding a subtraction for each of the additions shown. Project an open addition sentence and an open subtraction sentence. Place cards with numbers on them in the addition sentence to show $1 + 9 = 10$.

- Invite a volunteer to rearrange the cards to make a subtraction sentence. Repeat until each of the addition sentences have been written as a subtraction.

> **SMP Tip:** To emphasize the relationship between addition and subtraction, alter the above activity by creating either an addition or subtraction sentence and allowing children to find a related number sentence. Their work with related number sentences helps children recognize regularity and lays the groundwork for advanced addition and subtraction strategies. (SMP 8)

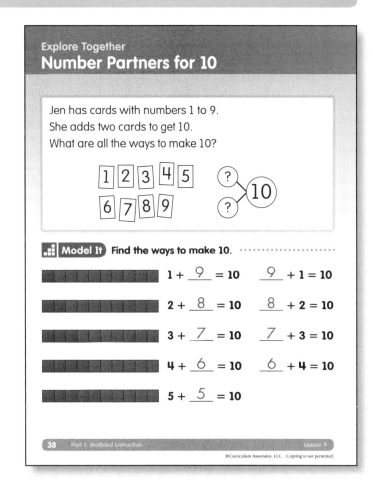

Mathematical Discourse

- *How are finding all the addition sentences for 10 like finding addition sentences for 8 and 9?*

  Some children may refer to the pattern, noting that as one addend increases, the other decreases. Others may suggest that when you know the addition for one set of numbers, you can "flip" it to find another addition.

Visual Model

Provide children with another visual representation of partners. Write the numbers 1–9 on the board horizontally. Ask children to find the partners for 10 and connect each partner pair.

$$1 \quad 2 \quad 3 \quad 4 \quad 5 \quad 6 \quad 7 \quad 8 \quad 9$$

STEP BY STEP

- Read the problem at the top of the page aloud. If children respond to "How do you know?" by saying they counted the yellow beads, discuss other ways they could know there are 4 yellow beads. Encourage children to recall strategies or visual models they used in the Opening Activity and on the previous page.

- Direct children's attention to the Model It. Ask: *How does the 10-frame show the partner for 6?* Invite children to demonstrate the addition and subtraction sentences for the number bond shown.

- **Error Alert** Have children discuss the Talk About It with a partner. Direct attention to the number bond. Guide children to model each number sentence on a ten-frame, then compare that to the sentences Buzz and Boom wrote. Ask children to discuss why the first sentence Buzz wrote does not make sense.

- To reinforce the concept of a "family" of numbers, ask: *If Buzz wrote the first number sentence correctly, would he then be correct, too?* Help children recognize that not all the numbers he used are included in the number bond so he would not be correct.

- Ask: *Why do you think Buzz wrote these number sentences?* Discuss how the numbers from the number bond were added or subtracted, but not in a way that resulted in another number from the number bond.

Hands-On Activity

Materials For each child: 10-Frame (Activity Sheet 11), red and yellow counters

- Provide each child with a 10-frame. Point out that each frame is divided into two groups of 5 just as their hands are divided into two groups of 5 fingers. Have children place 6 red counters on the frame and ask how many more they need to add to fill the frame. Instruct them to fill the remaining squares with yellow counters.

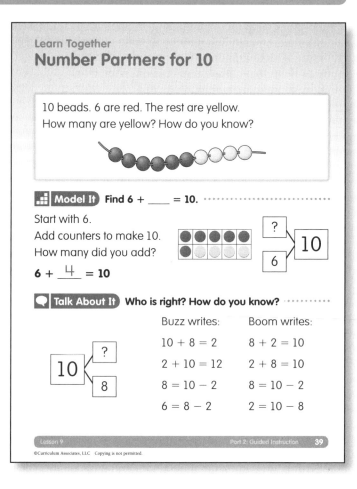

Mathematical Discourse

- *How is the ten-frame like the other models you have used? How is it different?*

  Children may notice similarities such as it is like holding up and folding down fingers. Children may say that a difference is that it is a rectangle divided into 10 squares.

SMP Tip: Making children aware of the relationship among all the models and strategies they have used provides a continual reminder of the regularity in reasoning used in mathematics and leads children to realize that they can apply what they have learned to many new situations, which engenders confidence. (SMP 8)

STEP BY STEP

Materials For each child: 10-Frame (Activity Sheet 11), 10 connecting cubes in two different colors

- Read the sample problem together. Ask: *Why are there only two number sentences for these partners?* Encourage children to associate the question to activities they have done in previous lessons that explored the concept of "twin" partners.

- Revisit the cube stacks from the Opening Activity and the Visual Model from the first page of the lesson to see that 5 stands alone. Model with cubes how "flipping" the addition sentence results in an identical number sentence.

- Direct children to Problem 1. Ask: *What strategy might you use to find the missing number in the number bond?* Listen for strategies that have been developed such as counting on, using fingers, etc. Model any strategies children suggest that have not been introduced or discussed previously.

- Have children model the number sentences by drawing counters in 10-frames. Ask the first Mathematical Discourse question to reinforce the application of the commutative property.

- Have children model the addends with connecting cubes and discuss how this model compares to their drawings in the 10-frames. Compare these models to the other models children have seen and discuss which model(s) each child prefers and why.

- As children discuss, make sure they understand that no one model is better than another and that their choices are individual. What works for one child may or may not work for another child.

- **Error Alert** Encourage children to model the subtraction sentences with 10-frames. Ask: *Why doesn't it make sense to write $9 - 1$ as a subtraction sentence for this number bond?* Revisit the problem on the previous page and the misconception Buzz had in combining the numbers in the bond inappropriately.

Fluency Practice

Materials For each child: Partners for 10 Practice (Activity Sheet 12)

Use the activity sheet to help children practice identifying partners for totals to 10 in a number bond.

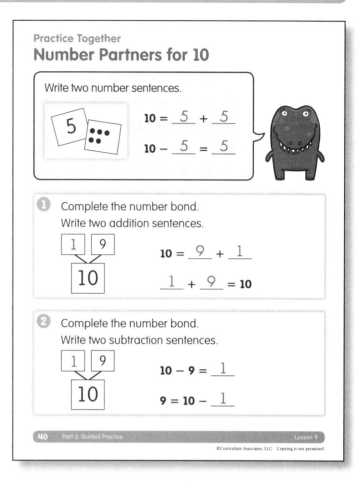

Mathematical Discourse

- *How do the 10-frame drawings show both addition sentences?*

    Children may respond that in the first 10-frame, one yellow is shown and then 9 red. In the second 10-frame, 9 red are shown and then one yellow. Children may also notice that the frames are "flipped" versions of each other.

- *How can thinking about a 10-frame or other model help you make sure you write the correct number sentences for a number bond?*

    Children may respond that when they "see" the problem they can tell what numbers go together and how to take one away to get the other number.

STEP BY STEP

- Before children work on this page, review the models used in the lesson. Emphasize that children are free to use whatever way helps them solve the problem.

- Read each problem aloud. Encourage children to notice what some of the differences among the three problems are.

- Some children may see that Problem 3 shows a digit card and a dot card as well as a number bond, that the totals in the number bonds and/or number sentences are displayed differently, or that there are both addition and subtraction sentences to solve.

- Have children work independently to solve the problems.

- You may wish to draw attention to Problem 5 and encourage children to draw a model of the number bond. Have children explain why they chose the model they did to show the number bond.

> **SMP Tip:** Have children model all the ways to decompose 10 in a 10-frame. As children organize counters on a 10-frame, they are repeatedly finding combinations whose sum is 10. *(SMP 8)* Lead them to recognize the way one color decreases in number each time the other color increases in number. *(SMP 7)* Relate this to the modeling done with partners for 8 and 9 in the previous lesson.

ELL Support

ELL students may find it difficult to express themselves in sharing what they notice about the differences among the problems, so may not offer ideas. To get a window on their thinking, encourage them to share ideas with a partner they trust, or speak with you later when there is no peer pressure.

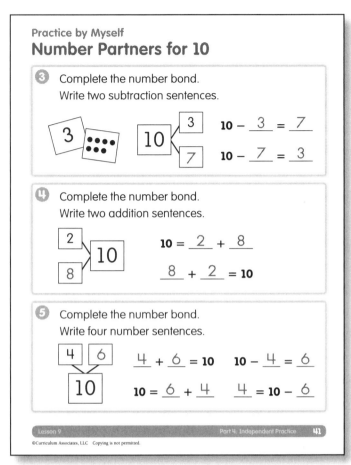

Practice by Myself
Number Partners for 10

3 Complete the number bond.
Write two subtraction sentences.

$10 - 3 = 7$
$10 - 7 = 3$

4 Complete the number bond.
Write two addition sentences.

$10 = 2 + 8$
$8 + 2 = 10$

5 Complete the number bond.
Write four number sentences.

$4 + 6 = 10$ $10 - 4 = 6$
$10 = 6 + 4$ $4 = 10 - 6$

Mathematical Discourse

- *How can you always know what number to start with when writing a subtraction sentence?*

    Some children may say to start with the greatest number. Others may notice that the number in the number bond from which both lines extend is the one to begin with.

Assessment and Remediation

- Ask children to write the four number sentences for the number bond including 10, 3, and 7. [3 + 7 = 10, 7 + 3 = 10, 10 − 3 = 7, 10 − 7 = 3]

- For children who are still struggling, use the chart below to guide remediation.

- After providing remediation, check children's understanding using the following problem: write the four number sentences for the number bond including 10, 4, and 6. [4 + 6 = 10, 6 + 4 = 10, 10 − 4 = 6, 10 − 6 = 4]

If the error is . . .	Children may . . .	To remediate . . .
10 + 3 = 13 3 + 7 = 10 10 − 7 = 3 7 3 = 4	be using any numbers in the number bond to create number sentences.	Write the number 10 in an open number bond. Have children model the two addends in the other sections of the number bond with bars of 3 and 7 cubes. Model combining and separating the two bars as children complete the number sentences.
7 − 10 = 3	applying the commutative property to subtraction.	Have children read the subtraction sentence and attempt to model it with a picture. Invite them to draw 7 circles and attempt to cross out 10. Lead them to recognize the corresponding subtraction sentences by modeling with counters or fingers.

Hands-On Activity

Play sums of ten memory game.

Materials For each pair: 9 cards of one color with numbers 1–9 printed on them, 9 cards of a different color each containing from 1 to 9 dots

- Mix up the cards and place them face down. Children take turns turning up two cards, one of each color. If the sum of the two cards is 10, the child keeps the cards. If not, the cards are turned face down again. Play continues until all combinations have been found.

- Optional: add cards with the numbers 10 and 0 and cards containing ten and 0 dots

Challenge Activity

Make a book.

Materials For each child: *Ten Black Dots,* by Donald Crew

- Have children read the book *Ten Black Dots.*

- Tell them they will work together in pairs to create a book that is similar to this book except each page will include a different combination of two colors of dots that make 10.

- Challenge pairs to put the dots into contexts different from what is in the book.

- When the pages are complete, help children think of a title and have them design a cover and then make a book for their classmates to read.

Lesson 10 (Student Book pages 42–45)

Understand the Equal Sign

LESSON OBJECTIVES

- Understand that the equal sign is used to indicate that one quantity is the same as another.

- Match equivalent expressions.

- Write and identify true and false number sentences.

- Rewrite a false number sentence so that it is true.

PREREQUISITE SKILLS

- Add to find totals up to 10.

- Find missing addends.

VOCABULARY

equal sign (=): a symbol that means "is the same as"

is the same as: indicates that quantities equal each other

number sentence: a sentence with symbols and numbers that compares two amounts as equal, less than, or greater than

THE LEARNING PROGRESSION

In Kindergarten, children work with number partners through 10 using mostly objects and drawings. Children solve joining situations that lead to an understanding of "equal" as groups that have the same amount or quantity.

In Grade 1, children connect the concepts of "joining," "separating," and "equal" to the symbols $+$, $-$, and $=$. Children understand that the equal sign signifies an equivalent relationship. **In this lesson,** children are introduced to the meaning of the equal sign working with picture models and number bonds that show equal quantities on both sides of the equal sign. Children also write number sentences to show that equivalent expressions are equal, identify true and false number sentences, and rewrite false number sentences as true.

In Grade 2, children use the equal sign to write number sentences for adding to, taking from, putting together, taking apart, and comparing situations. Children write number sentences to express uneven numbers as totals of two equal addends and represent rectangular arrays with number sentences expressing totals as sums of equal addends.

Ready *Teacher Toolbox*

Teacher-Toolbox.com

	Prerequisite Skills	1.OA.D.7
Ready Lessons	✓ ✓ ✓	✓
Tools for Instruction	✓	
Interactive Tutorials	✓	✓ ✓

CCSS Focus

1.OA.D.7 Understand the meaning of the equal sign, and determine if equations involving addition and subtraction are true or false. *For example, which of the following equations are true and which are false? $6 = 6$, $7 = 8 - 1$, $5 + 2 = 2 + 5$, $4 + 1 = 5 + 2$.*

ADDITIONAL STANDARDS: **1.OA.C.6, 1.OA.D.8** *(see page A36 for full text)*

STANDARDS FOR MATHEMATICAL PRACTICE: **SMP 2, 6** *(see page A9 for full text)*

Opening Activity: Understand the Equal Sign

Objective: Model that the same total can have different parts and write number sentences to show that the total is equal to the sum of the parts.

Materials For each child:
• none

Overview

Children act out two addition problems that have different parts and the same total. They identify the total as equal to the sum of the parts and write number sentences for each.

Step by Step (10–15 minutes)

1 Pose the problem.

• *The playground has new swings. At recess yesterday, there were 6 girls and 2 boys playing on the swings. At recess today, 4 girls and 4 boys play on the swings. How can you find out how many children played on the swings each day?*

2 Act out the problem.

• Have 6 girls and 2 boys go to one side of the classroom.

• Have 4 girls and 4 boys go to the opposite side of the classroom.

• Point to the side with 6 girls and 2 boys. Ask: *How many girls are there?* [6] *How many boys?* [2]

• Then point to the side with 4 girls and 4 boys. Ask: *How many girls are there?* [4] *How many boys?* [4]

3 Write addition number sentences.

• Write 6 + 2 on the board. Ask: *What is the total?* [8] Complete the number sentence by writing the equal sign and the total: 6 + 2 = 8.

• Write 4 + 4 on the board. Ask: *What is the total?* [8] Complete the number sentence by writing the equal sign and the total: 4 + 4 = 8.

4 Talk about the addition sentences.

• Ask: *What does 6 + 2 show?* [how many girls and how many boys]

• Ask: *What does 4 + 4 show?* [how many girls and how many boys]

• Point to the totals in the two number sentences on the board. Ask: *What do you notice about the totals?* [They are the same, 8.]

• Discuss how different parts can make the same total.

• Discuss how the number sentences show that the same number of children played on the swings each day.

Check for Understanding

Provide the children with the following problem: *Tom gets 3 books about dogs and 4 books about horses from the library. Dee gets 2 books about cats and 5 books about fish. Do Tom and Dee each get the same number of books? How do you know?* [Yes, the totals are the same, 5.]

Observe for children who do not see the quantities as equal after completing the additions. Additional support is provided in the Hands-On Activity on page 72.

STEP BY STEP

- Introduce the problem at the top of the page. Relate "is the same as" to the equal sign, =.

- Use the two picture models on the page to demonstrate the equality of the quantities on either side of the equal sign. The first model, 4 = 4, shows the identity property of addition. The second model shows that a quantity may be an expression or a number.

- Review the Think with the children. Reinforce the connection between the equal sign and the phrase "is the same as." Read the number sentence under the first number bond aloud and ask: *Is 1 + 3 the same as 4? Why or why not?* Ask a similar question for the second number sentence: *Is 4 the same as 1 + 3? How do you know?*

- Ask children what they notice about the placement of the equal sign. Children may say that it comes before the total in one number sentence and after the total in the other. Discuss how the equal sign still means "is the same as" no matter where it is placed in a number sentence.

- Present the Talk About It questions. Discuss that "true" means "correct" or "right." Children may identify the first number sentence as false and the second number sentence as true. Pose the Mathematical Discourse question.

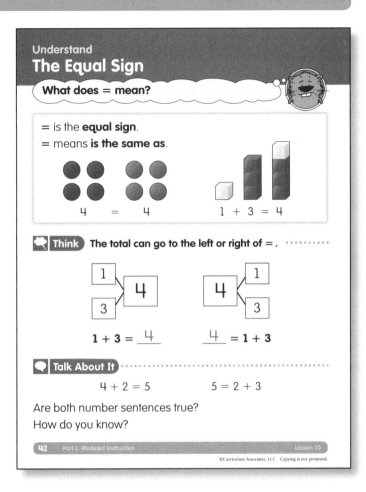

Hands-On Activity

Use counters to make equal quantities.

Materials For each child: 8 counters

- Have children make two groups of 4 counters.

- Children count and write the number sentence that shows the equality: 4 = 4.

- Have children repeat with groups of 1 and 3 counters and a group of 4 counters for the number sentence 1 + 3 = 4.

Mathematical Discourse

- *How do you know that 4 + 2 = 5 is not a true number sentence?*

   Children may say that first they find 4 + 2 (6), then compare the total they find to the total that is given (7). 6 is not equal to 5, so the number sentence is not true.

ELL Support

Provide cards to support the meaning of the mathematical symbols + and =. One card shows the symbol "+" with the word "plus" beneath it; another card shows "=" with the word "equal" beneath it. ELL children use the cards to talk about the concept of equality using mathematical language.

STEP BY STEP

- Provide connecting cubes of two different colors to children. Have children look at the first picture on the page and join cubes to model adding 4 + 1 and 3 + 2.

- Children may count cubes or compare lengths to find the total. Relate the parts and the total to the number sentences 4 + 1 = 5 and 5 = 3 + 2. Ask: *What do you notice about the totals?* [They are the same.] *Does 5 = 5?* [yes]

- After children have written the missing addends in the number sentences, draw attention to the one showing 4 + 1 = 3 + 2. Discuss the connection between the number bonds and the number sentences.

- Listen for statements that indicate children's understanding that the totals on each side of the equal sign are the same even though the parts are different.

- Have children work to complete Problem 1. Relate the number bond to the number sentence and have children complete the number sentences. Then pose the Mathematical Discourse question.

- Present the Talk About It problem and questions. Children may say that Mia and Dan do not have the same number of cubes. Children may find the total number of cubes each has and compare the totals: 2 + 6 = 8 and 4 + 3 = 7; 8 is not equal to 7.

Concept Extension

Make a false number sentence true.

- Talk with children about ways to change the number of cubes that Mia and Dan have so that they have an equal number of cubes.

- Ask: *Who has more cubes, Mia or Dan?* [Mia] *How many more cubes?* [1] *What could you do to make the number of cubes that they have equal?* [take 1 cube away from Mia or give Dan 1 more cube]

- Ask: *What number sentences could you write if you take 1 cube away from Mia?* [1 + 6 = 4 + 3; 2 + 5 = 4 + 3] *What number sentences could you write if you give Dan 1 more cube?* [2 + 6 = 5 + 3; 2 + 6 = 4 + 4]

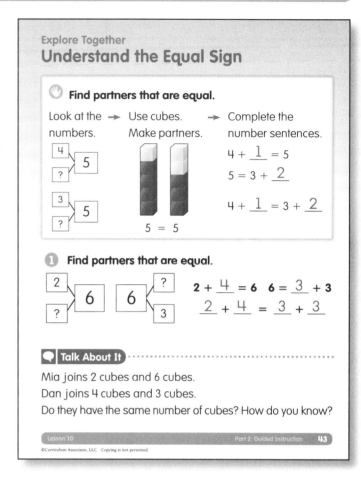

Mathematical Discourse

- *How can a number sentence that has different addends on each side of the equal sign be a true number sentence?*

    The addends make the same total; the totals are equal so the number sentence is true.

SMP Tip: In this lesson, children examine the precise meaning of the equal sign and realize that its position in a number sentence can convey a particular meaning. *(SMP 6)*

STEP BY STEP

- Discuss each Connect It problem as a class using the discussion points outlined below.

Draw:

- Guide children to recognize that both expressions have the same addends, but in a different order.

- Encourage children to think of a way they tell whether the number sentence is true without finding the totals on each side of the equal sign. [The addends are the same on both sides of the equal sign, so the number sentence is true.]

- Invite children to share their drawings. Ask questions such as: *Why did you draw the number of objects you did? Does anyone have a question about [child's name]'s drawing?*

- Encourage children to answer questions about their drawings. You may wish to have them modify their drawings or make new ones based on the questions from others.

Evaluate:

- As children decide whether the number sentences are true, revisit the earlier discussion about addends that make the same total. Guide children to recall that when any two addends on each side of an equal sign make the same total, the number sentence is true.

- Ask children to explain their reasoning about why each false number sentence is not true.

Create

- Ask children to talk to a partner about the problem. After a few minutes, begin a class discussion about the number sentences children have written.

- Have volunteers share their number sentences. Record their responses on the board. Then have children explain why they think there is more than one correct way to make the number sentences true.

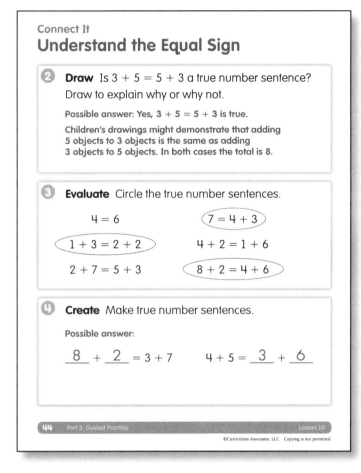

Connect It
Understand the Equal Sign

② **Draw** Is 3 + 5 = 5 + 3 a true number sentence? Draw to explain why or why not.

Possible answer: Yes, 3 + 5 = 5 + 3 is true.

Children's drawings might demonstrate that adding 5 objects to 3 objects is the same as adding 3 objects to 5 objects. In both cases the total is 8.

③ **Evaluate** Circle the true number sentences.

4 = 6   (7 = 4 + 3)

(1 + 3 = 2 + 2)   4 + 2 = 1 + 6

2 + 7 = 5 + 3   (8 + 2 = 4 + 6)

④ **Create** Make true number sentences.

Possible answer:

_8_ + _2_ = 3 + 7   4 + 5 = _3_ + _6_

©Curriculum Associates, LLC   Copying is not permitted.

SMP Tip: Finding equivalent and non-equivalent expressions involves making sense of quantities and their relationships. *(SMP 2)*

STEP BY STEP

- Tell children they will work on their own to complete the problems on this page.

- Review the directions aloud, making sure children understand what they are expected to do.

- In Part A, children count and write the number of shapes in groups to find addends in number sentences.

- In Part B, children correct the false number sentence from Part A.

- Observe children as they work. Ask questions such as the following to encourage thinking and problem-solving strategies.

  Do you write an equal sign in the box for the number sentence in Part B? Why or why not?

  What would happen if you remove 1 triangle from the right group in the right box? What would happen if you add 1 triangle to the left group in the right box?

  Do you think there is more than one way to fix the number sentence that is not true in Part A? Explain why you think so.

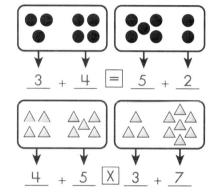

SCORING RUBRICS

Expectations for 4–3 Points

Points	Expectations
4	The child: • correctly identifies and writes the number of objects in each group as an addend. • finds the total for each expression and compares both totals correctly. • writes the equal sign between expressions in a true number sentence and marks an X between expressions in a false number sentence. • draws an accurate representation of groups to make a false number sentence true. • writes a number sentence that represents the drawing and uses an equal sign to show that the expressions have the same value.
3	The child: • may correctly identify and write the number of objects in each group as an addend, but find incorrect totals for one of the expressions. • may make an accurate drawing of groups to represent a number sentence, but may write an incorrect number sentence.

Expectations for 2–0 Points

Points	Expectations
2	The child: • may incorrectly count objects in a group and write incorrect addends. • may not recognize two separate groups as relating to the addends in a number sentence. • may inaccurately draw one group of objects to represent an expression. • may write an incorrect number sentence.
1	The child: • writes addends that have no relationship to the objects in the groups. • makes a drawing that has no connection to a number sentence. • fails to write a number sentence.
0	The child: • does not attempt to solve the problems.

Intervention Activity

Use a balance to model equal quantities.

Materials For each child: connecting cubes, pan balance

For children who have difficulty, provide connecting cubes and a pan balance to model making equal and unequal quantities.

- Have children place 1 connecting cube in each pan. Connect the idea of the balanced pans to the equal sign. Explain that the pans balance because the quantities in each pan are the same, or equal. Write 1 = 1 on the board.

- Repeat with different quantities, using the same number of connecting cubes in each pan to balance. Record examples on the board, e.g., 3 = 3, 4 = 4, etc.

- Connect the idea of pans that do not balance to quantities that are not equal: 3 cubes in one pan and 4 cubes in the other. Have children add 1 cube to the pan with 3 cubes and tell whether it balances. Record the number sentence on the board: 3 + 1 = 4.

- Have children determine by experimentation how many cubes on each side make the pans balance. Record the number sentences.

On-Level Activity

Match equal expressions.

Materials For each pair: index cards with a variety of expressions that make sums up to 10: for example, 6 + 1, 6 + 2, 0 + 8, 5, 3 + 1, 3 + 2, 4 + 1, etc.

- Have children work with a partner. Provide partners with a set of cards.

- Children place cards face down in a stack. One partner turns two cards over and tells whether the expressions are equal. The other partner agrees or disagrees, explaining the reasoning.

- Partners take turns recording true number sentences for each matched pair of equal expressions.

Challenge Activity

Make a false number sentence true.

Materials For each child: True and Untrue Number Sentences (Activity Sheet 13)

- Provide children with the True and Untrue Number Sentences worksheet.

- Have them write the number sentence represented by the drawing and tell whether it is true or false. [4 + 5 = 3 + 7 is a false number sentence because 4 + 5 = 9 and 3 + 7 = 10; 9 is not equal to 10.]

- Challenge children to fix the number sentence to be true and make a new drawing to represent the true number sentence.

- Discuss whether children found different ways to make a true number sentence. [Possible drawings and true number sentences: draw 1 more triangle in the group in the left box: 5 + 5 = 3 + 7; remove 1 star from the group in the right box: 4 + 5 = 3 + 6]

Lesson 11 (Student Book pages 46–49)

Facts I Know

LESSON OBJECTIVES

- Fluently add and subtract within 10.

- Use strategies such as counting on; using the relationship between addition and subtraction; and using a known sum or difference to find an unknown sum or difference to add and subtract.

PREREQUISITE SKILLS

- Add and subtract within 10.

- Understand the relationship between addition and subtraction.

VOCABULARY

addition table: a table showing expressions for sums to 20

During the lesson you will review the key term:

addend: a number being added

THE LEARNING PROGRESSION

In Kindergarten, children fluently add and subtract within 5 and record number partners within 10 by a drawing or number sentence.

In Grade 1, children develop fluency in addition and subtraction within 10 through the use of models and strategies. **In this lesson,** children complete and analyze addition tables, using strategies they have developed to find sums and differences. They demonstrate fluency by completing addition and subtraction number sentences in which the unknown is located in all positions.

In Grade 2, children become fluent in addition and subtraction within 20 applying strategies developed for addition and subtraction within 10.

Ready *Teacher Toolbox*   *Teacher-Toolbox.com*

	Prerequisite Skills	1.OA.C.6
Ready Lessons	✓ ✓ ✓	✓
Tools for Instruction	✓ ✓	✓
Interactive Tutorials	✓ ✓	✓ ✓

CCSS Focus

1.OA.C.6 Add and subtract within 20, demonstrating fluency for addition and subtraction within 10. Use strategies such as counting on; making ten (e.g., $8 + 6 = 8 + 2 + 4 = 10 + 4 = 14$); decomposing a number leading to a ten (e.g., $13 - 4 = 13 - 3 - 1 = 10 - 1 = 9$); using the relationship between addition and subtraction (e.g., knowing that $8 + 4 = 12$, one knows $12 - 8 = 4$); and creating equivalent but easier or known sums (e.g., adding $6 + 7$ by creating the known equivalent $6 + 6 + 1 = 12 + 1 = 13$).

ADDITIONAL STANDARDS: 1.OA.D.8 (*see page A36 for full text*)

STANDARDS FOR MATHEMATICAL PRACTICE: SMP 2, 3, 6, 7 (*see page A9 for full text*)

Opening Activity: Number Detectives

Objective: Build addition/subtraction fluency	**Materials** For each pair: • 20 two-color counters • white boards

Overview

Children apply familiar strategies for addition and subtraction to find a missing number from a set of clues provided by the teacher.

Step by Step (20–25 minutes)

1 Pose the problem.

- Tell children that today they are going to be detectives (remind them that a detective uses clues to solve a mystery). Explain that you will give them a clue that they will use to find missing numbers.

2 Playing the game.

- Place each child with a partner and provide them with counters and a white board. Tell them they can work together using counters, if desired, to find the missing number or numbers from the clue given.

- Once the "mystery" is solved, they should write a corresponding addition or subtraction sentence, circling the number or numbers they "found."

3 Mystery numbers.

- Read the following clue: *I have 6 marbles. Some are red and some are blue. There is the same number of red marbles as blue marbles. How many are red and how many are blue?*

- Watch children as they work together towards a solution, repeating the clue as necessary.

- Encourage children to share their number sentences and explain how they solved the mystery. Listen for and rephrase strategies to validate their use.

- Read the next clue: *I have 7 marbles. Some are red and some are blue. I have 2 blue marbles, how many are red?* This clue could result in an addition or subtraction sentence. Discuss why either sentence models the solution.

- Continue giving children clues similar to the first two clues, asking them to share solutions and strategies after each one.

4 One more or one less.

- Pose the open ended clue: *I have 9 marbles. Some are red and some are blue. There are more red marbles than blue marbles. How many red marbles and how many blue marbles could I have?*

- Allow children to share results and explain reasoning, then ask: *What if there was 1 more red marble than blue marbles? How many of each color would I have?* Ask for volunteers to demonstrate their strategy or thinking for the class to observe.

- Read the clue: *I have the same number of red marbles as blue marbles. If I take a blue marble away, I will have 7 marbles. How many red and how many blue marbles will I have?* Have children share solutions and strategies.

- Continue with similar clues as long as interest is sustained.

Check for Understanding

Pose the problem: *I have 8 marbles. 5 marbles are red, the rest are blue. How many are blue?*

Have children draw a picture and a number sentence for their solution and strategy. Observe as they work, asking questions that encourage reasoning.

STEP BY STEP

Materials For each child: different colored markers

- Begin with a discussion of the strategies children used to solve the clues from the Opening Activity. Provide necessary prompts to help them recall their strategies.

- Display the addition table shown on the page. Help children evaluate number partners by using a green marker to shade the boxes containing number partners that they already know, such as sums within 5; or that are easy to remember, such as +1 sums.

- Use red to shade addition facts that are more difficult—ones where children need to stop and think. This serves to build confidence by illustrating that there are only a limited number of addition facts such as these. Stress the benefit of using strategies to solve those addition facts.

- Provide children ample time to complete the table. Encourage them to solve the addition facts they know easily first and use strategies to find those they do not know.

- Discuss the strategies individual children employed to find the sums they did not know as easily. Help children notice how the sums on the table resemble parts of a number path. To find 4 + 3 by counting on they can find 4 + 1 and say 4 + 1 is 5 as the first count then move to the right saying 4 + 2 is 6, 4 + 3 is 7.

- Use this same technique to demonstrate how children can use a known fact such as 2 + 3 to find 2 + 4 by adding 1. You may want children to model with their fingers to show that when an addend increases by 1 the sum also increases by 1.

- Reinforce the way knowing addition facts helps know subtraction facts. Project and enlarge the table, isolating the column beginning with 1 + 4 and covering the 3 in 4 + 3. Ask children how the table could help them know what number you covered. Encourage children to notice structures like 2 + 4 is 6 and, since 7 is 1 more, it must be a 3 that is covered since 3 is 1 more than 2.

- Use the projected table to practice subtraction facts. Point to several addition facts, and have children name a related subtraction fact.

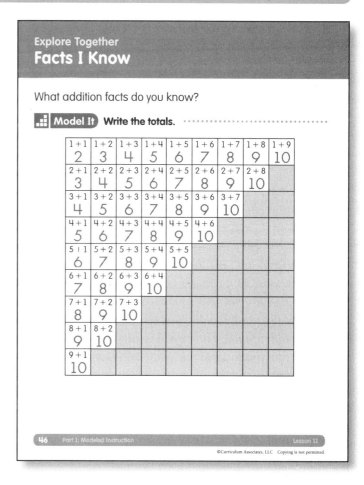

Mathematical Discourse

- *How can an addition table help you find sums you do not remember?*

  Children may respond that they can use the table to count on. Some may notice the "pattern" where the sum is increased by one when an addend is increased by one.

Fluency Practice

Materials For each pair: Addition Table 2 (Activity Sheet 14)

Distribute Addition Table 1. Have partners take turns covering an addend or sum in the table while their partner's eyes are closed. The partner must find the missing addend or sum and tell or write an addition and/or subtraction for the number sentence. Once successful, children cross out the fact. Play continues until all facts are crossed out.

STEP BY STEP

- Provide children time to examine the table on this page. Explain that it is the same addition table that they completed, but it is colored to show facts that are alike in some way.

- Direct attention to the yellow boxes. Ask: *What addend is the same in all boxes?* [1] *How are the facts in the yellow row different from the facts in the yellow column?* [The order of addends is different.] Use the same questions to talk about the green boxes.

- Ask children to describe how the facts in the orange boxes are alike. Guide them to recognize that these are all doubles facts.

- Have children examine the purple boxes and tell how these facts are alike. They should notice that these facts are all partners of 10. Use the Mathematical Discourse question to extend the discussion about patterns in the addition table.

> **SMP Tip:** As children examine the addition table, help them notice the structure inherent in the table—as an addend increases by one, the sum increases by one—leading them to recognize how the structure in our number system can be used to remember addition facts. *(SMP 7)*

Concept Extension

Examine doubles + 1 facts on the addition table

Have children find the doubles facts on the table (the orange boxes). Explain that they can use these facts to find other facts that they may not know. Direct attention to the doubles fact $4 + 4$. Have children circle the facts $4 + 5$ and $5 + 4$. Guide them to recognize that in these facts one addend is 4 and one is 1 more than 4. Write the three facts on the board as they appear in the table. Ask: *How many more is the total of $4 + 5$ than $4 + 4$?* [1 more] Explain that these facts are called doubles +1 because the total is 1 more than the related doubles fact.

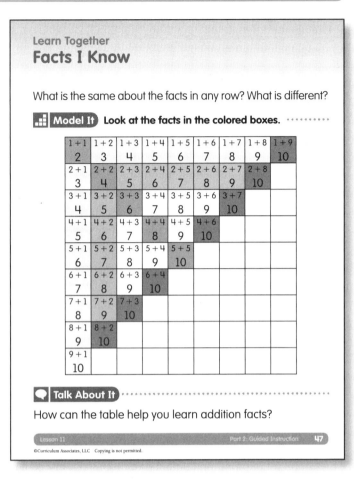

Learn Together
Facts I Know

What is the same about the facts in any row? What is different?

🔲 **Model It** Look at the facts in the colored boxes. ············

1+1 2	1+2 3	1+3 4	1+4 5	1+5 6	1+6 7	1+7 8	1+8 9	1+9 10
2+1 3	2+2 4	2+3 5	2+4 6	2+5 7	2+6 8	2+7 9	2+8 10	
3+1 4	3+2 5	3+3 6	3+4 7	3+5 8	3+6 9	3+7 10		
4+1 5	4+2 6	4+3 7	4+4 8	4+5 9	4+6 10			
5+1 6	5+2 7	5+3 8	5+4 9	5+5 10				
6+1 7	6+2 8	6+3 9	6+4 10					
7+1 8	7+2 9	7+3 10						
8+1 9	8+2 10							
9+1 10								

💬 **Talk About It** ·······················
How can the table help you learn addition facts?

Mathematical Discourse

- *Which other boxes could also be colored yellow? Green? Purple? Why?*

  Children should recognize that $1 + 1$ can be yellow since one addend is a 1 and $2 + 1$, $2 + 2$, and $2 + 8$ can also be green since one addend is 2. The facts $9 + 1$ and $5 + 5$ can be purple since they are partners of 10. Some children might respond that some facts fit with two different categories.

Fluency Practice

Materials for each child: Facts Practice 1 (Activity Sheet 16)

Use the Facts Practice 1 worksheet to provide children with practice with facts for sums 6, 7, 8, 9, and 10.

STEP BY STEP

- Draw attention to the problems shown on this page. Point out that each question shows a section of the addition table.

- Remind children of the activity they completed on the first page of the lesson. Help them see that this page is similar except that in some boxes more than one number is missing.

- Draw attention to the boxes at the end of each row in Problem 1. Ask: *Both of these boxes show 10 as the sum so how can you decide what numbers go in the empty spaces?* Help children notice that in each row the first addend remains the same while the second addend increases by one.

- Encourage children to use the observation above as they complete the sections of the table in each problem.

Visual Model

Write on the board.

$$4 + 3$$
$$7$$

Demonstrate writing subtraction sentences by changing the + to an = and drawing a line from the seven to each of the addends as shown.

$$4 = 3$$
$$\diagdown 7 \diagup$$

Discuss how the subtractions can be "seen" by making a path with your finger from 7 to 3 to 4 saying: *Seven minus 3 equals 4.* Repeat moving from 7 to 4 to 3.

Mathematical Discourse

- *How can you use what you know to find a fact you do not know?*

  Some children may respond that they know doubles so if 4 + 4 = 8, 4 + 5 = 9. Others may apply inverse operations, saying that if 5 + 3 is 8, then 8 − 5 is 3.

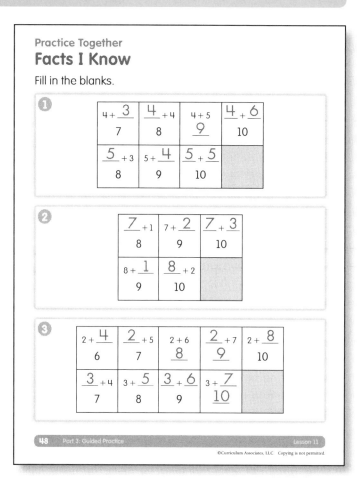

Practice Together
Facts I Know
Fill in the blanks.

1 | 4 + **3** / 7 | **4** + 4 / 8 | 4 + 5 / **9** | **4** + **6** / 10 |

| **5** + 3 / 8 | 5 + **4** / 9 | **5** + **5** / 10 | |

2 | **7** + 1 / 8 | 7 + **2** / 9 | **7** + 3 / 10 |

| 8 + **1** / 9 | **8** + 2 / 10 | |

3 | 2 + **4** / 6 | **2** + 5 / 7 | 2 + 6 / **8** | **2** + 7 / **9** | 2 + **8** / 10 |

| **3** + 4 / 7 | 3 + **5** / 8 | **3** + 6 / 9 | 3 + **7** / **10** | |

48 Part 3: Guided Practice — Lesson 11
©Curriculum Associates, LLC Copying is not permitted.

Concept Extension

Materials Optional: Addition Table 2 (Activity Sheet 14)

Draw attention to the two empty boxes on the page. Ask the children what addition sentences might go in those boxes. Remind them that although they have not learned those sums yet, they can use the table to find them. Discuss how they can use the structure of the table to find that 8 + 3 = 11 since 8 + 2 = 10.

For children needing an additional challenge, allow them to complete an Addition Table 3 (Activity Sheet 15) by filling in all the missing addition facts and then describe how the original addition facts in the table help them find those that are not shown.

STEP BY STEP

- Before children work on this page, discuss similarities and differences between the table on this page and the ones on previous pages. Emphasize that children are free to use whatever ways help them complete the table.

- Have children work independently to fill in the table. Remind children who are having difficulty completing the table that organizing information is a good strategy to use whenever there are many combinations to keep track of.

- Encourage children to relate number sentences where the numbers are written in reverse order. Listen for observations children make about the structure of the addition sentences.

- After children have completed their work, you may wish to ask the Mathematical Discourse question. If time allows, follow up by having children write subtraction facts for partners of 8, 9, and 10. Some children may notice the other subtraction that can be written for each addition. Encourage them to articulate a strategy, such as moving the sum to the other side of the addition fact then writing a subtraction fact.

Practice by Myself
Facts I Know

4 Fill in the table.

Partners of 7	Partners of 8	Partners of 9	Partners of 10
0 + 7 = _7_	0 + 8 = _8_	0 + 9 = 9	0 + 10 = 10
1 + _6_ = 7	1 + 7 = 8	1 + 8 = 9	1 + 9 = 10
_2_ + 5 = 7	2 + 6 = 8	2 + 7 = 9	2 + 8 = 10
3 + _4_ = 7	3 + 5 = 8	3 + 6 = 9	3 + 7 = 10
4 + _3_ = 7	4 + 4 = 8	4 + 5 = 9	4 + 6 = 10
_5_ + 2 = 7	5 + 3 = 8	5 + 4 = 9	5 + 5 = 10
6 + _1_ = 7	6 + 2 = 8	6 + 3 = 9	6 + 4 = 10
_7_ + 0 = 7	7 + 1 = 8	7 + 2 = 9	7 + 3 = 10
	8 + 0 = 8	8 + 1 = 9	8 + 2 = 10
		9 + 0 = 9	9 + 1 = 10
			10 + 0 = 10

ELL Support

During whole group discussions or when giving oral directions, assist children by either writing the given numbers on the board or repeating the numbers in the child's native language.

Mathematical Discourse

- *How could you find a subtraction sentence for any addition sentence?*

  Children should recognize that for any addition fact, the order of the addends and sum can be reversed and written as a subtraction fact.

SMP Tip: Emphasize the value of accuracy in calculations by displaying the incorrect addition 3 + 4 = 8 and the corresponding subtraction facts. (*SMP 6*) Tell children that the addition you just wrote is Boom's work and ask them to respond to it. Discuss how by miscalculating the addition, all the other sentences were incorrect as well. (*SMP 3*)

Assessment and Remediation

- Ask children to complete the Facts Practice 2 worksheet (Activity Sheet 17) containing sums for 6, 7, 8, 9, and 10.

- For children who are still struggling, use the chart below to guide remediation.

- After providing remediation, check children's understanding using the following problem: complete Facts Practice 3 worksheet (Activity Sheet 18) containing sums for 6, 7, 8, 9, 10 in a different arrangement.

If the error is . . .	Children may . . .	To remediate . . .
incorrect responses primarily among subtraction facts	not be relating subtraction to addition.	Model an addition fact with cubes, fingers, and number bonds. Write a related subtraction fact. Model and discuss with the children how knowing an addition fact can help find a difference. Write another subtraction fact and have children find a related addition fact.
incorrect responses primarily among missing addends	not recognize the application of partner pairs.	Provide children with additional opportunities to play partner games where the sum is known and one addend must be found.
incorrect responses among a specific fact family	not have developed strategies for that family.	Review possible strategies with the children allowing them to develop and practice strategies that enable them to work with the challenging facts.

Hands-On Activity

Play an addition/subtraction game.

Materials For each pair: 1 × 11 strip of heavy paper divided into a 0–10 game board, 12 counters, 1 set of colored cards numbered 1–10, 1 set of cards in another color numbered 0–5

- Place the two sets of cards face down. One partner turns up one card from each pile and uses them to make either an addition or subtraction sentence. They then place a counter on the sum or difference found on the game board. The cards are then placed back under the piles. The other partner repeats the activity. If both the sum and difference of the cards drawn are already covered, play goes to the other partner.

- Play continues until all the numbers on the strip are filled.

Options:

- Provide children with open number sentences for modeling with their cards.

- Allow children to place cards in any two spaces in the number sentence to allow for missing addend solutions.

Challenge Activity

Write clues for number partners.

Materials For each child: counters, heavy paper or cardstock

Remind children of the "Number Detectives" game from the Opening Activity. Challenge them to write their own "clues" for number partners. Tell them they may work in pairs to make up clues that are different from the ones in the Opening Activity. Encourage them to try "2 more or 2 less" clues. They should write each clue clearly on a card and then read it to their partner who works it out to make sure it is clear and has a solution. These clues can be placed in a container for other children to try to solve.

Unit 2 Review

Solve the problems.

1. Al has 5 toy trucks. He has 5 toy cars. How many toy trucks and cars does Al have?

   $5 + 5 = \underline{10}$

   [number bond: 10 → 5 and 5]

2. There are 3 birds. More birds join them. Now there are 7 birds. How many birds join?

   $3 + \underline{4} = 7$

   [number bond: 7 → 3 and 4]

3. Make a true number sentence.
   Possible answer:
   $\underline{8} + \underline{1} = 2 + 7$

4. $10 - 8 = \underline{2}$

5. $\underline{7} = 5 + 2$

6. Make a true number sentence.

   $5 + \underline{3} = 3 + 5$

7. 4 books and 2 books. How many books in all?

   $4 + 2 = \underline{6}$ $\underline{6} = 2 + 4$

   Is $4 + 2 = 2 + 4$ a true number sentence? $\underline{Yes}$
   Draw to explain why or why not.

   Possible answer: Drawings might demonstrate that adding 2 objects to 4 objects is the same as adding 4 objects to 2 objects.

   In both cases, the total is 6.

8. 10 beads in all. 3 are red. The rest are yellow. How many are yellow?

   Complete the number bond. Write four number sentences for this problem.

   [number bond: 3 and 7 → 10]

   $\underline{3} + \underline{7} = 10$ $10 - \underline{3} = \underline{7}$

   $10 = \underline{7} + \underline{3}$ $\underline{3} = 10 - \underline{7}$

STEP BY STEP

- Have children solve the problems individually and show their work. Emphasize that children are free to use whatever way helps them solve the problems.

- Observe as children work. Be alert to those who may still have difficulty with the meaning of the equal sign, particularly in problems 3, 5, 6, 7, and 8. Elicit that the equal sign means "is the same as."

- For Problems 1, 2, and 8, children model the given problem using number bonds and number sentences. If some children struggle, suggest that they draw a picture to help them understand what is happening.

STEP BY STEP

- On this page, children write the partners of 8 or 9 in number bonds and use these to write a true number sentence equating two sets of the partners.

- Direct children to complete the Put It Together on their own.

- Read the directions and task aloud. Make sure children understand what they need to do to complete the task.

- As children work on their own, observe their progress and understanding. Respond to their questions and provide additional support as needed.

- Have children share their number bonds and number sentences with the class.

- Have children explain how they know their number sentence is true. Explanations should state that the quantities are the same.

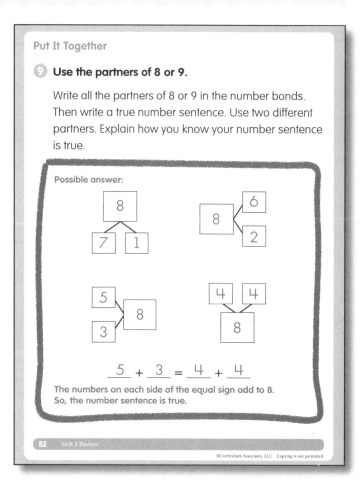

SCORING RUBRICS

Expectations for 4–3 Points

Points	Expectations
4	The child: • correctly completes all number bonds with partners of 8 or 9. • writes a correct addition sentence with two different sets of partners. • explains that the number sentence is true because both sides have the same total.
3	The child: • may complete three or four number bonds correctly. • may write a correct addition sentence with two different sets of partners. • may be able to explain why the number sentence is true, but the explanation may be unclear or incomplete.

Expectations for 2–0 Points

Points	Expectations
2	The child: • may complete two or three of the number bonds correctly. • may write a correct addition sentence with 8 or 9 on one side instead of a partner. • may not be able to clearly explain why the number sentence is true.
1	The child: • may complete fewer than two of the number bonds correctly. • may not write a correct addition sentence with two different sets of partners. • may not be able to explain why a number sentence is true or false.
0	The child: • does not attempt to complete the task.

Which lessons are students building upon?

Kindergarten, Lesson 21
Understand Teen Numbers
K.NBT.A.1, K.CC.A.2, K.CC.A.3, K.CC.B5

Kindergarten, Lesson 22
Count Teen Numbers
K.CC.A.3, K.CC.B.5, K.CC.A.2, K.NBT.A.1

Kindergarten, Lesson 18
Add Within 10
K.OA.A.1, K.OA.A.3, K.OA.A.5

Kindergarten, Lesson 19
Subtract Within 10
K.OA.A.1, K.OA.A.3, K.OA.A.5

Kindergarten, Lesson 23
Make Teen Numbers
K.NBT.A.1, K.CC.A.2, K.CC.A.3

Kindergarten, Lesson 18
Add Within 10
K.OA.A.1, K.OA.A.3, K.OA.A.5

Kindergarten, Lesson 19
Subtract Within 10
K.OA.A.1, K.OA.A.3, K.OA.A.5

Kindergarten, Lesson 23
Make Teen Numbers
K.NBT.A.1, K.CC.A.2, K.CC.A.3

Kindergarten, Lesson 18
Add Within 10
K.OA.A.1, K.OA.A.3, K.OA.A.5

Kindergarten, Lesson 19
Subtract Within 10
K.OA.A.1, K.OA.A.3, K.OA.A.5

Kindergarten, Lesson 23
Make Teen Numbers
K.NBT.A.1, K.CC.A.2, K.CC.A.3

Kindergarten, Lesson 18
Add Within 10
K.OA.A.1, K.OA.A.3, K.OA.A.5

Kindergarten, Lesson 19
Subtract Within 10
K.OA.A.1, K.OA.A.3, K.OA.A.5

Kindergarten, Lesson 23
Make Teen Numbers
K.NBT.A.1, K.CC.A.2, K.CC.A.3

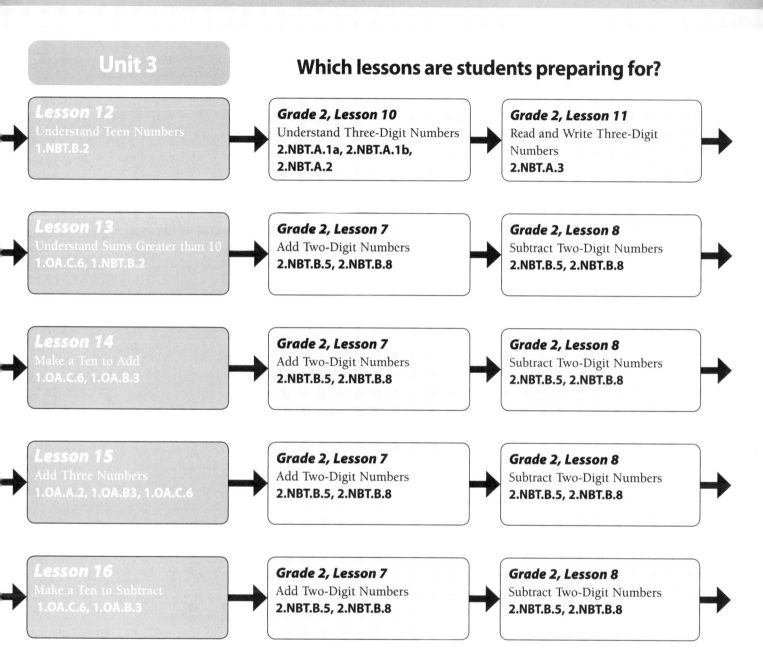

Unit 3

Which lessons are students preparing for?

Lesson 12
Understand Teen Numbers
1.NBT.B.2

→ **Grade 2, Lesson 10**
Understand Three-Digit Numbers
**2.NBT.A.1a, 2.NBT.A.1b,
2.NBT.A.2**

→ **Grade 2, Lesson 11**
Read and Write Three-Digit Numbers
2.NBT.A.3

→

Lesson 13
Understand Sums Greater than 10
1.OA.C.6, 1.NBT.B.2

→ **Grade 2, Lesson 7**
Add Two-Digit Numbers
2.NBT.B.5, 2.NBT.B.8

→ **Grade 2, Lesson 8**
Subtract Two-Digit Numbers
2.NBT.B.5, 2.NBT.B.8

→

Lesson 14
Make a Ten to Add
1.OA.C.6, 1.OA.B.3

→ **Grade 2, Lesson 7**
Add Two-Digit Numbers
2.NBT.B.5, 2.NBT.B.8

→ **Grade 2, Lesson 8**
Subtract Two-Digit Numbers
2.NBT.B.5, 2.NBT.B.8

→

Lesson 15
Add Three Numbers
1.OA.A.2, 1.OA.B3, 1.OA.C.6

→ **Grade 2, Lesson 7**
Add Two-Digit Numbers
2.NBT.B.5, 2.NBT.B.8

→ **Grade 2, Lesson 8**
Subtract Two-Digit Numbers
2.NBT.B.5, 2.NBT.B.8

→

Lesson 16
Make a Ten to Subtract
1.OA.C.6, 1.OA.B.3

→ **Grade 2, Lesson 7**
Add Two-Digit Numbers
2.NBT.B.5, 2.NBT.B.8

→ **Grade 2, Lesson 8**
Subtract Two-Digit Numbers
2.NBT.B.5, 2.NBT.B.8

→

Lesson 12 (Student Book pages 54–57)

Understand Teen Numbers

LESSON OBJECTIVES

- Recognize that ten ones and one ten represent the same quantity.

- Understand that numbers between 10 and 20 are composed of one ten and some ones.

- Model teen numbers.

PREREQUISITE SKILLS

- Count to 20.

- Interpret a number bond.

VOCABULARY

teen number: a ten and some number of ones from 1 to 9; the numbers 11–19

tens and ones: use concrete objects and visual models to teach the meaning of tens and ones. See the Hands-On Activity on page 91 and the Visual Model on page 93.

THE LEARNING PROGRESSION

In Kindergarten, children count to 20, connect the counts to objects and written numerals, and write numerals from 0 to 20. They compose and decompose numbers 11 to 19 into ten ones and more ones.

In Grade 1, children add and subtract within 20 and develop the concept of two-digit numbers. **In this lesson,** children explore the structure of numbers between 10 and 20, often referred to as *teen numbers*. They develop the concept that teen numbers are composed of a group of ten and a group of ones. This understanding leads to the idea that numbers 20 and greater are composed of multiple tens and from 1 to 9 ones.

In Grade 2, children continue to develop understanding of the structure of two-digit numbers and extend these concepts to three-digit numbers.

	Prerequisite Skills	1.NBT.B.2a, 1.NBT.B.2b
Ready Lessons	✓ ✓	✓
Tools for Instruction	✓ ✓	
Interactive Tutorials	✓ ✓	✓

Ready *Teacher Toolbox* — Teacher-Toolbox.com

CCSS Focus

1.NBT.B.2 Understand that the two digits of a two-digit number represent amounts of tens and ones. Understand the following special cases:

    a. 10 can be thought of as a bundle of ten ones — called a "ten."

    b. The numbers from 11 to 19 are composed of a ten and one, two, three, four, five, six, seven, eight, or nine ones.

STANDARDS FOR MATHEMATICAL PRACTICE: *SMP 1, 2, 3, 4, 5, 6, 7, 8* (see page A9 for full text)

Opening Activity: Ten Fingers

Objective: Children explore numbers between 10 and 20 as a group of ten and some ones.

Materials For each child:
• paper and pencil

Overview

Children discover ways to represent numbers greater than 10 with their fingers. They work with a partner to model teen numbers with their fingers.

Step by Step (20–30 minutes)

1 Pose the problem.

• Tell children you are going to say some numbers and you want them to show the number with their fingers as quickly as they can. Begin with numbers such as 4, 6, 3, and 8; then ask for 13. When children respond that they can't do it, ask for an explanation. Then ask: *Can you think of a way you could show 13 using fingers?*

2 Explore strategies.

• Allow children to discuss ways they can show 13 using fingers. Some may suggest thinking of 10 fingers and then using their hands to count on from 10. Others may suggest working with a partner to use two sets of hands. Listen to all responses.

• Have children model the suggested strategies. Begin with methods such as holding up ten fingers and then "thinking" of three more fingers and counting on. You may want to save the partner strategy until last as an introduction to the next step.

3 Partner counting.

• Have children work with a partner to show 13 with fingers. One partner shows 10 fingers and the other holds up 3 fingers.

• Ask children how they know which partner is showing 10 fingers. Discuss why they don't need to count all 10 fingers.

• Have the children showing 10 fingers move their hands together so that their thumbs touch each other (you may want to model this). Tell children that this shows there is one group of ten fingers.

4 Model teen numbers.

• Now say some teen numbers and ask children to work with a partner to show the numbers as quickly as possible. You may want them to take turns showing the ten and the extra fingers.

• As you call out several teen numbers, observe whether children are modeling correctly.

Check Your Understanding

Provide children with the following problem: *Draw or trace fingers on your paper to show 14 fingers. Show how you know there are 14.*

Some children may fail to identify 10 fingers as a group of ten. You can utilize the modeling options provided throughout the lesson to support these children.

STEP BY STEP

- Revisit the Opening Activity. Ask: *What was the same about all the teen numbers you and your partner made with your fingers?* Lead children to recognize that, in each case, one partner was showing 10 fingers locked together. As children share the drawings they made of 14, ask them to explain how they know there are 14 fingers.

- Read the question and directions at the top of the page. As children say the numbers, have them listen for the word "teen" in the number. Emphasize the connection between "teen" and "ten."

- Read through Think with the class. Ask the Mathematical Discourse question to help children connect the models to the Opening Activity.

- Use the Hands-On Activity to explore the concept that 10 ones can be described as 1 ten.

- As you discuss Talk About It, some children may focus on the digits rather than on the composition of each number as 1 ten and a different number of ones. Ask questions like: *Why do you think both 10 and 11 start with a one?*

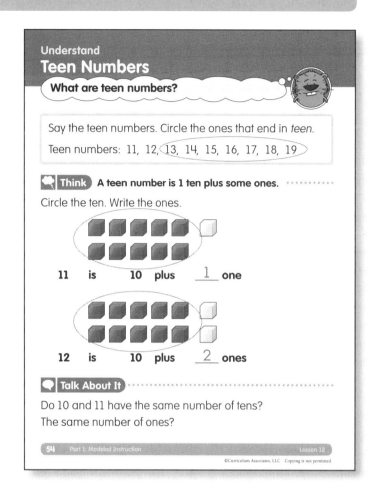

Hands-On Activity

Materials For each child: connecting cubes, a 10-frame

Have children work in pairs to count out 11 cubes and organize them on a 10-frame.

- Ask: *How do you know when you have a group of ten?* Have children connect the 10 cubes from the full frame. Say together: *One ten and one cube is eleven.* Repeat for 12. Ensure children recognize that the 10 cubes on the frame and the bar of cubes represent the same number of cubes.

- Ask children what they think 14 would look like on the 10-frame and then with 10 connected cubes. Ask: *What is another way you could say 14?* [1 ten and 4 ones]

Mathematical Discourse

- *How are the cubes like counting with your fingers?*

  Children should respond that 10 cubes are grouped together to make a ten just like connecting 10 fingers. You count on the extra cubes like you count on the extra fingers. Some may notice that the blocks are organized into 2 groups of 5 just as fingers are organized into 2 hands of 5 fingers.

ELL Support

Encourage children to tell the class how to count from ten to twenty in their native language. Help them see how teen numbers use *ten* in the number, such as in the Spanish word for 16, "**diez** y seis" (10 and 6), or the French word for 17, "**dix**-sept" (ten-7). Emphasize the similarity to the word "teen" used in English to name a ten.

STEP BY STEP

Materials For each child: 10-Frame (Activity Sheet 11), 20 connecting cubes in two different colors

- Distribute materials. Explain the directions at the top of the page. Model placing 13 cubes in the 10-frames and have children do the same.

- Now take the 10 cubes out of the first 10-frame and connect them. Help children make the connection between this train of 10 cubes and the red tens illustrated on the student page.

- Ask the Mathematical Discourse question to reinforce the concept that 10 ones is equal to 1 ten. For children who struggle with this concept, refer to the 1 ten as "1 group of ten."

- Allow children time to complete Problems 1–3. Circulate to check that they are displaying the cubes correctly and coloring to record their work.

> **SMP Tip:** Display the numbers 1, 21, 16 with distance between them. Ask: *Which of these numbers has 1 ten and some ones? How do you know?* Activities like this can help children focus on the structure of two-digit numbers and prepare them for understanding numbers greater than 19. *(SMP 7)*

- Discuss Talk About It. Help children recognize that the numbers 13–16 are all composed of 1 ten but of a different number of ones.

Fluency Practice

Materials For each child: Hundreds Chart (Activity Sheet 19), crayons

- Have children circle the number 15 on the hundreds chart. Lead them to see that 15 represents 15 squares on the chart. Have children shade the first row of 10 squares, emphasizing that this is 1 ten. Ask: *How many more squares do you count to get to 15? How many ones and tens are in 15?* Continue with other teen numbers.

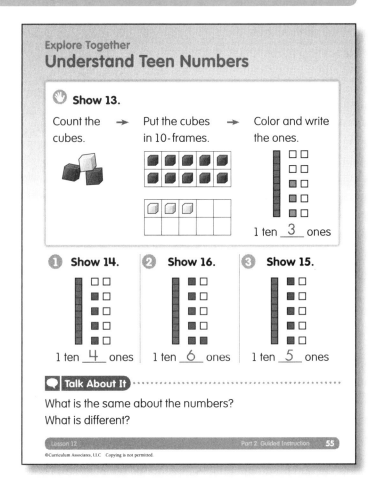

Mathematical Discourse

- Say: *10 cubes and 1 ten are the same amount. I thought 10 was more than 1. How can 10 and 1 ten be equal?*

    Children should respond that the 1 tens bar is the 10 cubes grouped together.

STEP BY STEP

Materials For each pair: 40 connecting cubes in two different colors

- Discuss each Connect It problem as a class using the discussion points outlined below.

Compare:

- If children struggle to get started, give pairs connecting cubes. Have one partner model 10 and 7 more while the other shows 18 as 1 ten and 8 ones.

- Ask children to name each model as a teen number, as ten cubes and some ones, and as one ten and some ones. This reinforces the fact that there are multiple ways to describe a number.

- Discuss the Mathematical Discourse question as a way to have children start thinking about tens and ones in a more abstract way.

Apply:

- Help children connect the number bond to other models they have explored, noting that each of the teen numbers is composed of 1 ten (shown in one part of the number bond) and some ones.

- Reinforce the concept of equality by asking children why the teen number is always shown on one side of the equal sign.

Explain:

- To introduce the problem, ask children to describe what the model shows. [1 ten and 3 ones]

- Invite children to present their arguments about whether they agree or disagree with Buzz. Encourage the use of mathematical language and precise explanations, prompting them with questions such as: *How do you know the model shows 13? Why is the bar the only one counted as 10?*

- Encourage children to demonstrate the correct way to count the cubes.

> **SMP Tip:** Extend children's ability to critique and justify their thinking by asking: *Why do you think Buzz said that the model shows 4? What did he do wrong?* (SMP 3)

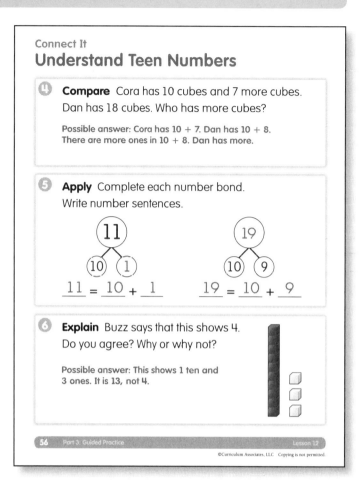

Mathematical Discourse

- *How can you know, just by looking at two numbers like 15 and 19, which one is more?*

   Some children may respond that they know by counting. Others may realize that both numbers have 1 ten, but 19 has 9 ones and 15 has 5 ones. Since 9 is more than 5, 19 is more than 15.

STEP BY STEP

- Encourage children to complete the problems on this page independently.

- As children work, support them with questions such as the ones below.

  What is the fewest number of star stickers you can draw to show a teen number?

  What is the greatest number of moon stickers you can draw to show a teen number?

  How can the stickers help you find the tens and ones?

  What number do you think should go in the top box of the number bonds? What does that number tell you? What does the number in the box next to the ten tell you?

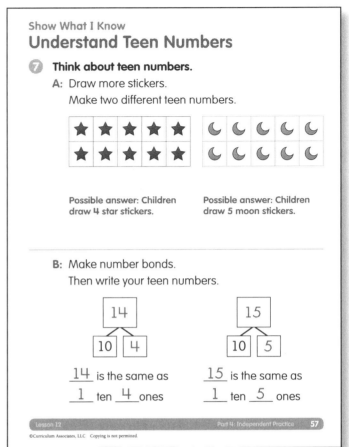

SCORING RUBRICS

Expectations for 4–3 Points

Points	Expectations
4	The child: • draws stickers to represent two different numbers from 11 to 19. • accurately decomposes each teen number in a number bond and represents it as a two-digit number and as a ten and some ones.
3	The child: • draws stickers to represent two different numbers from 11 to 19. • completes the number bonds and writes two-digit numbers; however, there may be minor errors with placement in the number bond or with the number of ones recorded.

Expectations for 2–0 Points

Points	Expectations
2	The child: • draws stickers to represent at least one number from 11 to 19. • may attempt to complete the number bonds; however, all numbers used do not correspond to the teen numbers drawn. This results in inaccuracies with the two-digit numbers and the tens and ones recorded.
1	The child: • may draw some stickers; however, there is no evidence the child relates the number drawn to a number bond, a two-digit number, or a number of tens and ones.
0	The child: • makes little or no attempt to solve the problem.

Intervention Activity

Relate cubes in 10-frames to digits in teen numbers.

Materials For each child: 10-Frame (Activity Sheet 11), 20 connecting cubes, one half of an $8\frac{1}{2} \times 11$ sheet of paper, 9 quarters of $8\frac{1}{2} \times 11$ sheets of paper

- Distribute the materials and instruct children to write 10 on the half sheet of paper and the numbers 1–9 on the quarter sheets of paper.

- Instruct children to mix up the set of 1–9 cards and set the pile face down next to the 10 card.

- Have children fill one of the 10-frames with ten cubes. Ask them to turn one of the digit cards face up and place that number of cubes on the other 10-frame. Lead children to read the total as, for example, "10 and 3 more is 13." Have them place the 3 card over the 0 on the 10 card to see the number 13 displayed.

- Repeat until all the cards are used.

On-Level Activity

Play: What's my number?

Materials For each child: pencil and paper or personal whiteboard

This is a teacher-led activity. You may want to display an open number bond and 10-frame on the board for reference.

- Think of a teen number, for example 14, and say: *I'm thinking of a number that has 1 ten and 4 ones. If you think you know my number, write it down.*

- Have children hold up their numbers and compare what they have written. Ask a volunteer to justify his or her answer using tens and ones.

- Continue giving other teen numbers and using different prompts such as: *I'm thinking of a number that has:*
  - *a 10 and a 6 on the bottom part of a number bond.*
  - *a full 10-frame and 5 extra ones.*
  - *one group of 10 cubes and one extra cube.*

- Make the prompts as challenging as your group of children allows.

Challenge Activity

Represent teen numbers in multiple ways.

Provide each child with a different *teen* number and challenge them to find as many ways as possible to show the number. Discuss how combining varied groups of numbers is a way, for example $8 + 7 = 15$. Encourage them to use more than two addends and to look for patterns that might help them find more ways to represent the number. Don't expect, but accept representations involving subtraction.

Have children compile their findings on a large sheet of paper for display. Encourage them to show each example clearly and write neatly so that everyone can read their work.

Lesson 13 (Student Book pages 58–61)

Understand Sums Greater than 10

LESSON OBJECTIVES

- Find the partners of teen numbers.
- Recognize the different ways that numbers can be decomposed and composed.

PREREQUISITE SKILLS

- Know the partner that makes 10 for any number.
- Know all decompositions for numbers within 10.
- Understand that teen numbers can be decomposed as 10 + some number.

VOCABULARY

During the lesson you will review the key terms:

addend: a number being added

teen number: a ten and some number of ones from 1 to 9; the numbers 11–19

total: a number found as the result of adding

THE LEARNING PROGRESSION

In Kindergarten, children learn to subitize, or recognize the number of objects in a group without counting. They begin to add and subtract by acting out situations and using physical models and drawings as they develop mathematical language.

In Grade 1, children develop strategies to extend addition and subtraction beyond 10 to include numbers within 20. They use numbers in diagrams that show the relationships between the quantities. **In this lesson,** children explore ways to compose and decompose teen numbers, using number bonds and systematic approaches to help build the conceptual foundation for fluency.

In Grade 2, children fluently add and subtract within 20, using a variety of strategies. They build on this fluency to add and subtract within 100.

▣ **Ready** *Teacher Toolbox*		*Teacher-Toolbox.com*
	Prerequisite Skills	*1.OA.C.6*
Ready Lessons	✓ ✓ ✓	✓
Tools for Instruction	✓ ✓	✓
Interactive Tutorials	✓ ✓	✓ ✓

CCSS Focus

1.OA.C.6 Add and subtract within 20, demonstrating fluency for addition and subtraction within 10. Use strategies such as counting on; making ten (e.g., $8 + 6 = 8 + 2 + 4 = 10 + 4 = 14$); decomposing a number leading to a ten (e.g., $13 − 4 = 13 − 3 − 1 = 10 − 1 = 9$); using the relationship between addition and subtraction (e.g., knowing that $8 + 4 = 12$, one knows $12 − 8 = 4$); and creating equivalent but easier or known sums (e.g., adding $6 + 7$ by creating the known equivalent $6 + 6 + 1 = 12 + 1 = 13$).

ADDITIONAL STANDARDS: ***1.NBT.B.2a, 1.NBT.B.2b*** *(see page A36 for full text)*

STANDARDS FOR MATHEMATICAL PRACTICE: **SMP 1, 2, 3, 4, 6, 7, 8** *(see page A9 for full text)*

Opening Activity: Act Out Partners of 11

Objective: Act out the various number partners that make 11 and model the partners with connecting cubes.	**Materials** For each child: • 20 connecting cubes in two colors • Cards with numbers 1–11

Overview

Children play a "Red Rover"-type game. They form two groups, starting with 10 and 1, and shift one child at a time to the smaller group. They model partners of 11 with connecting cubes.

Step by Step (10–15 minutes)

1 **Pose the problem.**

• Say: *Let's play a game! This game is a little like the game "Red Rover." How many of you have played "Red Rover"? It's a game with two groups of children. Each time, some children are called to switch groups. Now, let's say that 11 lucky children are going on a train ride. There are two train cars. How many different ways can the children get on the two cars? Let's act this out, using our game.*

2 **Model the problem.**

• Have 10 children stand in a group to model filling one car. Ask: *How many are in this car?* [Children hold up "10" card.]

• Have 1 child stand alone to model 1 child in the other car. Ask: *How many are in this car?* [Children hold up "1" card.]

• Ask: *How many are there in all?* [Children hold up "11" card.] Elicit that 11 is "10 and 1 more." Write 11 = 10 + 1 on the board.

• Children use connecting cubes to model the partners.

3 **Find the partners of 11.**

• Say: *Let's fill the cars a different way.* Have the child in the "1" car say, *"Red Rover, Red Rover, let [child's name] come over!"* That child moves from the group of 10 to the group of 1.

• Ask: *How many are in this car?* [9] Ask: *How many are in this car?* [2] Ask: *How many are there in all?* [11] Write 11 = 9 + 2 on the board.

• Children use connecting cubes to model the partners.

• Continue in this way until all the partners have been found.

4 **Discuss the findings.**

• Ask: *Did we find all the partners? How can you tell?*

• Elicit that, if another child "comes over," the partners will be the same as a previous pair of partners, but in reverse order. Show this by reversing a set of connecting cubes, and discuss.

Check for Understanding

If children lose track of the process (decreasing one car by 1 and increasing the other by 1) or don't understand that the sum remains the same, ask: *What happens to this car when [name] comes over? What happens to the other car? Is the total still 11, or did it change? How do you know?*

STEP BY STEP

Materials For each child: 20 connecting cubes in two colors, Number Bond Recording Sheet (Activity Sheet 2)

- Read aloud the question at the top of the page and encourage children to suggest answers.

- Remind children that they learned that teen numbers can be written as 1 ten and some ones. Elicit that 12 is 1 ten and 2 ones. Ask children to describe how this relates to the blue and red bar at the top of the page.

- Have children model 12 as 10 and 2, using connecting cubes.

- Point out the number bond. Have children explain how the number bond shows the same thing as the visual model. Ask the first Mathematical Discourse question to check that children can make connections among all the different models on the page.

- Read Think aloud. Ask the second Mathematical Discourse question to relate the visual models and number sentences to a familiar situation.

- Have children work in pairs to model the first number sentence with cubes. Then have them decrease the first addend and increase the second. They can record the results in number bonds and relate them to the number sentences on the page.

- Present the Talk About It question. Discuss why changing the order of the partners does not change the total.

Visual Model

Materials For each child: Number Paths (Activity Sheet 1), crayons or markers

Have children shade each number partner of 12 in a different color and then discuss the patterns they see. Help children recognize that as one addend increases by 1, the other decreases by 1.

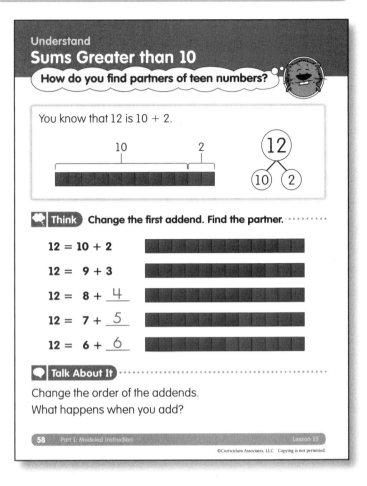

Mathematical Discourse

- *How does the number bond relate to the number sentence 12 = 10 + 2?*

  The number bond shows partners of 12. The number sentence is one of the two number sentences you can make using this number bond. You can also reverse the addends.

- *How are the pictures of the blue and red bars on this page like the game you played in the opening activity?*

  Children should be able to describe the process of taking 1 from one addend and increasing the other addend by 1.

STEP BY STEP

Materials For each child: 10-Frame (Activity Sheet 11), connecting cubes in two colors

- Read the directions aloud. Have children put 13 connecting cubes in their 10-frames to match the picture on the page.

- Draw a number bond on the board and invite a volunteer to write numbers in it that correspond to the 10-frame. Ask: *How did you know what numbers to write?*

- Have children work in pairs, using connecting cubes and 10-frames to complete the page. Circulate and monitor their work. If children seem stuck, make sure that they understand that they need to fill the 10-frame with 13 cubes each time, using different numbers of each color each time.

- When children are finished, ask pairs to come up and demonstrate the partners for 13 with connecting cubes. Have them write a number sentence. Ask a volunteer to reverse the order of the connecting cubes and write the number sentence. Use the Mathematical Discourse question to extend this idea to subtraction.

- Present the Talk About It question. Ask children how their various methods are the same or different and to explain why each method works.

SMP Tip: Encourage children to be aware of and make use of the structure of teen numbers: "10 and some more." When they see a teen number, ask them how many tens are in it [1 ten], and how many more ones. This concept can be reinforced with number bonds, number sentences, connecting cubes, and 10-frames. *(SMP 7)*

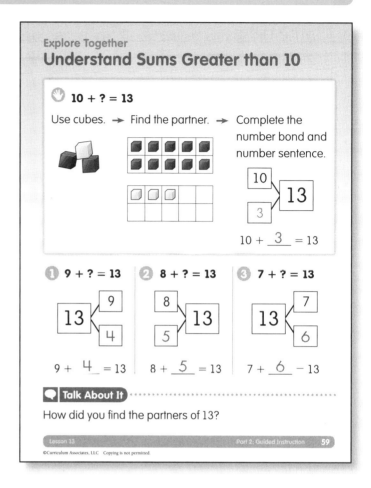

Mathematical Discourse

- *What subtraction sentences could you write for these number bonds?*

  Children should give two subtraction sentences for each number bond.

Concept Extension

Relate partners to the concept of equality.

Write the following on the board:

$$13 = 10 + 3$$
$$\_\_ - \_\_ + \_\_$$
$$13 = 8 + 5$$

Ask: *What number do you subtract from 10 to get 8? What number do you add to 3 to get 5?* Fill in the blanks. Continue with $9 + 4$ and $7 + 6$. Discuss that if the same number is subtracted from one addend and added to the other, the total remains the same.

STEP BY STEP

- Discuss each Connect It problem as a class using the discussion points outlined below.

Interpret

- You may want to have children work alone and then compare their responses with a partner.

- Ask: *How does the 8 in the number bond relate to the picture?* [It is the number of blue squares.] *How can you find the missing number in the number bond?* [Count the red squares.]

- Direct attention to the addition sentences. Ask children to explain why the addends are the same but in reverse order.

Illustrate

- Relate the circles in the 10-frames to the cube activity with the 10-frames on the Explore Together page. Ask children how the 10-frames on the Explore Together page show teen numbers. Guide them to understand that they show 1 ten in one color on the first frame and the ones in a different color on the second frame.

- Ask: *What if the first addend is 9?* Help children understand that part of the second addend is in the first frame and the rest is in the second.

- Have children explain how they wrote the addition sentences. You may wish to ask them to write and explain subtraction sentences for this number bond.

Explain

- Read the problem. Have children discuss it in pairs. Then bring the whole group together and have each pair share their conclusions and reasoning.

- Ask children: *Why do you think Buzz wrote that 8 + 6 equals 15? What would you say to help Buzz understand?*

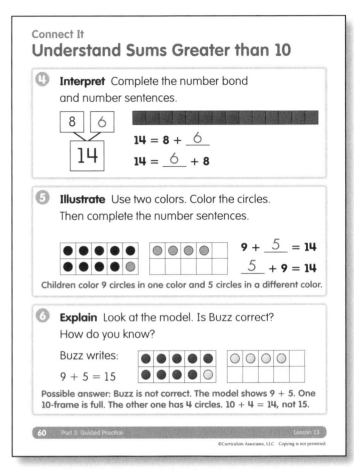

SMP Tip: On this page, children investigate different partners of 14. Support their learning by pointing out the relationship between the parts: for example, because $6 + 8 = 14$ and $9 + 5 = 14$, you know that $6 + 8 = 9 + 5$. To draw attention to the regularity in these relationships, have children apply the reasoning from the Opening Activity (decrease one addend by 1 and increase the other addend by 1) to the three problems on this page. *(SMP 8)*

STEP BY STEP

- Read the directions for Part A. Explain that children can choose how to draw the partners of 15.

- Read the directions for Part B. Children can use any of the models from this lesson to help find the partners of 16.

- Observe children as they work. Provide support by asking questions, such as the following, to encourage thinking and problem-solving strategies.

  How could a 10-frame help you with this page?

  How many tens and ones are in 16? How can this help you find the other partners of 16?

Show What I Know
Understand Sums Greater than 10

7 **Think about different ways to make totals greater than 10.**

A: Draw to show partners of 15.
Complete the number bonds.

 Possible answer: Children might use two different-colored objects in drawings to show the partners of 15.

B: Show how to find the partners of 16.

Possible answer: Children might make drawings, number bonds, or number sentences to show the partners of 16.

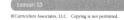

SCORING RUBRICS

Expectations for 4–3 Points

Points	Expectations
4	The child: • draws accurate models and completes number bonds correctly. • accurately shows all the number partners of 16.
3	The child: • may draw models and complete number bonds for 15; however, there are a few minor errors. • may correctly show most of the partners of 16 or show all of the partners with one or two errors.

Expectations for 2–0 Points

Points	Expectations
2	The child: • may have some incomplete or inaccurate drawings and number bonds. • may be able to show one or two accurate partners of 16, but not all.
1	The child: • attempts to draw partners of 15 and complete the number bonds, but may be unable to complete the task and shows little evidence of a strategy or understanding. • attempts to model the partners of 16, but the work is inaccurate and incomplete.
0	The child: • does not attempt to solve the problem.

Intervention Activity

Compose teen numbers in 10-frames

Materials For each child: 10-Frame (Activity Sheet 11), 20 two-color counters

• Have children count out 13 counters. Then have them put 10 of one color in the first frame and 3 of the second color in the second frame. Discuss how this shows 10 + 3. Have children write a number sentence. [10 + 3 = 13]

• Instruct children to turn over the last counter in the first frame so that it is now the same color as the counters in the second frame. Ask children to identify this new partner of 13 and write a number sentence. [9 + 4 = 13]

• Continue until you have found all the partners of 13. You may want to repeat with other teen numbers.

On-Level Activity

Explore equal partners.

Materials For each pair: 40 two-color counters

• Write two pairs of partners of 13 on the board as addition expressions (e.g., 9 + 4 and 10 + 3). Have children work in pairs to model both sums with counters, using one color for each partner.

• Ask: *Are these sums the same or different? Why do you think so?* Children may mention that both sets are partners of 13. Or they may say that by lining up the counters they can see that the total number of counters in each line is the same. Or they may note that 9 is one less than 10 and 4 is one more than 3. If a child thinks the sums are different, gently challenge that child to show and explain why.

• Continue with other partners of teen numbers.

Challenge Activity

Change one partner to 10.

Materials For each child: 10-Frame (Activity Sheet 11), 20 two-color counters, pencil and paper

Write 8 + 7 = 15 on the board. Point to the 8 and ask: *What can you do to make this 10?* Children may use counters and 10-frames as supports if needed. Guide children to understand that you need 2 more to make 10, so take 2 from the 7. The new addition sentence is 10 + 5 = 15. Repeat with other partners of teen numbers where one addend is 8 or 9, such as 9 + 3 = 12, 8 + 5 = 13, or 9 + 5 = 14. Consider having children work in pairs to check each other's work.

Lesson 14 (Student Book pages 62–65)

Make a Ten to Add

LESSON OBJECTIVES

- When adding two one-digit numbers, understand the rationale for decomposing one addend to make ten.

- Use the strategy of making ten to add numbers within 20.

- Use and articulate mental math strategies to add.

PREREQUISITE SKILLS

- Know the partner that makes 10 for any number.

- Know all decompositions for numbers within 10.

- Understand that teen numbers can be decomposed as 10 + some number.

VOCABULARY

make a ten: a strategy that uses combinations of numbers that add to ten when finding totals greater than 10

THE LEARNING PROGRESSION

In Kindergarten, children learn to count the number of objects and later to subitize, or recognize the number of objects in a group. They gain understanding of basic addition and subtraction situations and begin learning to compose and decompose numbers 10 or less.

In Grade 1, children learn strategies for adding and subtracting numbers within 20 and develop understanding of properties of addition. **In this lesson,** children learn the strategy of making ten to add within 20. This involves breaking apart an addend and associating one part of it with another addend to make 10, and then applying the understanding that teen numbers can be thought of as "10 + some number."

In Grade 2, children become fluent at adding and subtracting within 20. They use strategies to add and subtract within 100.

Ready *Teacher Toolbox*   *Teacher-Toolbox.com*

	Prerequisite Skills	1.OA.C.6
Ready Lessons	✓ ✓ ✓	✓
Tools for Instruction	✓ ✓	✓
Interactive Tutorials		✓ ✓

CCSS Focus

1.OA.C.6 Add and subtract within 20, demonstrating fluency for addition and subtraction within 10. Use strategies such as counting on; making ten (e.g., $8 + 6 = 8 + 2 + 4 = 10 + 4 = 14$); decomposing a number leading to a ten (e.g., $13 - 4 = 13 - 3 - 1 = 10 - 1 = 9$); using the relationship between addition and subtraction (e.g., knowing that $8 + 4 = 12$, one knows $12 - 8 = 4$); and creating equivalent but easier or known sums (e.g., adding $6 + 7$ by creating the known equivalent $6 + 6 + 1 = 12 + 1 = 13$).

ADDITIONAL STANDARDS: **1.OA.B.3** (see page A36 for full text)

STANDARDS FOR MATHEMATICAL PRACTICE: **SMP 1, 2, 3, 4, 6, 7, 8** (see page A9 for full text)

Opening Activity: Act Out Making a Ten

Objective: Act out a "Make Ten" problem and model with counters.	**Materials** For each child: • counters • an index card to represent the "bus"

Overview

Children act out a scenario in which 8 children are on a bus and 5 more board. They first board 2 children to make ten and then add the rest. They model the problem with counters and discuss.

Step by Step (10–15 minutes)

1 Pose the problem.

- Let's imagine you are getting on a bus for a fabulous field trip! So far there are 8 children on the bus. 5 more are ready to get on. Let's use a strategy to see how many that is in all.

2 Model the problem.

- Organize 10 chairs in 2 rows to be the "bus." Have 8 children sit down.

- Gather a group of 5 more children. Say: *We're going to let a few children on the bus at a time. How many more children do I need to have 10 on the bus?* [2]

- Separate the 5 children into a group of 2 and a group of 3. Have the 2 children sit with the "bus" children. Ask a child to count to verify that there are 10 children on the bus.

- Say: *There are 10 on the bus, and how many more children are there?* [3] *What's the total?* [13] Have the remaining 3 children join the "bus" children and have the class count to verify the total.

3 Use counters.

- Have children work in pairs to model the situation. They put 8 counters on the index card in 2 rows to represent 8 children on the bus. They put 5 more counters on the table.

- Remind children that at first 2 children are added to make 10 on the bus. Tell them to break apart their group of 5 counters and move 2 of them onto the index card.

- Then they put the remaining 3 counters on the index card.

3 Discuss.

- Ask: *How many children are there in all?* [13] Ask: *How do you know?*

- Have pairs explain how they used the counters to model the problem. Ask why they think making a ten is a good strategy for finding totals that are teen numbers.

Check for Understanding

Provide the children with the following problem: *What if there were 9 children on the bus and 5 wanted to get on? How would this change what you do?* Children should be able to explain that if one child boards, that makes 10; then there are 4 more, which makes 14 (10 and 4 more).

STEP BY STEP

- Begin by asking children what they have learned or remember from the Opening Activity. Elicit their thoughts on how making a ten helps when the total is more than ten.

- Read aloud the problem at the top of the page. Discuss how the picture is like what you did in the Opening Activity. Introduce the number sentence. Ask: *How does this number sentence relate to the picture?*

- Read Model It aloud. Direct attention to the first pair of 10-frames and have children identify which parts of the number sentence are being modeled. Ask the Mathematical Discourse question to emphasize the visual benefit the 10-frame provides.

- Ask: *What happens in the second pair of 10-frames? How are these different from the first pair? Is this the same total number of counters? How do you know?* Discuss children's responses, concluding that both pairs of 10-frames show a total of 13.

- Have children fill in the totals. Discuss with them how making ten helps them find the total.

> **SMP Tip:** The structure of 10-frames helps children understand the make a ten strategy. Encourage children to think and talk about how the 10-frames help them go from "8 and some more" to the known structure of "10 and some more." *(SMP 7)*

Hands-On Activity

Model adding numbers on 10-frames.

Materials For each child: 10-Frame (Activity Sheet 11), 20 two-color counters.

Write the problem 8 + 5 = ? on the board. Have children put 8 counters of one color in one 10-frame and 5 of another color in the second frame. Ask how they can use the 5 counters to fill the first 10-frame. [Remove 2 from the frame with 5 and use those to fill the frame with 8.] Have them actually move counters and describe what they did. Help them to conclude that the total number of counters didn't change. They just moved the counters around in the 10-frames to show a ten and some ones.

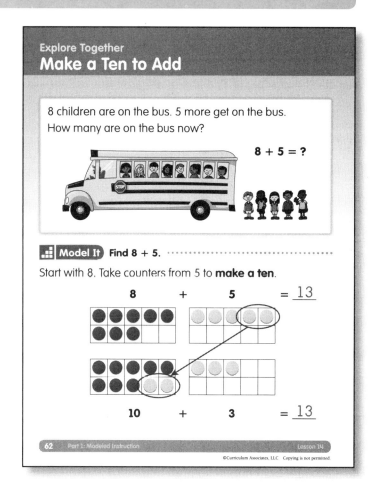

Mathematical Discourse

- *How does the model help you make a ten?*

  Children should see the empty spots in the 10-frame as a signal to what is needed to make a ten. With more practice, this visual clue will eventually translate to recognizing the number that makes ten.

STEP BY STEP

- Read aloud the problem at the top of the page. Ask children how they would approach the problem. Elicit the idea of making a ten and then seeing what's left to add.

- In Model It, direct attention to the number path. Ask children to describe what it shows. Guide children to see that 7 is circled because it is the addend you start with. Ask: *Why start with 7?* [It's easier if you start with the addend that is closer to 10. But the strategy will work either way.]

- Ask: *How many numbers is the blue jump? Why do you jump this many first?* [The blue jump is 3 because you want to make a ten. 7 + 3 = 10]

- Explain that now they have used 3 of the big blocks to make 10. Ask: *How many more do you have to add?* [2] Elicit that the total is 10 and 2 more, which is 12. Ask the Mathematical Discourse question to check understanding of this idea.

- You may want to have children verify the sum by laying green blocks or counters along the number path: 3 for the blue jump and 2 for the red jump.

- Present the Talk About It question. Have children describe the diagram and number sentence. Then have them answer the question and explain their thinking. [Boom is incorrect. It looks like Boom forgot to fill the 10-frame that has 9 counters but assumed that it had 10 in it. Actually, 9 + 5 = 14.]

Fluency Practice

Practice facts within 10.

Materials For each child: Facts Practice 4 (Activity Sheet 20)

Have children complete the facts sheet. Then have pairs work together to review the facts. One partner reads two addends and the other partner gives the sum. Children should go "out of order" for this, skipping around the worksheet and choosing addition sentences with different sums.

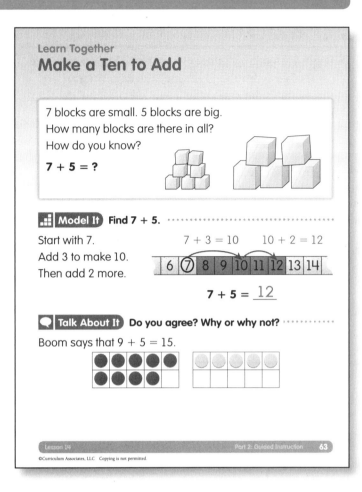

Learn Together
Make a Ten to Add

7 blocks are small. 5 blocks are big.
How many blocks are there in all?
How do you know?

7 + 5 = ?

Model It Find 7 + 5.

Start with 7.
Add 3 to make 10.
Then add 2 more.

7 + 3 = 10   10 + 2 = 12

| 6 | ⑦ | 8 | 9 | 10 | 11 | 12 | 13 | 14 |

7 + 5 = _12_

Talk About It Do you agree? Why or why not?

Boom says that 9 + 5 = 15.

Mathematical Discourse

- *How can you tell how big to make the jump from ten to the sum?*

  Children need to understand how many more are left after making the ten. They might respond that after a jump of 3, there is a jump of 2 left since the partner of 3 that makes 5 (the other addend) is 2.

STEP BY STEP

- Work through Practice Together. Read the model problem aloud and have children describe the two sets of 10-frames. Ask: *What can you do in the first 10-frame to get what is shown in the second 10-frame?* [Take 2 counters from the 6 and fill the first 10-frame.]

- Read Problem 1 aloud. Point out that the visual model only shows one set of 10-frames. Make sure children can identify the 8 and the 7 in the model. Have some children demonstrate how to solve this problem.

- In Problem 2, children need to draw jumps to 10 and then to the total. Suggest that they answer these questions: How many do I need to make 10? This number and how many more make the second addend? You may wish to have children work with a partner. Have some children demonstrate their solution and explain how they solved it.

> **SMP Tip:** Discuss the equivalent expressions on this page, for example $8 + 6$ and $10 + 4$. Continue to develop the repeated reasoning that as one addend increases, the other decreases by the same amount. *(SMP 8)*

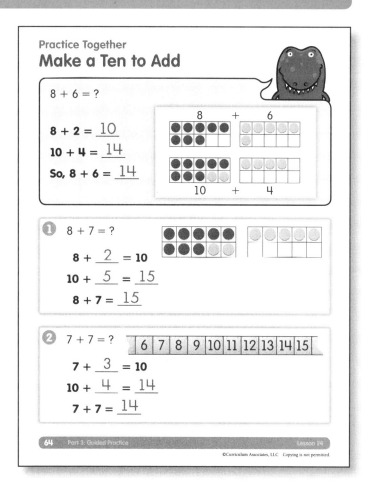

Visual Model

Use number bonds to make a ten and add within 20.

Write $7 + 5$ on the board. Then draw a circle around the 5 and connect it to two circles below to form a number bond. Ask: *Starting with 7, how can you make a ten?* [Add 3.] Write 3 in the left circle of the number bond. Ask children what needs to go in the right circle and why. [2, because 2 and 3 are the partners that make 5.] Below the number bond, write: $10 + \_\_\_ = \_\_\_$. Ask children what numbers go in the blanks. [2, 12] Consider trying this approach with different numbers for those who find it helpful.

Mathematical Discourse

- *Can you explain in your own words how to use the make a ten strategy to add two numbers?*

  Children should describe a two-part process. Start with one addend (preferably the greater addend) and find the partner that makes ten. To find what's left, remove the quantity added to make a ten from the other addend. In other words, the partner that makes ten has a partner that makes the other addend.

STEP BY STEP

- Read each problem aloud, then have children work independently to solve.

- If children struggle with Problem 3, ask what the red counters show. [The addend 7] Point out that they will make ten when the first frame is filled, and that they need to add more to add a total of 6.

- After children complete Problem 4, you may wish to present the following reasoning: *Nine is one less than 10, so 9 + 4 is one less than 10 + 4.* Ask the Mathematical Discourse question to continue discussing similar reasoning.

- For Problem 5, children can use any visual model or strategy that they choose. Invite several children to demonstrate their solutions, and then discuss the similarities and differences in their approaches.

Concept Extension

Use the associative property to make a ten and add within 20.

Write the problem 9 + 6 on the board. Have children work in pairs to make a ten and add. Have one pair describe what they did. When they tell how they made 10, write 9 + 1 on the board. When they explain how they added the remaining 5 to get 15, write + 5, to make the expression 9 + 1 + 5. Ask: *What happens if you add 9 + 1 first, then add 5?"* [We get 10 + 5 = 15.] Ask: *What happens if you add 1 + 5 first, then add 9?* [We get 6 + 9 = 15.] Lead children to conclude that grouping the addends differently does not change the total.

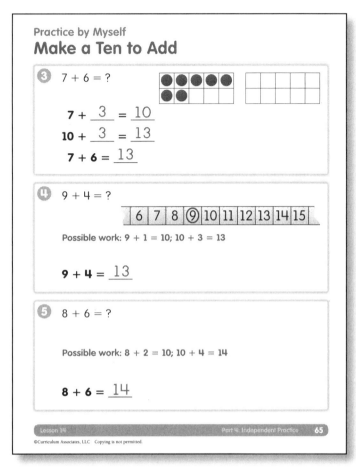

Mathematical Discourse

- *Why is the sum of 9 + 6 and 10 + 5 the same?*

  Children need to understand that as a number is decomposed and composed in different ways, the total stays the same. Responses should reflect the idea that some quantity has been taken from one addend and moved to the other, decreasing one addend and increasing the other by the same amount. So the overall quantity has not changed.

Assessment and Remediation

- Ask children to solve 8 + 7 = ? by making ten. [Add 8 + 2 to make 10. Then 10 + 5 = 15, so 8 + 7 = 15.]

- For children who are still struggling, use the chart below to guide remediation.

- After providing remediation, check children's understanding using the following problem: Solve 9 + 4 = ? by making ten. [Add 9 + 1 to make 10. Then 10 + 3 = 13, so 9 + 4 = 13.]

If the error is ...	Children may ...	To remediate ...
8 + 2 is 10, so 8 + 7 = 17	not understand the need to decompose the second addend.	Ask: *Where did you get the 2?* Use counters to model the problem with children. Elicit that the 2 comes from the 7, leaving 5 more to add.
14 or 16	be counting on instead of making ten, making a mistake in counting.	Have children demonstrate how they added. If they are counting on from 8, explain that it's easy to lose track when counting on more than 2 or 3. Guide children to use a make ten approach.
Any other teen number, or one of the addends	not have decomposed the addend correctly to make ten, or may have simply used an addend as the sum.	Have children model "10 and some more," using counters, for 12, 13, 15, and 16. Then have them model 8 + 7 using counters. Ask: *How can you change this model to show "10 and some more"?*

Hands-On Activity

Use connecting cubes to model making 10.

Materials For each pair: 20 connecting cubes in 2 colors

- Provide pairs of children with 10 each of two different color cubes. Give them an addition problem with a teen number sum, such as 8 + 6.

- Children write the problem and model it with two trains of different color connecting cubes, one for each addend.

- Children take cubes from one train and connect them to the other train to make a ten. Then they say how many are still left on the other train and solve the problem as "10 and 4 more," or 14. They write 10 + 4 = 14 and write = 14 after 8 + 6.

- Have pairs explain their work. You may wish to repeat the activity with other numbers.

Challenge Activity

Write and solve addition word problems.

Materials For each pair: paper and pencil, counters (optional)

- Have children work in pairs to write word problems involving teen numbers. They may wish to use counters to act out their ideas while they write.

- Circulate and offer support and feedback. When the pairs are finished, put the problems in a pile.

- Pairs take turns picking a problem, reading it, and solving by making a ten. The rest of the group listens to see if they are correct. Children may ask questions or recommend strategies as appropriate.

- For extra challenge, see if children can solve the problems without using manipulatives or even paper and pencil.

Add Three Numbers

LESSON OBJECTIVES

- Write addition expressions with three addends to represent word problems.
- Find the total of three addends, using strategies such as making a ten and using doubles.
- Use the associative and commutative properties to group addends in order to find known sums.

PREREQUISITE SKILLS

- Write addition sentences to solve word problems.
- Use doubles to add.
- Make a ten to add.
- Understand sums greater than 10.

VOCABULARY

Associative Property of Addition: when the grouping of 3 or more addends is changed, the total does not change

During the lesson you will review the key term:

addend: a number being added

THE LEARNING PROGRESSION

In Kindergarten, children solve addition and subtraction word problems and add and subtract within 10, using objects and drawings.

In Grade 1, children first learn to solve word problems that call for addition of two whole numbers. They learn strategies such as counting on, making ten, and creating equivalent but easier or known sums to add. Children also apply properties of operations as strategies to add and subtract. **In this lesson,** children solve word problems that involve three addends. They use the associative property to group addends to make a ten and then add the third addend.

In Grade 2, children continue to use the addition strategies they learned in Grade 1. They work with totals to 20 and then extend this understanding to solve problems involving addition and subtraction within 100, using diagrams and number sentences.

Ready *Teacher Toolbox*   Teacher-Toolbox.com

	Prerequisite Skills	*1.OA.A.2*
Ready Lessons	✓ ✓ ✓	✓
Tools for Instruction	✓ ✓	✓
Interactive Tutorials	✓ ✓	✓ ✓

CCSS Focus

1.OA.A.2 Solve word problems that call for addition of three whole numbers whose sum is less than or equal to 20, e.g., by using objects, drawings, and equations with a symbol for the unknown number to represent the problem.

ADDITIONAL STANDARDS: ***1.OA.B.3, 1.OA.C.6*** (see page A36 for full text)

STANDARDS FOR MATHEMATICAL PRACTICE: **SMP 1, 2, 3, 4, 7, 8** (see page A9 for full text)

Opening Activity: A Word Problem with Three Addends

Objective: Model writing a number sentence with three addends to solve an addition word problem.	**Materials** For each child: • pencil and paper

Overview

Children act out an addition problem with three addends and solve a number sentence to find the total. They identify ways to group two addends to find an easier or known sum.

Step by Step (10–15 minutes)

1 Pose the problem.

- Joe drops a container with pencils. The pencils spill on the ground. He picks up 7 pencils that drop near him. Carla picks up 3 pencils that fall near her desk. Pete finds 4 pencils that roll under the table. How many pencils do the children pick up?

2 Act Out the problem.

- Have three children stand at the front of the classroom. Give each child the appropriate number of pencils as you describe the situation.

- Say: *Here are the 7 pencils that Joe picks up. Here are the 3 pencils that Carla picks up. Here are the 4 pencils that Pete picks up.*

- Have the three children hold up their pencils. Ask: *How can you find how many pencils all three children pick up?* [Count all the pencils or add together the number of pencils that each child has.]

3 Write an addition sentence with three addends to represent the problem.

- Ask: *What number sentence can you write to show how to find the total number of pencils?* [$7 + 3 + 4 = ?$] Write the addition sentence on the board.

- Ask: *Why do you add the numbers?* [You are looking for the total number of pencils so you need to add the number that each child has.]

4 Talk about and solve the addition sentence.

- Ask: *What do the three addends in the number sentence stand for?* [the number of pencils each child picks up]

- Direct children's attention to the addition sentence on the board. Ask if anyone sees a way to make a ten with any of the numbers. Circle the 7 and 3 and write 10 on the board under these two numbers.

- Discuss why making a ten makes it easier to find the total. Then have children identify the next step in finding the total. [$10 + 4 = 14$] Write this number sentence on the board.

- Again, write $7 + 3 + 4 = ?$ on the board. Circle 3 and 4 and have children add these numbers first and give the total. Write 7 under the 3 and 4.

- Ask: *What strategy can you use to find the total of the remaining two numbers?* Guide children to see that they can use doubles to add $7 + 7 = 14$.

- Discuss the idea that you used different groupings to add the numbers and still ended up with the same total.

Check for Understanding

Provide children with the following problem: *Children go to the playground at recess. There are 6 children on the swings, 2 children on the slide, and 4 children on the seesaw. How many children are at the playground?*

Ask children to look for a way to group the addends to make a ten and to make doubles.

STEP BY STEP

- Explain that this page is about solving a word problem with three addends, just like the Opening Activity. Read aloud the problem at the top of the page. Encourage children to identify the three items that need to be added.

- Use the Hands-On Activity below to connect writing and solving a number sentence with three addends to the problem on the page.

- Direct children's attention to Model It. Ask: *What do the 8 red counters stand for in the problem?* [8 cans that Pat collects] *What do the 2 yellow counters stand for?* [2 cans that Max collects] *What do the 4 blue counters stand for?* [4 cans that May collects]

- Relate the three addends, $8 + 2 + 4$, to the counters. Discuss the strategy of making a ten with two of the addends, 8 and 2. Help children recognize that 4 more need to be added to the 10.

- Ask: *How many cans do all three children collect?* Have children write the total in the blank. Then pose the Mathematical Discourse question.

> **SMP Tip:** Continuing to emphasize the relationship between a real-life mathematical situation, a model, and a number sentence helps children develop skills that involve abstract reasoning. *(SMP 4)*

Hands-On Activity

Use counters and a 10-frame to add three addends.

Materials For each child: 10-Frame (Activity Sheet 11), 8 red, 2 yellow, and 4 blue counters

- Have children place the 8 red counters and 2 yellow counters in the 10-frame and place 4 blue counters in a row beneath the 10-frame.

- Ask: *How many counters are in the 10-frame?* [10] *What are the parts that make 10?* [8 and 2] *How many do you add to 10?* [4]

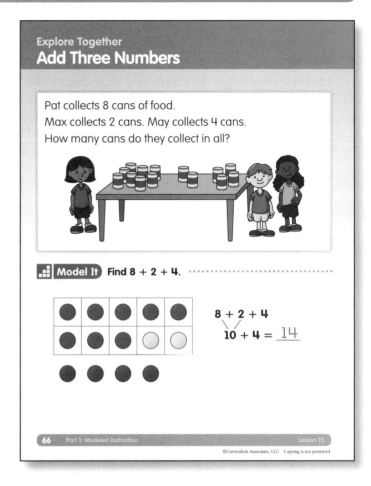

Explore Together
Add Three Numbers

Pat collects 8 cans of food.
Max collects 2 cans. May collects 4 cans.
How many cans do they collect in all?

Model It Find $8 + 2 + 4$.

$$8 + 2 + 4$$
$$10 + 4 = \underline{14}$$

Mathematical Discourse

- *How does making a ten make it easier to find the total of three numbers?*

  If you make a ten with two of the three addends, you are left with two addends to add. The two addends are 10 and the other number. It's easy to add 10 and the other number because they make a teen number whose parts are the 10 and the other number.

STEP BY STEP

- Read aloud the problem at the top of the page. Have children match each group of flowers in the picture to the numbers in the word problem.

- Direct children's attention to Model It. Read aloud the directive "Find 6 + 4 + 8." Relate the three addends to the picture above and to the numbers in the word problem. Then relate the three addends to the number path model.

- Ask: *Which two numbers do you add first to make a ten?* [6 + 4 = 10.] *What number do you add to the 10 to find the total?* [8] Have children complete the number sentences.

> **SMP Tip:** Children have found partners of 10 and have learned to use the make a ten strategy to add 2 one-digit numbers. Emphasize the benefit in making a ten to add 3 one-digit numbers. This important calculation will be repeated over and over as they add two-digit numbers and beyond. (*SMP 8*)

- Read aloud Talk About It. Encourage discussion by having children tell what is the same and what is different about the way Boom and Buzz write the addends for the problem.

- Use the Mathematical Discourse questions to engage children in a discussion about the commutative and associative properties of addition.

Hands-On Activity

Model the commutative and associative property of addition.

Materials For each child: 18 connecting cubes (6 of one color, 4 of a second color, and 8 of a third color)

- Ask children to count the connecting cubes, identifying that there are 18 in all.

- Have children use the connecting cubes to model putting the addends 6, 4, and 8 in different orders. Discuss how the total number of cubes is the same for each arrangement.

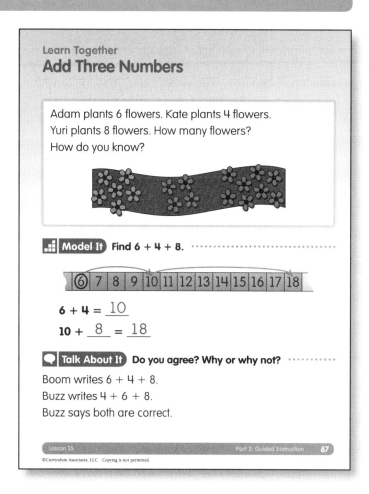

Learn Together
Add Three Numbers

Adam plants 6 flowers. Kate plants 4 flowers. Yuri plants 8 flowers. How many flowers? How do you know?

Model It Find 6 + 4 + 8.

| 6 | 7 | 8 | 9 | 10 | 11 | 12 | 13 | 14 | 15 | 16 | 17 | 18 |

$6 + 4 = \underline{10}$

$10 + \underline{8} = \underline{18}$

Talk About It Do you agree? Why or why not?

Boom writes 6 + 4 + 8.
Buzz writes 4 + 6 + 8.
Buzz says both are correct.

Mathematical Discourse

- *Is the total of 6 + 4 + 8 the same as the total of 4 + 6 + 8? How do you know?*

  Yes, the totals are the same. Both 6 + 4 = 10 and 4 + 6 = 10, so in both cases you add 10 + 8 to find the total of 18.

- *Is there another way you could write the addends? If so, explain whether the total remains the same.*

  Yes, you can write 6 + 8 + 4. You can add 6 + 4 = 10; 10 + 8 = 18, so the total remains the same. Children may give other ways to write the expression, such as 8 + 6 + 4 and 4 + 8 + 6 and say that the total remains the same for any order in which the addends are placed.

STEP BY STEP

- Read the example problem at the top of the page. Discuss with children that this is another situation in which you add three numbers to find the total.

- Ask children to identify the number of apples that each person has. As they do, write the addends $7 + 3 + 5$ on the board.

- Direct children's attention to the number path. Ask: *What number do you start with?* [7] *Why do you first add 3?* [to make 10] Relate to the number sentence $7 + \underline{3} = \underline{10}$.

- Ask: *How do you know how many more to add?* [Look at the third addend, so add 5 more.] Connect this to the number sentence $10 + \underline{5} = \underline{15}$. Then guide children to recognize that these two number sentences are the two separate additions needed to find $7 + 3 + 5$.

- Work together with children to complete Problem 1. Make sure they see the connection between the numbers in the problem, the circles in the model, and the numbers in the number sentences.

- In Problem 2, children make a ten with the second and third addends. Continue to emphasize that the order and grouping of the addends does not change the total.

Fluency Practice

Practice facts within 10.

Materials For each child: Number Bond Practice for 10 (Activity Sheet 21)

Have children complete the facts sheet. Then have pairs work together to review the facts. One partner reads two addends and the other partner gives the sum. Children should go "out of order" for this, skipping around the worksheet and choosing addition sentences with different sums.

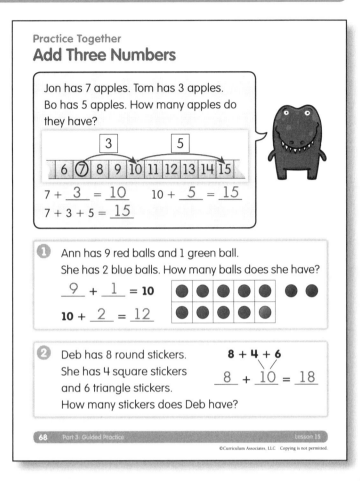

Mathematical Discourse

- *Are there other ways you could solve the word problem at the top of the page instead of using a number path to add the numbers? Tell about the other ways.*

    You could use counters or cubes to stand for each group of apples and then count to find the total. You could draw a picture or use 10-frames.

STEP BY STEP

- Read each problem aloud, then have children work independently to solve.

- Remind children to look for ways to add numbers whose sums they already know. They may use the strategy of making a ten or adding doubles to help them add two of the three addends in the number sentences for each word problem.

- In Problem 3, children may use the number path to make a ten and find the total. Some children may notice that the two addends that make a ten (5 + 5) are also doubles. These two addends are not next to each other in the number sentence. Use the Mathematical Discourse question to discuss grouping addends in a different order.

- In Problem 4, some children might draw in the 10-frames, while others just add 10 + 9.

- If children struggle with Problem 5, encourage them to find an easier way to add by grouping addends that make a ten.

Concept Extension

Solve word problems with zero as an addend.

Adapt the word problems on this page to have one addend of zero. For example, 8 children on the bus; no children get on at the next stop; then 9 children get on. Work with children to write the number sentence with a zero addend, 8 + 0 + 9, and find the total. Provide more examples for children to complete.

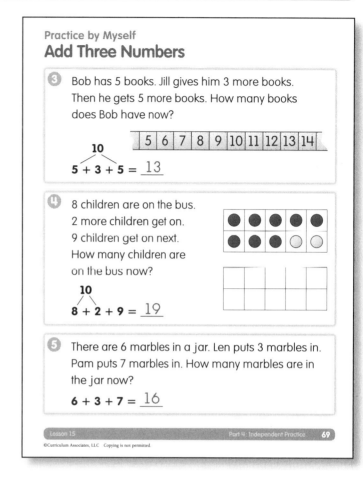

Mathematical Discourse

- *To solve Problem 3, Bob added 5 + 3 + 5. Tom added 5 + 5 + 3. Do you think they both got the same total? Why or why not?*

  Both ways give the same total. You are adding the same numbers, so the totals are the same. Changing the way you add the numbers together still gives you the same total.

Assessment and Remediation

- Ask children to find the total number of pets if there are 4 dogs, 7 cats, and 6 fish. [17 pets]

- For children who are still struggling, use the chart below to guide remediation.

- After providing remediation, check children's understanding using the following problem: Sam finds 7 shells. Brian finds 5 shells. Timmy finds 3 shells. How many shells do they find in all? [15 shells]

If the error is . . .	Children may . . .	To remediate . . .
10	have used the make a ten strategy to add 4 + 6 and forgotten to add the third addend, 7.	Have children use counters to show the number of each kind of pet. Then write a number sentence for the counters: 4 + 7 + 6. Have them combine the groups of 4 and 6 to make a ten, write the number sentence 10 + 7, and add to find the total, 17.
11	have added only the first two addends, 4 + 7, and forgotten to add the third addend, 6.	Have children draw a picture showing how many of each animal and then write the number beneath each picture. Ask them to write a number sentence to find the total.
16	have used the make a ten strategy to add 4 + 6 and then added 6 again instead of adding 7.	Have children use connecting cubes to model each addend. Have them join the 4-cube stick and 6-cube stick to make a stick of 10 cubes. Children use the 10-cube stick and the 7-cube stick to write the number sentence to find the total: 10 + 7 = 17.

Hands-On Activity

Use shapes to model adding three addends.

Materials For each pair: Pattern blocks (6 each of three different shapes)

- One partner uses any number of each of the three different shapes to make three separate groups.

- The other partner writes the addition number sentence using three addends to represent the shapes.

- Partners talk about what strategies they can use and then select an appropriate strategy to find the total.

Challenge Activity

Use strategies to add four addends to find sums less than 20.

- Have children use strategies such as making a ten and using doubles to solve addition number sentences with four addends:

9 + 7 + 1 + 2 = ___ [19]   4 + 5 + 4 + 5 = ___ [18]

8 + 6 + 2 + 3 = ___ [19]   3 + 5 + 2 + 3 = ___ [13]

7 + 4 + 3 + 5 = ___ [19]   7 + 0 + 3 + 7 = ___ [17]

8 + 1 + 8 + 2 = ___ [19]   9 + 4 + 2 + 1 = ___ [16]

6 + 3 + 2 + 7 = ___ [18]   5 + 4 + 3 + 2 = ___ [14]

Lesson 16 (Student Book pages 70–73)

Make a Ten to Subtract

LESSON OBJECTIVES

- Recognize that teen numbers can be decomposed and composed to subtract.

- Use the "make a ten" strategy to subtract single-digit numbers from teen numbers.

PREREQUISITE SKILLS

- Count on to add and subtract.

- Add and subtract in word problems.

- Know number partners for numbers within 10.

- Understand teen numbers.

- Understand totals greater than 10.

- Make a ten to add.

VOCABULARY

During the lesson you will review the key terms:

make a ten: a strategy that uses combinations of numbers that add to ten when finding totals greater than 10

teen number: a ten and some number of ones from 1 to 9; the numbers 11–19

THE LEARNING PROGRESSION

In Kindergarten, children add and subtract within 10, know decompositions for all numbers within 10, and know the partner that makes 10 for numbers within 10. Children understand teen numbers as 10 and some ones.

In Grade 1, children add and subtract within 20. They solve addition problems with two single-digit addends and solve related subtractions. **In this lesson,** children use the "make a ten" strategy to subtract single-digit numbers from teen numbers. They use 10-frames and number paths to decompose a teen number, subtract in parts that allow them to make a ten, and then subtract the other part to find the difference.

In Grade 2, children add and subtract within 100 using strategies based on place value, properties of operations, and the relationship between addition and subtraction.

Ready *Teacher Toolbox*		Teacher-Toolbox.com
	Prerequisite Skills	*1.OA.C.6*
Ready Lessons	✓ ✓ ✓	✓
Tools for Instruction	✓ ✓	✓ ✓
Interactive Tutorials	✓	✓ ✓

CCSS Focus

1.OA.C.6 Add and subtract within 20, demonstrating fluency for addition and subtraction within 10. Use strategies such as counting on; making ten (e.g., $8 + 6 = 8 + 2 + 4 = 10 + 4 = 14$); decomposing a number leading to a ten (e.g., $13 − 4 = 13 − 3 − 1 = 10 − 1 = 9$); using the relationship between addition and subtraction (e.g., knowing that $8 + 4 = 12$, one knows $12 − 8 = 4$); and creating equivalent but easier or known sums (e.g., adding $6 + 7$ by creating the known equivalent $6 + 6 + 1 = 12 + 1 = 13$).

ADDITIONAL STANDARDS: **1.OA.B.3** *(see page A36 for full text)*

STANDARDS FOR MATHEMATICAL PRACTICE: **SMP 1, 2, 3, 4, 7, 8** *(see page A9 for full text)*

Opening Activity: Make a Ten to Subtract

Objective: Model solving a subtraction problem.	**Materials** For each child: • 16 markers • transparent bag

Overview

Children act out a subtraction problem and solve a subtraction number sentence to find the solution.

Step by Step (10–15 minutes)

1 **Pose the problem.**

- Say: *Maria put 16 markers in her bag to bring to school. 9 markers fell out of her bag. How can you find out how many markers Maria has left in her bag?*

2 **Act out the problem.**

- Have 3 children stand at the front of the classroom.

- Say: *Let's count to show the 16 markers Maria put in her bag.* Have one child place the markers, one by one, into a transparent bag, as the class counts aloud together.

- Discuss with children how they can show the 9 markers that fell out of Maria's bag. [take 9 markers out of the bag]

- Have the second child remove 9 markers from the bag, counting aloud together with the class, one by one, until 9 markers are removed.

- Ask children how they can tell how many markers are left in the bag. Some children may suggest counting them. Listen for responses from children who suggest subtracting 9 from 16.

3 **Write a subtraction number sentence to represent the problem.**

- Say: *Let's write a number sentence to solve the problem.* Ask children if they think the number sentence should be an addition sentence or a subtraction sentence. [subtraction] Encourage children to explain their reasoning.

- Write $16 - 9 = ?$ on the board.

4 **Talk about and solve the subtraction sentence.**

- Discuss with children what the 16 in the number sentence stands for. [the number of markers Maria put in her bag]

- Then have children identify what the 9 in the number sentence stands for. [the number of markers that fell out of Maria's bag]

- Ask children to tell why 9 is subtracted from 16 in the number sentence. [to find how many markers are left in the bag]

- Say: *One way you can find how many markers are left is to count them.* Have the third child count aloud with the class, one by one, the 7 markers left in the bag.

- Say: *Another way you can find out how many markers are left is to start at 9 and then count up from 9 to 16.* Place the 9 markers in view. Say: *Nine.* Then pick up and display each of the 7 markers and count aloud, one by one: *10, 11, 12, 13, 14, 15, 16.*

Check for Understanding

Provide children with the following problem: *Rina has 13 apples. She gives away 6 apples. How many apples does she have left?* Children should be able to understand that this is a "take away" situation, and that 6 needs to be subtracted from 13.

STEP BY STEP

- Have a child retell the important math idea from the Opening Activity.

- Explain that this page is about solving a subtraction problem, just like the Opening Activity. Read aloud the problem at the top of the page.

- Direct children's attention to Model It with the 10-frames and counters.

- Remind children that they can use what they know about addition to help them subtract. Read aloud: *15 − 7 = ? is the same as 7 + ? = 15.* Pose the Mathematical Discourse question.

- Use the Hands-On Activity below to connect solving the number sentence to the problem.

- Discuss which number to start with. [the number being subtracted, or 7] Have children count up 3 to make 10; then count 5 more to reach 15.

- Point out how the 3 and 5 they just counted make 8. Then ask children how many they counted in all to get from 7 to 15. [8] Relate the numbers to the subtraction number sentence 15 − 7 = 8.

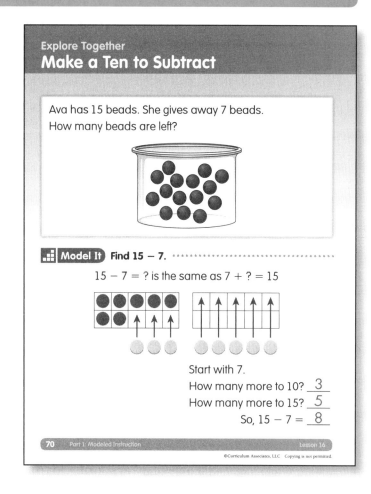

Hands-On Activity

Use 10-frames to subtract.

Materials for each child: two 10-frames, 15 two-color counters

Distribute the counters and have children count to confirm there are 15 in all. Have children place 7 red counters in a 10-frame and tell how many more counters are needed to fill it. [3] Have children place 3 yellow counters in the 10-frame and discuss their understanding that 7 and 3 make 10. After children place the remaining counters (yellow side up) in the second 10-frame, ask: *How many counters are in the other 10-frame?* [5] *How many do 5 and 3 make?* [8] Guide children to see that the 8 yellow counters and 7 red counters make 15 counters in all. To connect the number of counters to the subtraction, conclude by saying: *15 counters minus 7 counters is 8 counters. 15 minus 7 is 8.*

Mathematical Discourse

- *How can you use the idea of parts and the whole to explain that 15 − 7 = ? is the same as 7 + ? = 15?*

  15 is the whole. 7 and another number are the parts. You can add the parts together to get the whole. You can also subtract one part from the whole to get the other part.

SMP Tip: Algebraic ideas underlie what children are doing when they create equivalent expressions to solve a problem. Children begin to consider the relationship between the parts. Provide children with physical models such as counters, 10-frames, connecting cubes, and number paths to strengthen the connections they are making between objects and abstract reasoning. *(SMP 8)*

STEP BY STEP

- Read aloud the problem at the top of the page. Ask children what operation they can use to solve the problem. [subtraction] Have them explain their reasoning.

- Direct children's attention to the Model It. Read aloud the directive: *Find 14 − 6.* Relate the 14 hats to the 14 counters in the two 10-frames.

- Ask children what strategies they would use to help them subtract. Listen for children who suggest making a ten. Point out the 10-frames on the page and discuss how they can be used to make a ten to subtract.

- Have children identify which number to start with. [14] Ask: *How can you make a ten?* [take away 4] Point out that the bracket under the 4 counters indicates they are taken away. Relate the number sentence 14 − 4 = 10 to the 4 taken-away counters and the 10-frame that contains 10 counters.

- Ask: *How many more do you need to take away?* [2] *Why?* [because you need to take away 6 and you already took away 4; 4 and 2 are 6] Ask: *How many counters are left?* [8] Relate the number sentence 10 − 2 = 8 to the 2 taken-away counters and the 8 counters remaining in the 10-frame.

- Reinforce children's understanding by asking them how many counters they started with [14], how many counters were taken away [4 counters and 2 counters: 6 counters in all], and how many counters are left [8 counters]. Then direct their attention to the final number sentence and discuss.

- Use the Mathematical Discourse question to talk about how the make a ten strategy makes it easier to subtract from a teen number.

- **Error Alert** Read aloud the Talk About It. Children may recognize that 2 counters, not 5, need to be taken away from the left 10-frame. Discuss that 5 is taken away in all: first 3 and then 2.

ELL Support

Create language cards for "subtract," "take away," and "minus." For the number sentence 14 − 4 = 10, show: "fourteen minus four equals ten"; "take away four from fourteen to make ten"; "subtract four from fourteen to get ten."

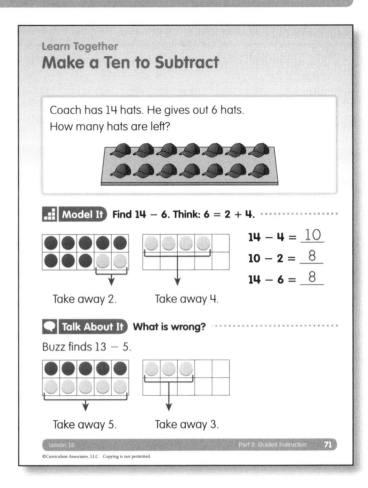

Mathematical Discourse

- *How does making a ten make it easier to subtract from a teen number?*

  You can think of a teen number as 10 and some ones. You can subtract the ones to get to 10. Then you subtract from the 10 as many more ones as you need to subtract in all. It's easier to subtract from 10 because you know the number partners that make 10.

STEP BY STEP

- Read aloud the problem at the top of the page. Discuss with children what strategies they could use to solve subtraction problems.

- Direct children's attention to the number path. Ask what strategy they think it shows. [make a ten] Guide children to name the number to start with if they were to use this strategy. [16] Ask: *How many from 16 to 10 on the number path?* [6]

- Connect this 6 to the box above the number path and to the first number sentence beneath the number path. Have children touch the 6 in the box and the 6 in the number sentence, $16 - 6 = 10$.

- Ask: *You subtracted 6 to get to 10. How many more do you need to subtract?* [1] *How do you know?* [you need to subtract 7 altogether] Relate this to the jump from 10 to 9 on the number path and to the second number sentence. Have children touch the 1 in the box above the path and the 1 in the number sentence, $10 - 1 = 9$.

- Ask: *What number do you end at after two jumps on the number path?* [9] Connect this to the final number sentence, $16 - 7 = 9$.

- Work together with children to complete Problem 1 using the same strategy.

- For Problem 2, children use 10-frames and counters to find $17 - 8$. Ask children whether they prefer to use a number path or 10-frames to make a ten to subtract. Encourage children to understand that neither model is better than the other by discussing how both methods give the same answer.

Visual Model

Materials For each child: 16 dried beans or other small objects

Have children use dried beans to help them visualize subtraction on the number path. For $16 - 7 = 9$, have children place 6 beans beneath 10 through 16 on the number path and 1 bean beneath 9 on the number path. Children first take away 6 beans and then take away 1 bean to model taking away 7 beans in all.

Mathematical Discourse

- *How is making a ten to subtract on a number path like counting back to subtract?*

   It's like counting back two times to subtract. First you count back to 10 on the number path. Then you count back a second time, from 10.

- *How do you know how many to count back each time?*

   Break the number you are subtracting into two parts. Count back to subtract one part to get to 10 on the number path. Then count back to subtract the other part from 10.

SMP Tip: Children use number paths and number sentences to represent decompositions when subtracting from teen numbers. Connecting the two strategies, making a ten to subtract and counting back to subtract, helps children look for and make use of structure. (*SMP 7*)

STEP BY STEP

- Before children work on this page, review the models used in this lesson. Emphasize that children are free to use whatever way helps them solve the problem.

- Read each problem aloud, then have children work independently to solve.

- As children work, walk around to assess their progress and understanding.

- In Problem 3, some children may choose to solve the problem by drawing 3 counters to make a ten, then 3 more to make 13. You may wish to pose the Mathematical Discourse questions to discuss other ways children could solve the problem.

- Ask children who solve Problem 5 without showing their work to explain what strategy they used.

Fluency Practice

Materials For display: Teen Number Cards (Activity Sheet 22)

Use digit cards to provide children with practice breaking apart teen numbers into a 10 and some ones. Display a card and have children call out 10 and the number that together make the teen number. For example, hold up a card marked 17. Children call out: *10 and 7 make 17.*

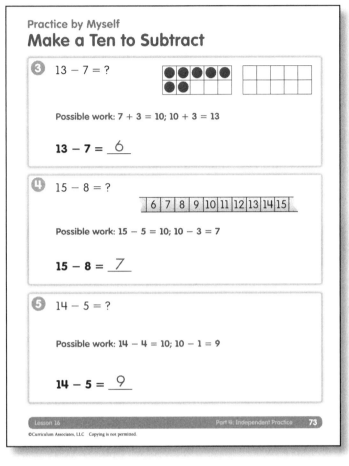

Practice by Myself
Make a Ten to Subtract

3. $13 - 7 = ?$

Possible work: $7 + 3 = 10; 10 + 3 = 13$

$13 - 7 = \underline{6}$

4. $15 - 8 = ?$

Possible work: $15 - 5 = 10; 10 - 3 = 7$

$15 - 8 = \underline{7}$

5. $14 - 5 = ?$

Possible work: $14 - 4 = 10; 10 - 1 = 9$

$14 - 5 = \underline{9}$

Mathematical Discourse

- *Explain a strategy you could use to find $13 - 7$ in Problem 3.*

  You have 7 counters in one 10-frame. You need to know how many more counters to make 13. So you can draw 3 more counters to make 10. Then you can draw 3 more counters to make 13. You put together the 3 counters and 3 counters to get 6. So you know you need 6 counters to get from 7 to 13. So you know that $13 - 7 = 6$.

- *Did anyone else use the same strategy? If not, how did you find $13 - 7$?*

  Children may say they used the same method or that $13 - 3 = 10$ and $10 - 3 = 7$, so $13 - 7 = 6$.

Assessment and Remediation

- Ask children to find 14 − 8. [6]

- For children who are still struggling, use the chart below to guide remediation.

- After providing remediation, check children's understanding using the following problem: 13 − 6. [7]

If the error is . . .	Children may . . .	To remediate . . .
2	have taken away 4 to make 10 and then, instead of taking away 4 more, taken away 8 more to find 14 − 12 = 2.	provide children with 14 counters and two 10-frames to model the problem so that they can count the 8 counters to take away.
7	have included 8 as one of the numbers they counted as they counted up from 8 to 14.	have children use a number path to draw individual jumps from 8 to 14 and then count the number of jumps (6) to find the difference between 14 and 8.
10	have decomposed 14 into 10 and 4 and taken away 4 to get 10 without continuing on to take away another 4 from 10 to get 6.	have children connect 14 cubes and break them apart to make a ten-stick and a stick of 4 ones. Have them take away 8 cubes, 4 from the 4 ones and 4 from the 10-stick, and count the remaining cubes to find how many remain.

Hands-On Activity

Use shapes to make a ten to subtract.

Materials For each child: 17 triangle shapes

- Distribute triangle shapes. Write the subtraction 16 − 9 on the board. Have children count out 16 triangles in a horizontal row.

- Have children move 6 triangles into a second row. Discuss how 10 and 6 still show 16 in all.

- Point to the problem on the board and ask how many they need to take away. [9] Have them take away the 6 triangles in the second row.

- Tell children they can count on from 6 to find out how many more triangles they need to take away from the 10 to take away 9 in all.

- Have them count 7, 8, 9 as they take away 3 triangles from the 10. Say: *Now you've taken away 9 triangles. Count how many are left.* [7]

- Repeat for other subtraction problems such as 17 − 9, 15 − 9, 15 − 6, 14 − 8, and 13 − 9.

Challenge Activity

Use number bonds to make a ten to subtract.

- Have children solve subtraction problems using number bonds. Present the first problem, showing the decomposition of both 15 and 9. Guide children to recognize that breaking the teen number into a ten and some ones helps them decide how to break apart the other number.

$$15 \quad - \quad 9 \quad = \underline{}$$
$$10 \quad 5 \qquad 5 \quad 4$$

- Give children just the subtraction problem 14 − 6 and 17 − 9. Ask them to break apart the numbers like you did in the example to solve.

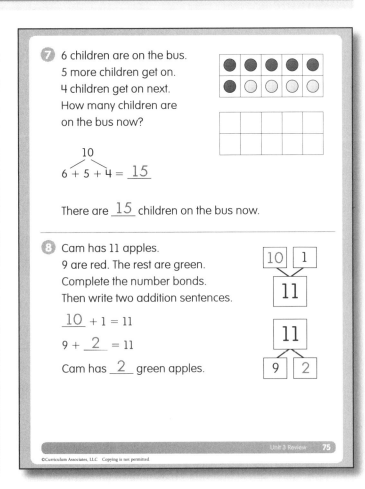

Unit 3 Review

Solve the problems.

① 8 blocks are big. 7 blocks are small.
How many in all?

8 + _2_ = _10_
10 + _5_ = _15_
8 + 7 = _15_

② Max has 14 stickers. He gives away 5 stickers.
How many stickers are left?

14 − _4_ = 10
10 − _1_ = _9_
14 − 5 = _9_

| 6 | 7 | 8 | 9 | 10 | 11 | 12 | 13 | 14 | 15 |

③ 4 green balls. 7 red balls. 3 blue balls.
How many in all?

4 + 7 + 3 = _14_

④ _7_ = 13 − 6

⑤ 16 is the same as

_1_ ten and _6_ ones

⑥ 17 = 10 + _7_

17 = _9_ + 8

---

⑦ 6 children are on the bus.
5 more children get on.
4 children get on next.
How many children are
on the bus now?

10
6 + 5 + 4 = _15_

There are _15_ children on the bus now.

⑧ Cam has 11 apples.
9 are red. The rest are green.
Complete the number bonds.
Then write two addition sentences.

| 10 | 1 |

11

_10_ + 1 = 11

9 + _2_ = 11

Cam has _2_ green apples.

11

| 9 | 2 |

STEP BY STEP

- Have children solve the problems individually and show their work. Emphasize that children are free to use whatever way helps them solve the problems.

- Observe as children work. Watch for those who struggle with the idea of "1 ten and some number of ones". Help these children identify the ten and ones in each teen number. Have them write, draw, and talk about making a ten as they add.

- For Problem 8, children find number partners for 11, starting with 10 and 1, and then moving to 9 and 2 in order to solve the word problem. For children who struggle, point out that the first number bond shows 1 one and ask: *What else does 11 have?* [1 ten] Then remind children that they can find another partner of 11 by subtracting 1 from one addend and adding 1 to the other addend.

STEP BY STEP

- On this page, children start with 10 and then add some ones to make a teen number. Then they subtract 7 from the number they made.

- Direct children to complete the Put It Together on their own.

- Read the directions and task aloud. Make sure children understand what they need to do to complete the task.

- As children work on their own, observe their progress and understanding. Respond to their questions and provide additional support as needed.

- If time permits, have children share their drawings and solutions with the class. Have them show the partners of 7 that they used to do their subtraction.

- Ask: *How did you know those were the partners of 7 to use?* [The first partner should be the same as the number of ones in their teen number.]

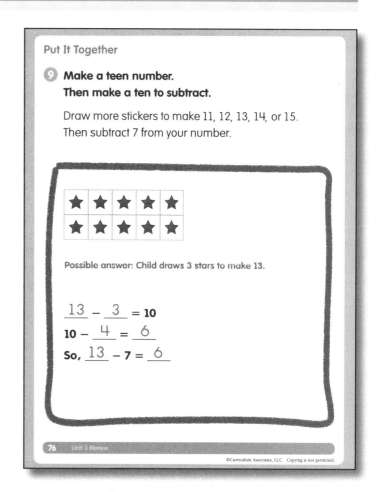

Put It Together

9 **Make a teen number.**
Then make a ten to subtract.

Draw more stickers to make 11, 12, 13, 14, or 15. Then subtract 7 from your number.

Possible answer: Child draws 3 stars to make 13.

$\underline{13} - \underline{3} = 10$
$10 - \underline{4} = \underline{6}$
So, $\underline{13} - 7 = \underline{6}$

76   Unit 3 Review

©Curriculum Associates, LLC   Copying is not permitted.

SCORING RUBRICS

Expectations for 4–3 Points

Points	Expectations
4	The child: • creates a teen number. • correctly uses the "make a ten" strategy to subtract.
3	The child: • may create a teen number. • may have a minor error when subtracting 7.

Expectations for 2–0 Points

Points	Expectations
2	The child: • may create a teen number. • may incorrectly identify the partners of 7 or the difference.
1	The child: • may show errors in creating a teen number. • may make multiple errors when subtracting.
0	The child: • does not attempt to complete the task.

Unit 4: Number and Operations in Base Ten—Tens

Which lessons are students building upon?

Kindergarten, Lesson 21
Understand Teen Numbers
K.NBT.A.1, K.CC.A.2, K.CC.A.3, K.CC.B5

Kindergarten, Lesson 22
Count Teen Numbers
K.CC.A.3, K.CC.B.5, K.CC.A.2, K.NBT.A.1

Kindergarten, Lesson 22
Count Teen Numbers
K.CC.A.3, K.CC.B.5, K.CC.A.2, K.NBT.A.1

Kindergarten, Lesson 24
Count to 100 by Tens
K.CC.A.1, K.CC.A.2

Kindergarten, Lesson 25
Count to 100 by Ones
K.CC.A.1, K.CC.A.2

Kindergarten, Lesson 22
Count Teen Numbers
K.CC.A.3, K.CC.B.5, K.CC.A.2, K.NBT.A.1

Kindergarten, Lesson 23
Make Teen Numbers
K.NBT.A.1, K.CC.A.2, K.CC.A.3

Kindergarten, Lesson 24
Count to 100 by Tens
K.CC.A.1, K.CC.A.2

Kindergarten, Lesson 21
Understand Teen Numbers
K.NBT.A.1, K.CC.A.2, K.CC.A.3, K.CC.B5

Kindergarten, Lesson 22
Count Teen Numbers
K.CC.A.3, K.CC.B.5, K.CC.A.2, K.NBT.A.1

Kindergarten, Lesson 24
Count to 100 by Tens
K.CC.A.1, K.CC.A.2

Which lessons are students preparing for?

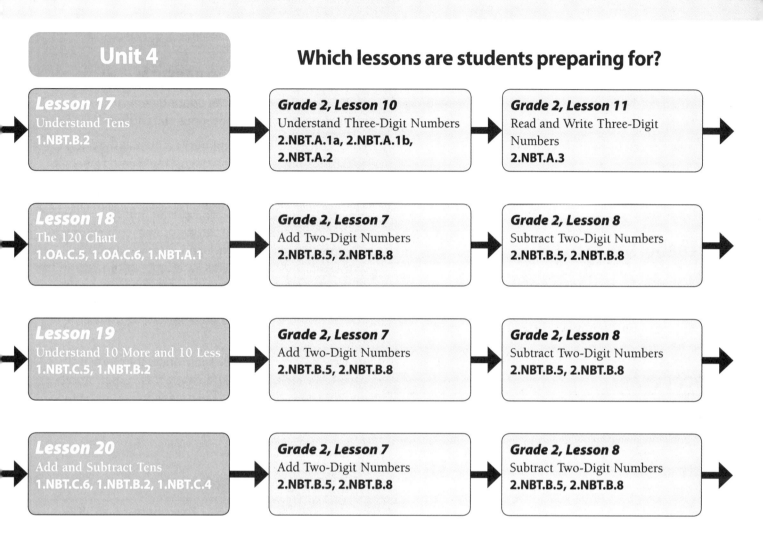

Lesson 17
Understand Tens
1.NBT.B.2

→ **Grade 2, Lesson 10**
Understand Three-Digit Numbers
**2.NBT.A.1a, 2.NBT.A.1b,
2.NBT.A.2**

→ **Grade 2, Lesson 11**
Read and Write Three-Digit Numbers
2.NBT.A.3

Lesson 18
The 120 Chart
1.OA.C.5, 1.OA.C.6, 1.NBT.A.1

→ **Grade 2, Lesson 7**
Add Two-Digit Numbers
2.NBT.B.5, 2.NBT.B.8

→ **Grade 2, Lesson 8**
Subtract Two-Digit Numbers
2.NBT.B.5, 2.NBT.B.8

Lesson 19
Understand 10 More and 10 Less
1.NBT.C.5, 1.NBT.B.2

→ **Grade 2, Lesson 7**
Add Two-Digit Numbers
2.NBT.B.5, 2.NBT.B.8

→ **Grade 2, Lesson 8**
Subtract Two-Digit Numbers
2.NBT.B.5, 2.NBT.B.8

Lesson 20
Add and Subtract Tens
1.NBT.C.6, 1.NBT.B.2, 1.NBT.C.4

→ **Grade 2, Lesson 7**
Add Two-Digit Numbers
2.NBT.B.5, 2.NBT.B.8

→ **Grade 2, Lesson 8**
Subtract Two-Digit Numbers
2.NBT.B.5, 2.NBT.B.8

Lesson 17 (Student Book pages 78–81)

Understand Tens

LESSON OBJECTIVES

- Understand that the base-ten system is made up of groups of tens and ones.

- Organize ten ones into groups of ten.

- Express ten ones as one ten and one ten as ten ones.

- Identify and write two-digit numbers in terms of tens and ones.

PREREQUISITE SKILLS

- Count to 100.

- Add within 10.

- Understand teen numbers as 1 group of ten and some ones.

VOCABULARY

ones: single units or objects

tens: groups of ten ones

THE LEARNING PROGRESSION

In Kindergarten, children count by tens to 100 and write numbers to 20, observing place value.

In Grade 1, children explore tens by making a ten to add and subtract and by recognizing teen numbers as a composition of a ten and some ones. **In this lesson,** children explore the concept of ten as 10 ones by counting, recording, and comparing multiple groups of ten. They reason that 10 can be shown as one group of 10 or as 10 individual ones and compare numbers expressed in the two forms. Concepts in this lesson lay groundwork for understanding the idea that the two digits in two-digit numbers represent a number of tens and ones and for adding and subtracting multiples of ten.

In Grade 2, children use their understanding of the base-ten system to add and subtract two-digit numbers and extend the concept of place value to understand three-digit numbers.

Ready *Teacher Toolbox*		*Teacher-Toolbox.com*
	Prerequisite Skills	**1.NBT.B.2a, 1.NBT.B.2c**
Ready Lessons	✓ ✓	✓
Tools for Instruction	✓ ✓	✓
Interactive Tutorials		✓ ✓

CCSS Focus

1.NBT.B.2 Understand that the two digits of a two-digit number represent amounts of tens and ones. Understand the following special cases:

   a.   10 can be thought of as a bundle of ten ones—called a "ten."

   c.   The numbers 10, 20, 30, 40, 50, 60, 70, 80, 90 refer to one, two, three, four, five, six, seven, eight, or nine tens (and 0 ones).

STANDARDS FOR MATHEMATICAL PRACTICE: **SMP 2, 3, 5, 7, 8** (*see page A9 for full text*)

Opening Activity: Make a Ten

Objective: Explore groups of ten as a way to express ten ones.	**Materials for each child:** • Connecting cubes (at least 20) • 10-Frame (Activity Sheet 11)

Overview

Children explore the concept of tens beyond teen numbers by building groups of 10 connecting cubes and describing the total number of cubes.

Step by Step (20–25 minutes)

1 Introduce the activity.

- Distribute 10-Frame activity sheet and cubes to children. Write the number 6 on the board. Model for children how to place the corresponding number of cubes (ones) on their 10-frames. Explain that children will add cubes to the 10-frame to build groups of 10.

2 Build one group of 10.

- Ask children how many more cubes need to be added in order to make 10. Then have them add that number of cubes to the 10-frame. Reinforce addition by stating the sum (e.g., 6 + 4 = 10. 10 cubes on the frame.).

- When the 10-frame is full, tell children to connect 10 ones (cubes) to make 1 ten. Have them place the ten to the left of the 10-frame.

- Discuss that children now have one group of 10 (pointing to the connected cubes) and 0 ones (pointing to an empty 10-frame).

- To emphasize that 1 ten is the same as 10 ones, ask children to break apart the ten, place the individual cubes in the 10-frame, then connect the cubes again to make a ten. Again, have children put the ten to the left of the 10-frame.

3 Build two groups of 10.

- Repeat the process used for building the first 10, but start with 3 cubes (ones) this time and ask children how many more cubes need to be added to make another ten.

- After children have placed 7 more cubes on the 10-frame to build a second ten, have them connect the cubes and place it next to the first ten.

- Ask: *How many tens do you have now?* [2 tens] *How many ones are in 2 tens?* [20 ones] Have children take apart each ten and place the individual cubes in two 10-frames to verify that there are 20 counters.

Check for Understanding

As children build and break apart tens, look for an understanding that 1 ten and a group of 10 ones are the same. Some children may think of a ten as a one and count 1, 2 instead of 1 ten, 2 tens. Children will have opportunities to develop thinking as they work through the lesson. Additional support is provided in the Hands-On Activity on page 130 and the Visual Model on page 131.

STEP BY STEP

- Read aloud the question at the top of the page and ask children why they think it is important to know about tens. Emphasize that numbers 10 or greater are made up of tens and ones.

- Direct attention to the 10 ones and 1 ten on the student page. Ask children to describe how the pictures remind them of what they did in the Opening Activity. Ask: *How can you tell that both pictures show ten cubes?*

- As the children explain their thinking, reinforce the idea that when the cubes are separate, they are expressed as *ones* and when they are connected, they are expressed as *tens.*

- Display a train of 10 cubes and 3 single cubes. Ask: *Would it make sense to count these as* [point as you count] *1, 2, 3, 4 cubes? Why or why not?* Make sure children understand that the ten and the ones are counted differently because they represent different quantities.

- Present the Talk About It question. Encourage discussion by asking questions, such as: *Do you agree with what [child's name] said? Does someone have a different way to tell how the pictures are the same?* [Both pictures have 10 cubes. The cubes are connected in the ten and separate in the ones.]

> **SMP Tip:** Asking children to express and justify mathematical ideas clearly reinforces understanding of concepts and promotes mathematical reasoning. As you listen to their thinking, validate and support the way they expressed their ideas, and help them develop their reasoning skills through further questioning. *(SMP 3)*

Hands-On Activity

Materials For each pair: 50 connecting cubes

Have children work in pairs. One child counts out a group of 20 cubes, while the other counts out a group of 30 cubes. Ask partners to switch groups of cubes and connect them to form tens. Together partners count the tens (by ten) and verify that 20 is 2 tens and 30 is 3 tens.

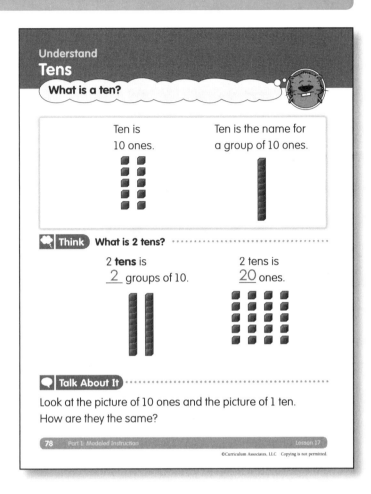

Mathematical Discourse

- *When you make tens like this, how can you tell for sure that each group has ten cubes in it?*

  Some children will count the cubes in each group. Others may count the number in one group and compare the others to it.

- *If you had a lot of cubes to count, how might making tens help you count them?*

  If you make groups of ten, you can count the cubes by tens. If you count lots of cubes one by one, it could take a long time and you may lose count. Counting by tens is faster and you won't lose count as easily.

STEP BY STEP

- Explain the directions at the top of the page. Have children follow the model by counting out 20 cubes and making groups of 10. Ask why 2 groups of cubes are colored. Ensure that children make the connection between the physical model and the picture.

- Allow children time to complete Problems 1–3. Watch to make sure they count, color, and record the number of tens, not the number of cubes, on the lines.

- Discuss the structure of the numbers 20, 30, 40, 50, connecting each one to the number of tens recorded. Make sure children understand that the zero shows there are only tens and no extra ones.

- Write the number 30 on the board and cover the zero. Ask: *If I told you to show this number of cubes, what would you do?* Children should see that without the zero, the number is read as 3 ones, not as 3 tens.

- Read the Talk About It question aloud. Encourage children to justify their decision. Ask the second Mathematical Discourse question to extend the idea of comparing tens.

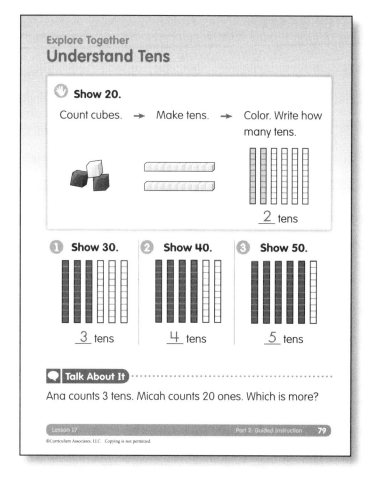

Visual Model

Materials For each child: Hundreds Chart (Activity Sheet 19), crayons

Display a Hundreds chart. Ask children to find the row of squares showing 1–10 on their own charts and color it. Demonstrate on the displayed chart. Have children shade in the next row of ten with a different color. Ask how many rows are shaded and how many squares are shaded. Encourage children to justify their answers by counting, or by recognizing that the numbers on the chart tell how many in all. Continue to have children shade in rows and find totals. Discuss how each row is like a ten they made with connecting cubes. Point out that the numbers in the rightmost column are the numbers you say when you count by tens.

Mathematical Discourse

- *How could you see that 40 is more than 30 just by looking at the numbers?*

   Look for an understanding that the digits 3 and 4 in 30 and 40 indicate a number of tens. Since 4 is more than 3, 4 tens or 40 is more than 3 tens or 30.

- *How did you decide whether Ana or Micah has more cubes?*

   Some children might suggest building each group of cubes and counting them. Others may suggest thinking of 3 tens as 30 ones and comparing 20 ones to 30 ones or thinking of 20 as 2 tens and comparing 3 tens to 2 tens.

STEP BY STEP

Materials Optional: 10 connecting cubes

- Discuss each Connect It problem as a class using the discussion points outlined below.

Draw:

- If children need help getting started, provide a set of 10 cubes linked together to help them remember what is meant by 1 ten.

- Invite children to share their drawings. Ask questions, such as: *Why did you draw your tens the way you did? Does anyone have a question about [child's name]'s drawing?*

- Encourage children to answer questions about their drawings. You may wish to have them modify their drawings or make new ones based on the questions from others.

- Revisit the earlier discussion about why it makes sense to group 10 ones as 1 ten. Remind children that counting by tens makes sense when there are many items to count.

Reason:

- Circulate the room to check understanding by asking questions like: *What does your picture show? How is the picture of 1 ten different than the picture of 10 ones?*

- Invite children to share their drawings and explain how they found the number of tens in all. Encourage all to comment on drawings and explanations.

Explain:

- Ask children to talk to a partner about the problem. After a few minutes, start a class discussion about the counting method David may have used.

- **Misconception Alert** Point to each ten on the student page as you say: *10, 11, 12, 13, 14.* Then ask: *Why doesn't David's counting on strategy work?* Children should recognize that he counted the first ten correctly, but then he counted all the other tens as if they were ones instead of tens.

- Invite volunteers to show the correct way to count the tens. Then ask children to make a drawing that correctly shows 14 using base-ten blocks.

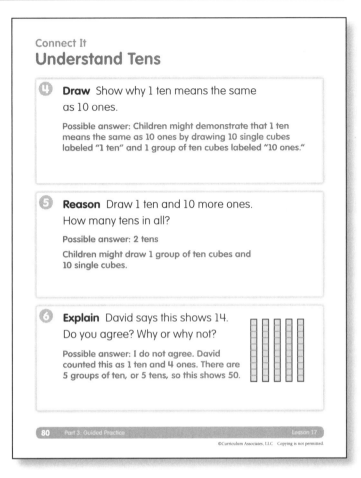

SMP Tip: As children learn to see a set of multiple parts (ten individual items) as one single part (one ten) they are building understanding of the structure and power of the base ten counting system. Provide multiple opportunities for children to compose and decompose tens to reinforce this concept. *(SMP 7)*

STEP BY STEP

- Tell children that they will complete this page independently.

- Read the directions and questions aloud, making sure children understand what they are expected to do.

- In Part A, children circle groups of ten, write how many groups of ten there are, and tell how many objects there are in all.

- In Part B, children make 2 tens and 1 one.

- Observe children as they work. Ask questions such as the following to encourage thinking and problem-solving strategies:

How can you be sure you have circled ten?

How can you check that you have the correct number of stars?

What does 21 mean? How many tens does 21 have? How many ones?

Is there a way to show 21 that makes it easy to count?

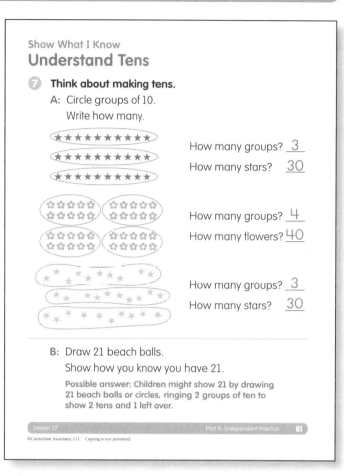

SCORING RUBRICS

Expectations for 4–3 Points

Points	Expectations
4	The child: • accurately circles groups of ten and identifies the number of groups and totals. • draws the correct number of balls and justifies by labeling each ball, or groups balls into tens and ones and gives the total.
3	The child: • may circle groups of ten, but show minor errors in the number of groups and totals. • may show the correct number of balls, but presents a justification that is inaccurate or incomplete.

Expectations for 2–0 Points

Points	Expectations
2	The child: • may circle groups of ten in some, but not all of the sets and does not accurately identify all groups or totals. • shows the correct number of balls, but provides no justification.
1	The child: • attempts to circle groups of ten and show the correct number of balls, but there is no evidence of a strategy or understanding of the problems.
0	The child: • does not attempt to solve the problems.

Intervention Activity

Record groups of ten and ones.

Materials For each pair: connecting cubes, 10-Frame (Activity Sheet 11), 1–6 number cube, white boards or recording sheets

- Organize children into pairs and explain that they will play a game that is like the Opening Activity.

- Give children the target number 30. Tell them that when one of them reaches this number or gets beyond it, the game is over and they play again.

- To play, children take turns rolling the number cube and placing that number of cubes on their 10-frame. After each roll, children add cubes to the 10-frame and record the total number of cubes. When the 10-frame is full, they connect the cubes to make a ten and place it to the left of the frame. Instruct children to record the total by counting and writing the tens (outside of the frame) and the ones (inside the frame). For example: 2 tens and 3 ones.

On-Level Activity

Record tens and some ones.

Materials For each child: 11 to 29 dry beans

- Put children into groups of 2 or 3 and give each child a different numbers of beans. Use amounts greater than 10 but less than 30. Have each child arrange his or her beans into groups of 10 and extra ones.

- Encourage children to record the number of tens they made. Ask each group to count by tens to determine the total number of tens they have.

- Groups then combine the leftover beans to see if they can create additional groups of ten and again find the total number of tens.

- You may want to have children put all beans together in a large group, redistribute them among members, and repeat the activity.

Challenge Activity

Make more than 9 tens.

Materials Optional: Hundreds Chart (Activity Sheet 19), 12 connecting cubes

As a preview to the next lesson, challenge children to find out how many cubes are equal to 10 tens, 11 tens, 12 tens. You might give them a hundreds chart, connecting cubes, or suggest that they make drawings. Encourage them to think about the strategies they used to find the total number of cubes and share these ideas with the class.

Lesson 18 (Student Book pages 82–85)

The 120 Chart

LESSON OBJECTIVES

- Count on from any number on the 120 chart.
- Connect counting on to addition.
- Count by 1s, 2s, and 5s within 120.

PREREQUISITE SKILLS

- Count by ones.
- Count by twos.
- Count on to add.

VOCABULARY

120 chart: a chart labeled with numbers from 1 to 120 set across 10 columns and down 12 rows

row: a horizontal arrangement of items in a chart

column: a vertical arrangement of items in a chart

During the lesson you will review the key term:

tens: groups of ten ones

THE LEARNING PROGRESSION

In Kindergarten, children learn the relationship between a quantity of objects and the number representing the quantity. They understand that the last number name said tells the number of objects counted. They count to 100 by 1s and 10s, count up from a given number, and write numbers from 0 to 20.

In Grade 1, children understand counting as a thinking strategy. They relate counting on to addition and subtraction and counting back to subtraction. They relate the counting sequence to the cardinality of numbers: each number is one more or one less than the number after or before. Children read and write numbers from 1 to 120 and use strategies that involve 10 as a benchmark number. **In this lesson,** children use a 120 chart to count up from any given number within 120. They look for patterns in the 120 chart that show relationships between numbers. They count up by 1s, 2s, and 5s and identify numbers that are 1, 2, or 5 more than a given number.

In Grade 2, children count within 1,000 and skip count by 5s, 10s, and 100s. Children read and write numbers to 1,000. They identify groups as having an odd or even number of objects.

■ Ready *Teacher Toolbox*

Teacher-Toolbox.com

	Prerequisite Skills	1.OA.C.5
Ready Lessons	✓ ✓ ✓	✓
Tools for Instruction	✓ ✓	✓
Interactive Tutorials	✓ ✓	✓

CCSS Focus

1.OA.C.5 Relate counting to addition and subtraction (e.g., by counting on 2 to add 2).

ADDITIONAL STANDARDS: **1.OA.C.6, 1.NBT.A.1** (*see page A36 for full text*)

STANDARDS FOR MATHEMATICAL PRACTICE: **SMP 2, 3, 5, 7, 8** (*see page A9 for full text*)

Opening Activity: The 120 Chart

Objective: Count on from any given number within 120.	**Materials** For display: 120 Chart

Overview

Children act out counting numbers from 1 to 10. They count on a 120 chart from given numbers.

Step by Step (10–15 minutes)

1 Act out counting 1 to 10.

- Arrange 10 chairs in a row at the front of the classroom. Have 10 children stand in front of the chairs.
- Together with the class, count aloud from 1 to 10 as the children sit down in the chairs one by one.
- When the number 10 is reached, the class repeats "10" again and the last child stands back up. Have the class count back aloud together from 10 to 1 as the children stand back up one by one.
- Repeat the activity, this time having children clap on each number as the class counts up from 1 to 10 and back from 10 to 1.

2 Display the 120 chart.

- Cover the bottom two rows of a classroom 120 chart so children see the numbers 1 to 100 on the chart.
- Point to the first row on the chart and ask children how it relates to the activity they just completed. [You can count up from 1 to 10 and back from 10 to 1 on it.]

3 Talk about the 120 chart.

- Have children name the numbers that the displayed chart starts and ends with. [1 and 100] Ask: *How do you think you can count numbers greater than 100?* [Start over with 1, 2, 3, and so on, but say "one hundred" in front of each number: 101, 102, 103, and so on.]
- Uncover the bottom two rows of the chart. Discuss how the two rows at the bottom are different from the rest of the chart. [They have 3 digits; they show numbers in the hundreds.] Count aloud from 100 to 120 with children, pointing to each number on the chart as the class counts it.

4 Use the 120 chart to count on from a given number.

- Ask children how the chart might be used to help them count. [You can start counting at any number on the chart. You can stop counting at any number.] Count aloud from 21 to 30 with children.
- Repeat counting aloud together with the class, starting at and ending on different numbers. For example, count from 11 to 25, 27 to 40, 52 to 56, 58 to 60, 84 to 91, 95 to 104, and so on.

Check for Understanding

Ask children the following questions: *How many numbers are across the first row of the chart?* [10] *How do you know?* [The numbers go from 1 to 10.] *Do you think there are 10 numbers in the next row?* [yes] *Why?* [Because there are the same amount of boxes in the next row.] Observe to see that children recognize that the last number in each row makes a ten.

STEP BY STEP

- Begin by asking children what they remember about the Opening Activity. Have a child retell what the class did with the 120 chart.

- Explain that this page is about the 120 chart, just like the Opening Activity. Read aloud the question.

- Direct children's attention to the Model It. Have children look at the first column in the 120 chart, pointing out that a column goes from top to bottom. Then ask children what is the same about the numbers in the column. [The numbers all end with "1;" all the numbers have 1 one.]

- Read the numbers in the column aloud. Then have children tell what is different about the numbers. [They each begin with a different number; the tens get higher by one.]

- Have children look at the third row in the chart. Point out that a row goes from left to right. Read aloud the numbers in the row, and have children describe how the numbers are alike and how they are different.

- Children should notice that all the numbers in the row begin with 2, or 2 tens, except for the last number, which begins with 3, or 3 tens. They should also notice that each number ends with a different number and may see that the ones get higher by one.

- Read the directive and two sentences and have children color the boxes of the numbers that have 2 ones and circle the numbers that have 3 tens. After they have completed their work, discuss the patterns they see. Guide children to see that the same patterns repeat in all the columns and rows of the chart.

Hands-On Activity

Materials For each pair: 120 Chart (Activity Sheet 23), crayons

Provide pairs of children with a 120 chart. Have them work together to color to find patterns on the 120 chart. Have children share their ideas with the class, explaining the patterns they have discovered. Different children will describe the same pattern differently. Guide the discussion to be sure all the ideas being suggested are understood.

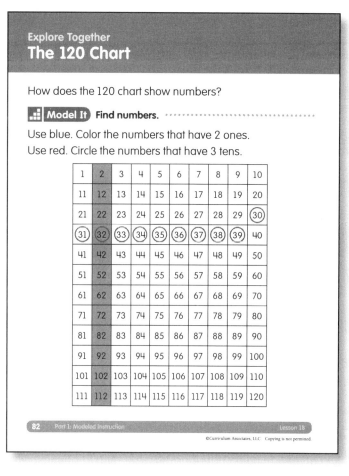

Explore Together
The 120 Chart

How does the 120 chart show numbers?

Model It Find numbers.

Use blue. Color the numbers that have 2 ones.
Use red. Circle the numbers that have 3 tens.

©Curriculum Associates, LLC   Copying is not permitted.

Mathematical Discourse

- *How do the numbers change in each row? In each column?*

   Children may say that in each row the ones change from 1 to 9 (1, 2, 3, 4, 5, 6, 7, 8, 9), until the last number, which ends in zero. They may also recognize that in the rows, the ones go up by 1. Children may say that as you go down each column, the tens go up by 1.

SMP Tip: Children carefully look for patterns and structures in the number system. Studying the relationship between the numbers in the columns and rows of the 120 chart helps children connect the numbers in the chart to the place-value concepts of tens and ones. (*SMP 7*)

STEP BY STEP

- Read aloud the question at the top of the page and the directive to count up.

- Direct children's attention to the Model It. Read the first two sentences. Have children count up 1 from 5 by first having them place their finger on the circled number, 5, then touching the colored number 6 with their finger. Have children count aloud as they do so: 5, 6.

- Ask: *How many numbers are colored next to the 5?* [1] *How many more than 5 is 6?* [1 more] Have children complete the sentence "5 and 1 more is 6." Relate the sentence to the circled 5 and the one colored square. Repeat for the circled number 18.

- Have children count up 2 and then 5 from the given numbers. Guide children by asking questions such as: *When you start at 62 (or 75) and count up 2, how many numbers are colored?* [2] *When you start at 85 (or 90) and count up 5, how many numbers are colored?* [5] *How many more than 75 is 77?* [2] *How many more than 90 is 95?* [5] *How do you know?* [I counted up.]

- After children complete the sentences in each problem, have them point to additional numbers in the rows and tell the number that is 1, 2, or 5 more. Ask them to explain their reasoning.

- **Error Alert** Read aloud the Talk About It. Children may see that Buzz is correct. Children who think Boom is correct may have difficulty with the transition between the tens on the number chart and counted 70 as one of the five counts: 70, 71, 72, 73, 74.

Mathematical Discourse

- *How is counting on 2 like adding 2?*

  They are both about 2 more. When you count on 2, you move two spaces on the number chart and stop at the number that is 2 more than the number you start with. When you add 2, you get the number that is 2 more than the number.

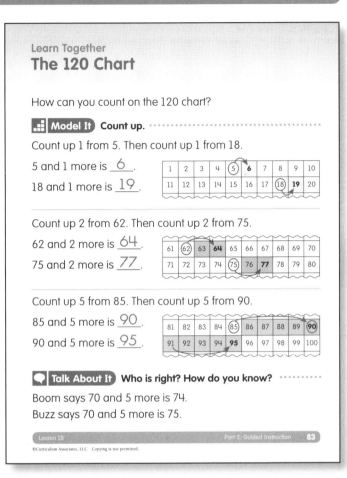

Learn Together
The 120 Chart

How can you count on the 120 chart?

Model It Count up.

Count up 1 from 5. Then count up 1 from 18.

5 and 1 more is __6__.

18 and 1 more is __19__.

Count up 2 from 62. Then count up 2 from 75.

62 and 2 more is __64__.

75 and 2 more is __77__.

Count up 5 from 85. Then count up 5 from 90.

85 and 5 more is __90__.

90 and 5 more is __95__.

Talk About It Who is right? How do you know?

Boom says 70 and 5 more is 74.

Buzz says 70 and 5 more is 75.

Lesson 18 · Part 2: Guided Instruction · 83

©Curriculum Associates, LLC · Copying is not permitted.

Visual Model

Materials For display: 120 Chart (Activity Sheet 23)

Use the classroom 120 chart to reinforce the concept of counting on by 1 and 2. Draw a circle around 43 on the chart. Say: *Let's count up by 1*. Move your finger one space to the right and stop on 44 as the children count: *43, 44*. Then demonstrate counting up by 2 by drawing a circle around 58 and moving your finger to point to 59 and 60. Have children count: *58, 59, 60*. Repeat, beginning at different numbers on the chart. Include starting at numbers such as 89, to give children practice transitioning between the decades on the chart.

STEP BY STEP

- Have children look at the section of the 120 chart at the top of the page. Discuss the numbers it shows.

- Direct children's attention to Problem 1. Have children circle the number 40 on the number chart. As children find 1 more, 2 more, and 5 more than 40, encourage them to see the relationship between the number they start with and the number of counts they make for each.

- As children find 1 more, 2 more, and 5 more than 55, ask them to explain how they know which number to stop at. [by counting up 1, 2, or 5; by counting the number of squares]

- For Problem 2, encourage children to move their fingers along the rows and columns of the chart at the top of the page as they count by 1, 2, and 5.

- As children begin, ask: *What number is 1 more than 33?* [34] *than 35?* [36] *How does using the number chart help you count?* [It can help me keep track of my counts. I know that the numbers in a row go up by one.]

- As children count by 2 and then 5, have them discuss the patterns they see. For counting by 2, they may say that they count every other number. For counting by 5, they may recognize that the ones number is either a 5 or a 0.

Concept Extension

Materials For each child: 120 Chart (Activity Sheet 23)

Distribute the 120 chart. Ask questions like the following and have children use their 120 charts to respond. Have them tell the answers without counting on the chart.

- *What number is 2 more than 16? 2 more than 70? 2 more than 109?*

- *What number is 5 more than 35? 5 more than 41? 5 more than 76?*

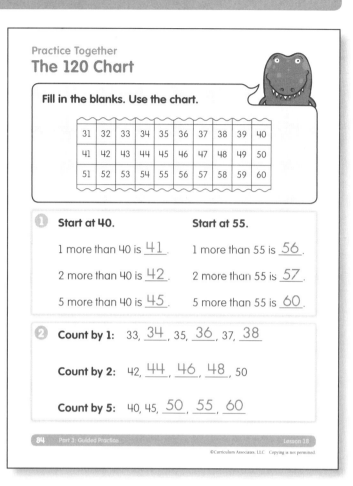

Practice Together
The 120 Chart

Fill in the blanks. Use the chart.

31	32	33	34	35	36	37	38	39	40
41	42	43	44	45	46	47	48	49	50
51	52	53	54	55	56	57	58	59	60

1 **Start at 40.**   **Start at 55.**

1 more than 40 is _41_ .   1 more than 55 is _56_ .

2 more than 40 is _42_ .   2 more than 55 is _57_ .

5 more than 40 is _45_ .   5 more than 55 is _60_ .

2 **Count by 1:**   33, _34_ , 35, _36_ , 37, _38_

Count by 2:   42, _44_ , _46_ , _48_ , 50

Count by 5:   40, 45, _50_ , _55_ , _60_

SMP Tip: By discussing and connecting relationships on the 120 chart, children begin to see how the sequence of numbers is related to the numeric relationships in the numbers. *(SMP 8)*

STEP BY STEP

- Before children work on this page, review some of the ways they used the 120 chart when counting. Emphasize that children are free to use whatever way helps them solve the problem.

- Read each problem aloud, then have children work independently to solve.

- For both Problems 3 and 4, observe to see if some children are having difficulty with numbers greater than 100.

- If time allows, after children have completed their work, introduce the Mathematical Discourse question to encourage discussion about the strategies they used.

Fluency Practice

Materials For display: 120 Chart (Activity Sheet 23)

Display the 120 chart. Have the class count on by 1, 2, and 5, using examples like the following.

- count by 1:
  start at 11 and end at 20
  start at 56 and end at 70

- count by 2:
  start at 2 and end at 30
  start at 88 and end at 110

- count by 5:
  start at 5 and end at 120
  start at 45 and end at 70

ELL Support

To present visual language support for children who need help distinguishing between a row and a column, provide a 120 chart labeled with the words "column" and "row." The labels should each include an arrow pointing to a column and a row.

Practice by Myself
The 120 Chart
Fill in the blanks. Use the chart.

91	92	93	94	95	96	97	98	99	100
101	102	103	104	105	106	107	108	109	110
111	112	113	114	115	116	117	118	119	120

3   **Start at 100.**   **Start at 115.**

1 more than 100 is 101.   1 more than 115 is 116.

2 more than 100 is 102.   2 more than 115 is 117.

5 more than 100 is 105.   5 more than 115 is 120.

4   **Count by 1:**   104, 105, 106, 107, 108, 109

     Count by 2:   98, 100, 102, 104, 106

     Count by 5:   95, 100, 105, 110, 115

Mathematical Discourse

- *How did you know what numbers to write to complete the sentences in Problem 3?*

  For finding "1 more," children may say they used the number chart and looked at the number to the right of the given number, or that they counted on by 1. For finding "2 more," children may share that they counted on by 2, or looked at every other number. For finding "5 more," children may suggest counting on by 5 or looking for numbers that end in either 5 or 0 as strategies.

Assessment and Remediation

- Ask children to tell which number on the 120 chart is 5 more than 65. [70]

- For children who are still struggling, use the chart below to guide remediation.

- After providing remediation, check children's understanding using the following problem: Which number is 2 more than 34? [36]

If the error is . . .	Children may . . .	To remediate . . .
66	have counted by 1 instead of 5.	Provide children with a 120 chart and have them circle 65 and 66. Guide them to see that 66 is 1 more than 65. Ask children to count up 5 to find 5 more than 65.
67	have counted by 2 instead of 5.	Provide children with a 120 chart and have them circle 65, color the five numbers to the left, and count the numbers. Then have them write: *5 more than 65 is 70.*
69	have started with 65 as the first counting number.	Provide children with a 120 chart and have them circle 65, then count on 5 as they touch and say each number: 66, 67, 68, 69, 70.

Hands-On Activity

Use a 120 chart to count by 2s and 5s.

Materials For each child: one blue and one yellow crayon, 120 Chart (Activity Sheet 23)

- Distribute the 120 chart and two crayons to each child.

- Have children count by 2 from 2 to 120 on the chart and color each square the same color.

- Have children count by 5 from 5 to 120 and color each square the same color.

- Tell children that some squares will be colored with more than one color.

- Discuss the patterns children see.

Challenge Activity

Find the difference between two numbers on a 120 chart.

Materials For each child: 120 Chart (Activity Sheet 23)

- Have children find 16 and 27 on the 120 chart. Ask: *How many more is 27 than 16?* [11] Have children explain the strategy they use to find the answer. Ask them whether they found the difference without counting.

- Have children find the differences for other pairs of numbers:

25 and 34 [9]	101 and 114 [13]
48 and 60 [12]	52 and 96 [44]
57 and 87 [30]	39 and 44 [5]
63 and 89 [26]	75 and 107 [32]
78 and 92 [14]	6 and 106 [100]

Lesson 19 (Student Book pages 86–89)

Understand 10 More and 10 Less

LESSON OBJECTIVES

- Mentally add and subtract 10 from any number within 120.

- Recognize that adding or subtracting a ten results in a change in the tens digit alone.

PREREQUISITE SKILLS

- Count to 120 by tens.

- Understand that 10 ones can be represented as 1 ten.

VOCABULARY

10 less: 1 less ten or 10 less ones than a given number

10 more: 1 more ten or 10 more ones than a given number

THE LEARNING PROGRESSION

In Kindergarten, children explore 10 as a group of objects within a teen number and count by tens to 100.

In Grade 1, children view 10 ones as a unit called a ten. They build on their "counting by tens" skills by mentally finding 10 more and 10 less than a number. **In this lesson,** children mentally add and subtract 10 to any number within 120. As they explore "10 more" and "10 less" with connecting cubes and on a 120 chart, they use the mental image formed to recognize that when adding or subtracting a ten, the tens digit increases or decreases by one respectively.

In Grade 2, children build on this concept, using it to add and subtract two-digit numbers. They extend the use of mental imagery through open number lines.

Ready *Teacher Toolbox*		Teacher-Toolbox.com
	Prerequisite Skills	*1.NBT.C.5*
Ready Lessons	✓ ✓ ✓	✓
Tools for Instruction	✓ ✓	✓
Interactive Tutorials	✓ ✓	✓

CCSS Focus

1.NBT.C.5 Given a two-digit number, mentally find 10 more or 10 less than the number, without having to count; explain the reasoning used.

ADDITIONAL STANDARDS: **1.NBT.B.2a, 1.NBT.B.2c** (*see page A36 for full text*)

STANDARDS FOR MATHEMATICAL PRACTICE: **SMP 2, 3, 5, 7, 8** (*see page A9 for full text*)

Opening Activity: Build 10 More or 10 Less

Objective: Explore the concept of 10 more and 10 less.	**Materials** For each pair: • 52 connecting cubes • white board

Overview

Children model a problem finding 10 more than a given number. They then explore the meaning of and strategies for finding 10 more and 10 less.

Step by Step (15–20 minutes)

1 Pose the problem.

- *There are 27 monkeys living in the zoo. There are 10 more birds than monkeys. How many birds live in the zoo?*

2 Solve the problem.

- Have children work in pairs to solve the problem using any strategy. Tell them to model the problem and solution with connecting cubes and write the number of monkeys and the number of birds on a white board.

- Watch as children complete the problem, ensuring they understand that to find the number of birds, 10 must be added to the number of monkeys.

3 Share strategies.

- Invite volunteers to share their results and explain the strategy they used by demonstrating it for the class to observe.

- Encourage children to ask questions by modeling with questions such as: *Why do you have 2 bars and 7 extra cubes instead of 27 cubes? Why did you add 10 ones to 27? Or: Why did you add 1 ten instead of 10 ones?*

4 Explore and extend.

- Compare the strategies children used. Discuss how adding 10 single cubes and 1 ten train resulted in the same answer.

- Tell children to show 42 with connecting cubes. Have them show 10 more in two different ways. Discuss how "10 more" implies adding 10, and explore the concept that 1 ten train is composed of 10 ones so adding 10 ones and 1 ten bar results in the same total.

- Have children show 42 again. Discuss how 10 were taken away from 52—either 10 ones or 1 bar of ten—therefore 42 is "10 less" than 52.

Check for Understanding

Provide children with 41 connecting cubes. Then pose the following problem: *Find 10 more than 31. Write the total on a white board.*

Watch children as they work, observe the strategies they employ. Some children may make trains of 10 and 1 extra cube to show 31. Others may count out 31 cubes. To find 10 more, some children may add another bar of 10, with others adding 10 cubes and recounting.

Encourage children to show each number using ten trains and extra ones, but do not expect them all to see 10 more as adding a ten.

Part 1: Modeled Instruction

STEP BY STEP

- Read aloud the question at the top of the page. Ask children why it is important to know about 10 more or 10 less than a number.

- Direct attention to the "42 and 10 more" on the student page. Ask children to describe how the pictures are like what they did in the Opening Activity. Ask: *How can you tell that 42 and 10 more is the same as 4 tens, 2 ones, and 1 ten?*

- As children explain their reasoning, reinforce the idea of "10 more" as 1 ten. Discuss how this relates to the addition sentence in the Think, 42 + 10 = 52, and to the picture of tens and ones below. Guide children to see that the two pictures of tens and ones show the same quantity.

- Present the Talk About It question. Encourage discussion by asking questions such as: *Does anyone have a different way to tell how the pictures are the same? Do you agree or disagree? Why?*

Hands-On Activity

Materials For each child: 52 connecting cubes, digit cards

- Ask children to show 42 cubes as tens and ones. Have them place the digit card "4" under the 4 trains and "2" under the 2 ones. Discuss how the 4 tells the number of tens shown.

- Tell children to add another ten train to their group of cubes and adjust the cards to show how many tens and ones they have now. Ask: *What card did you change? Why? Why didn't you need to change the card showing the ones?* Discuss how adding 1 ten to a number increases the tens by 1.

- Repeat the activity using other two-digit numbers, then for finding 10 less than a number.

SMP Tip: As children model 10 more and 10 less by adjusting digit cards, they recognize the repeated reasoning that allows them to increase or decrease the digit in the tens place. They then can connect it to the process of adding or subtracting 1 in single digit operations. *(SMP 8)*

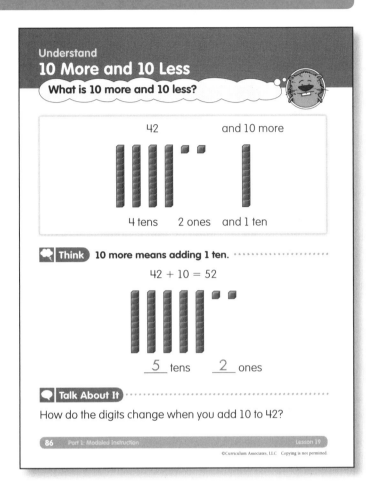

Mathematical Discourse

- *How is adding 10 to 40 like adding 1 to 4? How is it different?*

  Children may recognize that 40 + 40 is 50 and 4 + 1 is 5; 40 becomes 50 and 4 becomes 5, and in each case a 4 and 5 are used. They are different because 40 and 50 include a zero. Other children may focus on the number of tens. Adding 40 + 10 is like adding 4 tens and 1 ten which is like 4 + 1, the difference being they are tens and not ones.

ELL Support

In some languages the words for multiples of ten are more explicit than the English words. Many languages use words that describe them as 2 tens, 3 tens, etc. Help children relate the terms used in their native language to English by saying: *42 is 4 tens and 2. When you add a ten, you have 5 tens and 2, or 52.*

STEP BY STEP

Materials For each child: 120 Chart (Activity Sheet 23), 3 small objects to be used as markers

- Prior to introducing the activities on this page, provide each child with a 120 chart. Have them place a marker on 42 and a marker on 52.

- Then ask children to place a marker on the number 13. Have them count on 10 and place a marker where they land.

- Finally, ask children to place a marker on the number 76 and ask: *Where do you think you can find 10 more than 76? How do you know?*

- Discuss how, in each case, the number representing 10 more is found directly below the number on the chart. Ask: *Do you think this will work for finding 10 more than any number on the chart? Explain.*

- Encourage children to explore finding 10 more than several numbers, helping them to recognize that, as they move down on the chart, the tens place increases by 1 and the ones place is unchanged.

- Repeat the activity above, finding 10 less than the given numbers. Make sure children see that when moving up a row the tens digit decreases by 1 and the ones digit remains unchanged.

- Draw attention to the problems shown and explain to children that, on this page, only a section of a 120 chart is displayed for each problem.

- As children find 10 less than 37, project the rows shown. Emphasize the difference between adding 1 one and adding 1 ten by moving your finger from 37 to 38 and asking: *What happens when I move over one in this direction? How is it different from moving down one?*

- Help children articulate that moving to the right shows 1 more, so the change occurs in the ones digit while the digit in the tens place remains the same. Contrast this to the change that occurs in "10 more" and "10 less" as children complete Problems 1 and 2.

- Read the Talk About It. Encourage children to justify their responses.

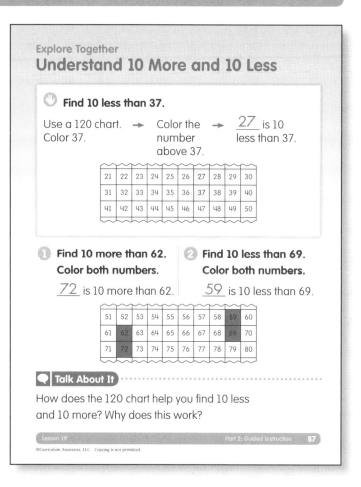

Mathematical Discourse

- *How is finding 10 more and 10 less on the 120 chart like adding and subtracting 10 cubes?*

  Children should notice that, in both cases, the tens digit changes by 1 while the ones digit remains the same. Some may recognize that moving down on the chart is like adding 10 ones, just as adding a ten train is like adding 10 ones. The inverse is true for 10 less.

Fluency Practice

Materials For each child: 120 Chart (Activity Sheet 23)

Use the 120 chart to reinforce the concept of 10 more and 10 less. Make sure children understand that they are to circle the number in the color as directed that is 10 greater than and 10 less than a given number.

STEP BY STEP

Materials For display: Classroom 120 chart

• Discuss each Connect It problem as a class using the discussion points outlined below.

Identify:

• This problem extends the concept of 10 more beyond 100. Ask children to retell how they found 10 more and 10 less in the previous activity. Then ask if it is possible to use the same strategy to find 10 more than a number beyond 100. Encourage them to explain their thinking.

• Compare and contrast the results of finding 10 more than a number beyond 100 by asking: *When you move down one, what changes? What stays the same?* To help children realize that the tens increase by 1, have them cover the 6 in both numbers to reveal the 9 and 10.

• Project a 120 chart. Shade in the number 108. Have children find 10 more on the chart. Discuss how both the 1 (in the hundreds place) and the 8 remain unchanged while the zero changed to a 1. Challenge children to think beyond the chart by asking: *If you added another row of numbers to this chart, what number do you think will be below 118? How do you know?*

Choose:

• Have children look at the numbers that end each sentence and the numbers in the yellow box. Ask them what they notice about these numbers. [The ones are all the same; the tens in some of the numbers are different.]

• As children complete each sentence, encourage them to explain how they decided which number to use. Ask questions such as: *How did you know to choose the number you did in the first sentence? How are the last two sentences alike? How are they different?*

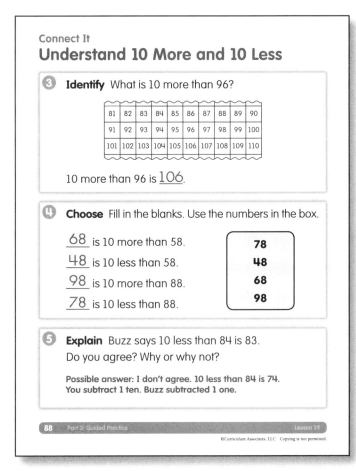

Connect It

Understand 10 More and 10 Less

3 **Identify** What is 10 more than 96?

81	82	83	84	85	86	87	88	89	90
91	92	93	94	95	96	97	98	99	100
101	102	103	104	105	106	107	108	109	110

10 more than 96 is __106__.

4 **Choose** Fill in the blanks. Use the numbers in the box.

__68__ is 10 more than 58.
__48__ is 10 less than 58.
__98__ is 10 more than 88.
__78__ is 10 less than 88.

| **78** |
| **48** |
| **68** |
| **98** |

5 **Explain** Buzz says 10 less than 84 is 83. Do you agree? Why or why not?

Possible answer: I don't agree. 10 less than 84 is 74. You subtract 1 ten. Buzz subtracted 1 one.

88   Part 3: Guided Practice   Lesson 19

©Curriculum Associates, LLC Copying is not permitted.

Explain:

• **Misconception Alert** You may wish to have children answer the questions in pairs before discussing them as a class. As they talk to each other, remind them of what they learned about the difference between adding 1 more and adding 10 more.

• Support children who offer explanations during class discussion with questions such as: *How is finding 10 less different from finding 1 less? What happens to the tens and the ones when you find 10 less? 1 less?*

SMP Tip: As children examine the 120 chart, emphasize how the structure of the chart enables them to mentally see "10 more" and "10 less" than a number. Ask them to close their eyes and "see" the number that is 10 more than 57; 10 less than 81. (*SMP 7*)

STEP BY STEP

- Tell children that they will complete this page independently.

- Read the directions aloud, making sure children understand what they are expected to do.

- In Part A, children make two 2-digit numbers, then write the numbers that are 10 more and 10 less.

- In Part B, children find 93 + 10 and explain the strategy they used.

- Observe children as they work through the problems. Ask questions such as the following to encourage thinking and problem-solving strategies:

    How many digits should you write on each card? Why?

    Does thinking about the cubes or the 120 chart help you find 10 more or 10 less? How?

    What happens to a number when you add/subtract 10? Why does that happen?

    What is the easiest way for you to think about 10 more than 93? Can you draw a picture of it?

    Do you think 10 more than 93 will be more than 100 or less than 100? Why?

Show What I Know

Understand 10 More and 10 Less

6 **Think about 10 more and 10 less.**

   A: Use digit cards to make numbers.

   `0` `1` `2` `3` `4` `5` `6` `7` `8` `9`

   Write a number. Find 10 less and 10 more than your number.
   Possible answer:

   | 3 | 6 |

   10 less than _36_ is _26_.
   10 more than _36_ is _46_.

   Write a different number. Find 10 less and 10 more than your number.
   Possible answer:

   | 8 | 9 |

   10 less than _89_ is _79_.
   10 more than _89_ is _99_.

   B: Find 93 + 10. Tell how you know.

   **93 + 10 = ** _103_   Possible answer:
   On the 120 chart, 103
   is 10 more than 93.

SCORING RUBRICS

Expectations for 4–3 Points

Points	Expectations
4	The child: • writes one digit on each card and accurately records 10 more and 10 less. • correctly identifies 103 as the total and provides an accurate explanation of the strategy employed.
3	The child: • writes one digit on each card and records 10 more and 10 less but may request to use cubes or a 120 chart to check accuracy. • correctly identifies 103 as the total but provides only a partial or unclear explanation of the strategy used.

Expectations for 2–0 Points

Points	Expectations
2	The child: • writes digits on the cards, but inaccurately records 10 more and 10 less. • correctly identifies 103 as the total but provides an unclear explanation of the strategy used.
1	The child: • may write one or more digits on each card, but there is no connection between the numbers shown on the cards and the 10 more or 10 less that is recorded. • does not find the correct total and may not attempt to provide an explanation.
0	The child: • does not attempt to write digits or complete the problems.

Intervention Activity

Build 10 more or 10 less.

Materials: For each child: "10 more" and "10 less" cards, Teen Number Cards (Activity Sheet 22), 30 counters

- Provide each child with a set of counters, teen number cards, and the "10 more" and "10 less" cards.

- Have children select a card containing a teen number and instruct them to model the number with counters. Encourage them to line up the group of ten counters.

- Children then randomly select a "10 more" or "10 less" card. They create another model next to the original showing 10 more or 10 less than that number. Remind them to line up the tens.

- Have children record on paper or a white board the two numbers and write either "10 more" or "10 less" next to the number that shows the result of the addition or subtraction they performed.

On-Level Activity

Model 10 more and 10 less.

Materials For each pair: workmat containing two attached rectangles, 2 sets of digit cards, "10 more" and "10 less" cards, base-ten blocks, 120 Chart (Activity Sheet 23)

- Place children in pairs, providing them with a set of materials.

- One child selects two digit cards and places them in the boxes on the workmat to show a 2-digit number. The partner chooses a "10 more" or "10 less" card. The first child selects a digit card to make the number show 10 more or 10 less by placing the new digit on top of the original one.

- Partners work together to model both numbers and/or find them in the 120 chart to check the answer. If correct, they clear the board and roles are reversed.

- If incorrect, they find the digit card that will make the number correct and place it on the workmat. The board is cleared, roles are reversed and play resumes.

Challenge Activity

Find multiples of 10 more and 10 less.

Materials For each child: worksheet including several problems such as: Find 20 more than 36, Find 40 less than 95, and challenge problems such as: Find 30 more than 127. For more advanced children, include adding and subtracting multiples of 10 to numbers in the 200–1,000 range.

- Distribute a worksheet to each child, instructing them to find the solutions and show the strategy they used for each one. Challenge them to utilize a variety of strategies, reminding them to draw a picture of what they "see" in their brain when finding each sum or difference.

- Challenge children to complete the work mentally without the support of physical models or a 120 chart. Tell them that they can draw pictures of either of those models, if that is what they "see" in their brain, but to rely on the mental rather than physical image.

Lesson 20 (Student Book pages 90–93)

Add and Subtract Tens

LESSON OBJECTIVES

- Count tens as 1 ten, 2 tens, 3 tens, . . . tens or as 10, 20, 30 . . .
- Add multiples of 10 to multiples of 10 and subtract multiples of 10 from multiples of 10.
- Relate adding tens to adding ones.

PREREQUISITE SKILLS

- count by tens to 100
- represent a multiple of 10 as a number of groups of ten.

VOCABULARY

During the lesson you will review the key term:

tens: groups of ten ones

THE LEARNING PROGRESSION

In Kindergarten, children organize 10 objects into a group of 10 and count by tens to 100.

In Grade 1, children view 10 ones as a unit called a ten. They compose two-digit numbers into groups of tens and some ones. **In this lesson,** children model the relationship between groups of 10 and an equal number of units of 10 and apply it to adding and subtracting multiples of 10. Children compare physical/visual representations to number sentences and analyze the ways in which the models relate to each other. As they recognize how adding tens and adding ones correlate to each other, children move beyond physical and visual models to compute mentally.

In Grade 2, children apply concepts of adding and subtracting within place values to number sentences involving regrouping where a ten may be composed or decomposed to add or subtract a two-digit number.

Ready *Teacher Toolbox*   Teacher-Toolbox.com

	Prerequisite Skills	1.NBT.C.6
Ready Lessons	✓ ✓ ✓	✓
Tools for Instruction	✓ ✓	✓
Interactive Tutorials		✓ ✓ ✓

CCSS Focus

1.NBT.C.6 Subtract multiples of 10 in the range 10–90 from multiples of 10 in the range 10–90 (positive or zero differences), using concrete models or drawings and strategies based on place value, properties of operations, and/or the relationship between addition and subtraction; relate the strategy to a written method and explain the reasoning used.

ADDITIONAL STANDARDS: **1.NBT.B.2, 1.NBT.C.4** *(see page A36 for full text)*

STANDARDS FOR MATHEMATICAL PRACTICE: **SMP 1, 2, 3, 4, 5, 6, 7, 8** *(see page A9 for full text)*

Opening Activity: One Ten, Ten Ones

Objective: Relate counting groups of 10 to adding multiples of 10.	**Materials** For each pair: • foam shapes, beads, or other art material • base-ten blocks or connecting cubes • 120 Chart (Activity Sheet 23)

Overview

Children solve a problem, model the addition with base-ten blocks, and connect counting tens to addition of multiples of 10.

Step by Step (20–30 minutes)

1 Pose the problem.

- Say: *Buzz uses 30 foam shapes (or other art material) for his art project. He wants to use 20 more. How many shapes does Buzz use altogether?*

2 Solve the problem.

- Have children work with a partner to find a solution to the problem. Make varied counters, 120 charts, and white boards available. Remind children to use whatever they need to help them solve.

- Watch children as they work, taking note of the strategies and/or materials they use. Provide suggestions for ways to get started to struggling pairs, but generally use this time to observe only.

3 Share strategies.

- Invite volunteers to share their solution and strategy with the class. Make sure all the strategies children used are represented.

- Help children recognize that not only do all the strategies lead to the same solution, but some of the strategies also use the same reasoning. For instance, finding 30 on a 120 chart and counting on 2 more tens is similar to taking 3 tens and counting on 2 more tens.

4 Connect counting methods.

- Project a group of 30 objects, organize them into groups of 10, and lay a tens block above one of the groups. Ask: *How is this ten the same as the group of 10? How is it different?* Discuss that both show a group of 10 but the tens block is one piece.

- Count the groups of objects together (*10, 20, 30*) writing the numbers on cards as children count. Place these cards below the groups. Then count the tens blocks together (*1 ten, 2 tens, 3 tens*) recording on cards as you count, and placing them below the tens blocks.

- Compare the recorded numbers, asking how they are the same and how they are different. Switch the cards, placing 10, 20, 30 below the tens blocks and 1 ten, 2 tens, 3 tens below the groups. Ask: *How do the numbers shown count these groups?*

- Lead children to see that since both the objects and tens blocks are in groups of 10, they can be counted either way.

- Ask: *If I add 2 more tens blocks, how many blocks will I have? If I add 2 more groups of (objects), how many (objects) will I have? How many groups will I have?*

Check for understanding:

Provide children with the following problem:

Show 20 and 10 more with either counters or tens blocks. Write the number of blocks (or counters) both ways.

As children work, observe those who connect adding tens to adding ones. Use the Hands-On Activity on page 151 and the Visual Models on page 151 and 153 for children who may require additional support to solidify this concept.

STEP BY STEP

- Revisit the Opening Activity, discussing how tens can be counted as 10, 20, 30. . . . or as 1 ten, 2 tens, 3 tens. . . . Have children retell the strategies they used to find 20 and 10 more. Ask them to describe how they used the two counting methods to find a solution to the problem.

- You may wish to engage children in a quick counting-by-10s warm-up. Project a tens block and invite children to count with you as you add 1 tens block at a time up to 10 blocks, or 100. Then count back to 0 as each block is removed.

- Direct attention to the erasers shown at the top of the page, comparing them to the Opening Activity. Ask children how they might make this problem easier to solve. Listen for suggestions of grouping erasers into tens or using tens blocks to count. Ask the Mathematical Discourse question to reinforce the idea of modeling with blocks.

- Discuss how the Model It represents the erasers. Use the Hands-On Activity to help children connect adding tens blocks to adding multiples of 10 as they complete the number sentence.

Mathematical Discourse

- *Why might it be easier to add blocks of ten rather than add all the erasers?*

  The blocks are already grouped into 10, which is easier than circling groups of 10 erasers. It is easier to see how many blocks there are than how many erasers there are. Some children may notice that 5 tens show 50, which is easier than seeing 50 erasers.

Hands-On Activity

Materials For each child: 5 tens blocks, Tens Cards (Activity Sheet 24)

Have children model the addition problem 30 + 20 with tens blocks, placing the tens cards under each group. Ask: *What part of the number on the card tells how many blocks there are?* Then have children place a finger on the zero in each number. Ask: *What is 3 + 2? What is 30 + 20? How do the digits help you add tens?* Repeat the above activity using several other addition sentences.

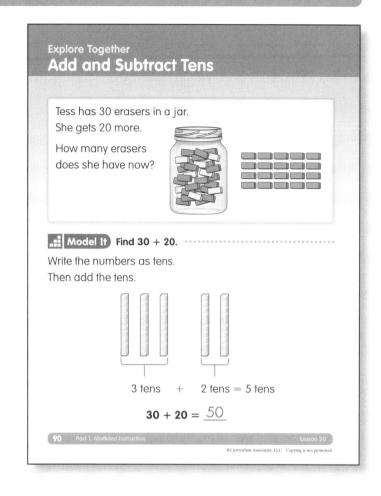

Visual Model

Materials For display: 50 connecting cubes

- Display 2 trains of 10 connecting cubes each and ask: *How many cubes do you see?* [20] *How many trains?* [2] *Add 3 more trains and ask: How many cubes did I add?* [30] *How many trains did I add?* [3]

- Recite together: *2 tens and 3 tens makes 5 tens; 20 and 30 is 50.*

- Display groups of 4 trains and 2 trains, encouraging children to recite together: *4 tens and 2 tens makes 6 tens; 40 and 20 is 60.* Repeat with varied multiples of ten.

STEP BY STEP

- Read aloud the problem at the top of the page. Say: *I don't see 7 tens. I just see lots of berries.* Ask: *How is 70 equal to 7 tens when there are no tens showing?* Reinforce the concept that within 70 are 7 groups of ten. Allow children who need additional support to count and circle the groups of 10 in 70 and 40.

- Direct children's attention to the Model It. Explain that the picture shows quick drawings of tens, where each stick represents one tens block. Review how both the addition and subtraction number sentences model the problem by encouraging children to share how they used addition to help them solve subtraction in previous lessons.

- Prior to completing the Model It, use the Concept Extension below to strengthen the connection to modeling a problem involving a missing addend.

- As children discuss Talk About It, suggest that they model both subtractions with blocks to justify their responses. Emphasize that "60" is another way to describe "6 tens," making both Buzz and Boom correct.

Concept Extension

Model a Missing Addend.

Materials For each child: 120 Chart (Activity Sheet 23), crayons or markers in two colors

- Give each child a 120 chart and two crayons or markers. Have children circle the number on the chart that tells how many berries Julie picks. Demonstrate how to use a marker of one color to draw a line through each row up to 70. Discuss how this shows all of Julie's berries.

- Then have children circle the number that shows how many berries Al picks and use the other marker to draw a line through each row up to 40.

- Ask: *What shows how many more berries Julie picks? How can you find out how many more there are?* Relate counting the groups of 10 that fall between 40 and 70 to finding a missing addend and discuss how it models subtraction.

- Use an interactive white board or project a clean chart and repeat the activity several times using other numbers.

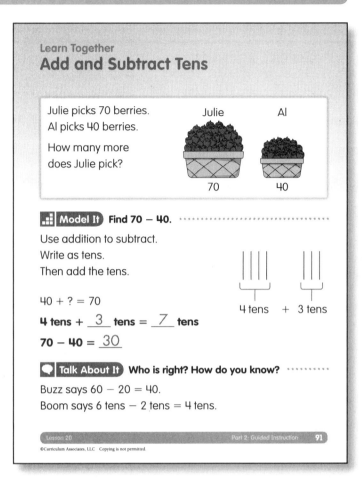

Mathematical Discourse

- *What are some other ways to find the answer to the problem on this page?*

  Some children may count on using their fingers to keep track of the number of tens between 40 and 70. Others may count backwards from 70 to 40. Some may suggest putting 4 tens blocks on top of 4 of the 7 blocks and count the rods that aren't covered.

SMP Tip: As children explore the many ways to model the problems in this lesson, they recognize that physical and visual models build an understanding of the number sentences that represent a problem. They also recognize the structure involved in representing a subtraction as a missing addend. *(SMP 4, SMP 7)*

STEP BY STEP

- Read the practice problem aloud. Use tens blocks to model both operations shown and ask the Mathematical Discourse question to help children see how the two number sentences represent the same situation.

- Use the Visual Model below to help children connect a familiar model to the problem situations found on this page.

- For Problem 1, reinforce children's understanding that both number sentences represent the 3 groups of flowers by displaying the counting cards recorded in the Opening Activity. Ask questions such as: *Which cards could I place below the blue flowers? The groups of yellow flowers? Are there any cards I could place below all the flowers? Why?*

- For Problem 2, encourage children to use the space provided to show how they thought about the problem. Have children share their strategies with the class, explaining what they did.

Visual Model

Show children the number bond:

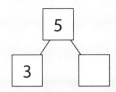

Remind children of how they used the number bond in previous lessons to solve a subtraction. Review methods they use to find the missing number.

Show the number bond:

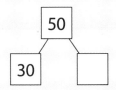

Discuss how the numbers in this number bond compare to those in the first bond. Relate 50 to 5 tens and 30 to 3 tens and ask: *How does knowing how to solve the first number bond help you solve the second one?*

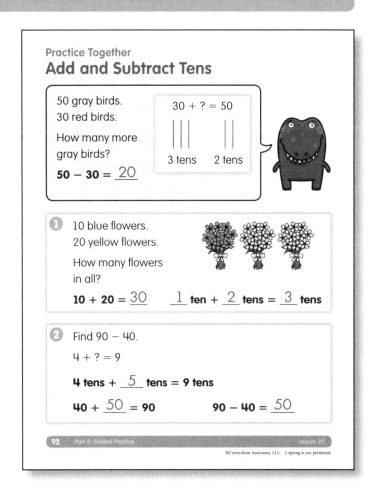

Mathematical Discourse

- *How do the number sentences describe the problem?*

  Since there are 50 gray birds, when you take away the number of red birds, what is left are how many more gray birds there are. Since there are 30 red birds, you can put together the number of red birds and how many more gray birds to make 50 gray birds in all.

Fluency Practice

Add and subtract multiples of 10.

Materials: For each child: Tens Cards (Activity Sheet 24)

Instruct children to select any two numbers from those shown to write a number sentence, reminding them to attend to the operation sign and making sure that each number sentence is different from the others they made. Encourage children to use any method or strategy to solve the problems.

STEP BY STEP

- Before children work on this page, review how tens blocks, number bonds, and the 120 chart help them add groups of ten. Emphasize that children are free to use whatever way helps them solve the problem.

- Point out that the problems on this page are similar to the problems the children worked together on the previous page.

- Read each problem aloud, then have children work independently to solve.

- You may wish to draw attention to the model in Problem 3, asking children how the ten sticks are related to the paper clips described in the problem.

- For Problem 4, observe to see if children are drawing 30 basketballs or representing them with ten sticks or other representations of ten.

> **SMP Tip:** As children work to add multiples of ten in Problem 4, encourage those children who draw 30 balls to organize them in a way that makes it easy to count accurately and check the precision of their calculation. (*SMP 6*)

- For those children who solve the addition problem by counting on by ones and making 10 marks for each count, suggest that they circle the group of ten marks to represent one ten.

- Encourage children to use the space provided to show the strategy they used to solve Problem 5. Ask those who used a strategy other than a visual model to explain the strategy they employed.

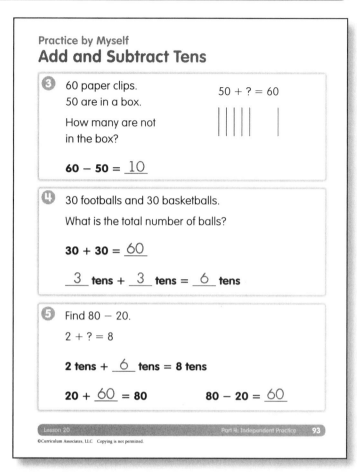

ELL Support

Some children may struggle with comprehending the language used in a word problem. You may wish to write each sentence of the two problems on this page on a separate line followed by a picture that represents it. Then underline the important words.

Assessment and Remediation

- Ask children to solve the addition sentence 20 + ___ = 70 and show their thinking. [50]

- For children who are still struggling, use the chart below to guide remediation.

- After providing remediation, check children's understanding using the following problem: Find the answer to 60 − 20 in two ways. [Answers will vary.]

If the error is . . .	Children may . . .	To remediate . . .
90	have added 20 + 70	Have children model the addition with blocks or on a 120 chart, reminding them of the meaning of the equal sign. Compare the model to their solution, discussing how their answer is one of the two numbers whose sum is 70.
60	have included 20 in their counts when counting on by tens.	Show children a 120 chart. Circle 20 and have children draw a line through each row to 20. Circle 70 and have children count on with you as you swipe your finger along each row. Explain that the row of 20 has already been counted so it isn't part of the counts when counting on.
5	have found the solution for 2 + ___ = 7.	Write: 2 tens + 5 tens = 7 tens. Praise the strategy children used reminding them that the 5 they found is 5 tens or 50. Return to their solution and ask if it makes sense. Have them calculate 20 + 5 to find that 25 is not equal to 70.

Hands-On Activity

Construct number sentences.

Materials For each pair: 2 sets of 10–120 multiples-of-ten cards, workmats containing an addition and a subtraction open number sentence, extra blank cards, tens blocks, 120 Chart (Activity Sheet 23)

- Place children with a partner and give each child a set of cards.

- One partner chooses two cards to create an addition or subtraction sentence, placing them in the appropriate open number sentence. The other partner finds the solution to the sentence and places it on the mat. Check using blocks or the 120 chart.

- The first partner reorganizes the numbers to create the inverse sentence. Together, partners check that the sentence is correct.

- Children may challenge themselves with sums greater than 120 by writing the sum on a blank card.

Challenge Activity

Construct advanced number sentences.

Materials For each pair: 2 sets of 10–200 multiples-of-ten cards, workmats containing an addition and a subtraction open number sentence, extra blank cards

- Place children with a partner and give each child a set of cards. Instruct them to complete the activity as in the Hands-On Activity on the left.

- Children will notice their cards include numbers beyond 120. Tell them that their challenge is to work with those larger numbers. If they require a greater challenge, provide them with multiples-of-ten cards greater than 200. They may use the blank cards to record sums that exceed the numbers on their cards.

- Challenge children to compute without the aid of blocks or 120 charts; however, make them available.

Unit 4 Review

Solve the problems.

1 35 ducks and 2 more ducks.

2 more than 35 is __37__ .

23	24	25	26	27	28
33	34	35	36	37	38
43	44	45	46	47	48

2 52 paper clips. 10 are in a box.
How many are not in the box?

41	42	43	44	45	46	47	48	49	50
51	52	53	54	55	56	57	58	59	60
61	62	63	64	65	66	67	68	69	70

52 − 10 = __42__

3 **86 + 10 =** __96__ 　|　 **4** __70__ **= 80 − 10**

5 **Count by 1: 108,** __109__ **, 110,** __111__ **,** __112__ **, 113**

6 The number of birds is the same as 6 tens.

Draw 6 tens.

Children draw six tens.

6 tens is __6__ groups of 10.　6 tens is __60__ ones.
There are __60__ birds.

7 Jo has 24 markers.

24 is __2__ tens and __4__ ones.

Bo has 10 more than Jo.　Mo has 10 fewer than Jo.
__34__ = 24 + 10　　　24 − 10 = __14__
Bo has __34__ markers.　Mo has __14__ markers.

STEP BY STEP

- Have children solve the problems individually and show their work. Emphasize that children are free to use whatever way helps them solve the problems.

- Circulate and observe children's work. Problems 1 and 2 are based on the 120 Chart. For children who struggle, discuss the ways to count by ones, twos, and tens on the chart.

- If children have difficulty drawing tens for Problem 6, review that 1 ten is 10 ones. Consider showing children a tens block and and having them brainstorm fast ways to draw tens using lines or rectangles.

- **Error Alert** Look for children who add or subtract 1 instead of 10 in Problems 2, 3, 4, 7, and 8. Guide them to understand that "1 ten" is the same as "10 ones." Have them identify where in the number the tens are written. Emphasize the difference between the tens and ones places.

STEP BY STEP

- On this page, children draw several tens, then use this number to complete a problem that involves subtracting 10.

- Direct children to complete the Put It Together on their own.

- Read the directions and task aloud. Make sure children understand what they need to do to complete the task.

- As children work on their own, observe their progress and understanding. Respond to their questions and provide additional support as needed.

- Have children share their drawing and problem with the class. Guide them to make a connection between their drawing and the numbers they wrote in the word problem.

- Have children demonstrate and justify the strategies they used to solve the problem.

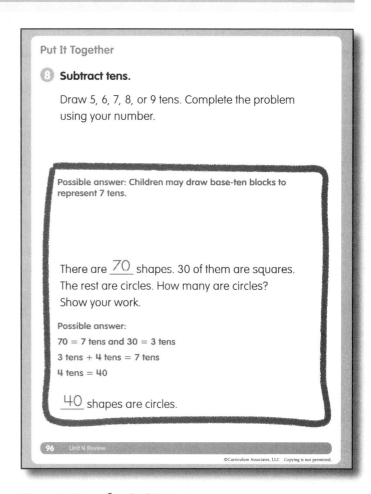

Put It Together

8 **Subtract tens.**

Draw 5, 6, 7, 8, or 9 tens. Complete the problem using your number.

Possible answer: Children may draw base-ten blocks to represent 7 tens.

There are _70_ shapes. 30 of them are squares. The rest are circles. How many are circles? Show your work.

Possible answer:

70 = 7 tens and 30 = 3 tens

3 tens + 4 tens = 7 tens

4 tens = 40

_40_ shapes are circles.

96　Unit 4 Review

©Curriculum Associates, LLC　Copying is not permitted.

SCORING RUBRICS

Expectations for 4–3 Points

Points	Expectations
4	The child: • draws the same number of tens as the number in the problem. • uses an appropriate strategy to subtract 30 and correctly solves the problem.
3	The child: • may draw the same number of tens as their number in the problem. • may use an appropriate strategy to subtract 30, but with a minor computation error.

Expectations for 2–0 Points

Points	Expectations
2	The child: • may not draw the same number of tens as the number in the problem. • may show signs of using a strategy to subtract 30, but the work has some errors.
1	The child: • may not draw the same number of tens as the number in the problem or does not draw any tens. • may not show signs of using a strategy to subtract 30 and the work has many errors.
0	The child: • does not attempt to complete the task.

Unit 5: Number and Operations in Base Ten—Tens and Ones

Which lessons are students building upon?

Kindergarten, Lesson 21
Understand Teen Numbers
K.NBT.A.1, K.CC.A.2, K.CC.A.3, K.CC.B5

Kindergarten, Lesson 24
Count to 100 by Tens
K.CC.A.1, K.CC.A.2

Kindergarten, Lesson 25
Count to 100 by Ones
K.CC.A.1, K.CC.A.2

Kindergarten, Lesson 5
Compare Within 5
K.CC.A.3, K.CC.B.4c, K.CC.C.6, K.CC.C.7

Kindergarten, Lesson 12
Compare Within 10
K.CC.B.4c, K.CC.C.6, K.CC.C.7

Kindergarten, Lesson 25
Count to 100 by Ones
K.CC.A.1, K.CC.A.2

Kindergarten, Lesson 22
Count Teen Numbers
K.CC.A.3, K.CC.B.5, K.CC.A.2, K.NBT.A.1

Kindergarten, Lesson 24
Count to 100 by Tens
K.CC.A.1, K.CC.A.2

Kindergarten, Lesson 25
Count to 100 by Ones
K.CC.A.1, K.CC.A.2

Kindergarten, Lesson 23
Make Teen Numbers
K.NBT.A.1, K.CC.A.2, K.CC.A.3

Kindergarten, Lesson 24
Count to 100 by Tens
K.CC.A.1, K.CC.A.2

Kindergarten, Lesson 25
Count to 100 by Ones
K.CC.A.1, K.CC.A.2

Kindergarten, Lesson 23
Make Teen Numbers
K.NBT.A.1, K.CC.A.2, K.CC.A.3

Kindergarten, Lesson 24
Count to 100 by Tens
K.CC.A.1, K.CC.A.2

Kindergarten, Lesson 25
Count to 100 by Ones
K.CC.A.1, K.CC.A.2

Unit 5

Which lessons are students preparing for?

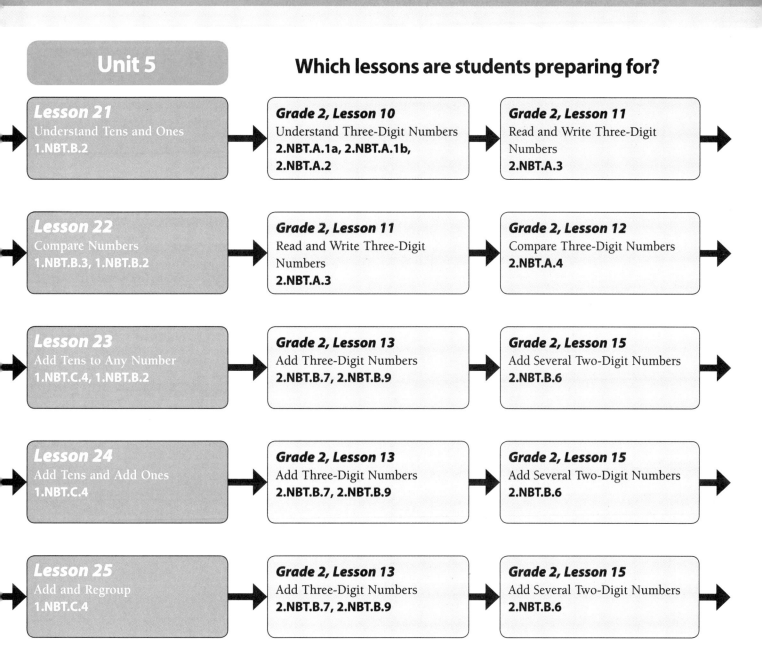

Lesson 21
Understand Tens and Ones
1.NBT.B.2

→ **Grade 2, Lesson 10**
Understand Three-Digit Numbers
2.NBT.A.1a, 2.NBT.A.1b, 2.NBT.A.2

→ **Grade 2, Lesson 11**
Read and Write Three-Digit Numbers
2.NBT.A.3 →

Lesson 22
Compare Numbers
1.NBT.B.3, 1.NBT.B.2

→ **Grade 2, Lesson 11**
Read and Write Three-Digit Numbers
2.NBT.A.3

→ **Grade 2, Lesson 12**
Compare Three-Digit Numbers
2.NBT.A.4 →

Lesson 23
Add Tens to Any Number
1.NBT.C.4, 1.NBT.B.2

→ **Grade 2, Lesson 13**
Add Three-Digit Numbers
2.NBT.B.7, 2.NBT.B.9

→ **Grade 2, Lesson 15**
Add Several Two-Digit Numbers
2.NBT.B.6 →

Lesson 24
Add Tens and Add Ones
1.NBT.C.4

→ **Grade 2, Lesson 13**
Add Three-Digit Numbers
2.NBT.B.7, 2.NBT.B.9

→ **Grade 2, Lesson 15**
Add Several Two-Digit Numbers
2.NBT.B.6 →

Lesson 25
Add and Regroup
1.NBT.C.4

→ **Grade 2, Lesson 13**
Add Three-Digit Numbers
2.NBT.B.7, 2.NBT.B.9

→ **Grade 2, Lesson 15**
Add Several Two-Digit Numbers
2.NBT.B.6 →

Lesson 21 (Student Book pages 98–101)

Understand Tens and Ones

LESSON OBJECTIVES

- Represent two-digit numbers as tens and ones.
- Decompose a two-digit number as some tens and some ones in multiple ways.
- Model a two-digit number in multiple ways.

PREREQUISITE SKILLS

- Count by tens to 100.
- Represent ten ones as one ten.

VOCABULARY

digit: any of the ten symbols used in the base-ten numeration system 0, 1, 2, 3, 4, 5, 6, 7, 8, 9

place value: the value of the place of a digit, such as tens and ones

During the lesson you will review the key terms:

ones: single units or objects

tens: groups of ten ones

THE LEARNING PROGRESSION

In Kindergarten, children decompose numbers from 11–19 using objects or drawings, understanding that these numbers are composed of a group of ten ones and one to nine additional ones.

In Grade 1, children extend their understanding of two-digit numbers to include those beyond 19. They also learn to see 10 as 10 ones or 1 ten. **In this lesson,** children decompose two-digit numbers into groups of tens and ones, representing them in multiple ways. They recognize that the digit in the tens place of a two-digit number denotes a number of tens and they write two-digit numbers by placing each digit in the appropriate place value location. The focus on tens and ones continues in grade 2 as children learn to compare and add two-digit numbers.

In Grade 2, children build on place-value concepts as they decompose two- and three-digit numbers and apply the decomposition to add and subtract numbers with regrouping.

Ready *Teacher Toolbox*

Teacher-Toolbox.com

	Prerequisite Skills	1.NBT.B.2a, 1.NBT.B.2c
Ready Lessons	✓ ✓ ✓	✓
Tools for Instruction	✓	
Interactive Tutorials		✓ ✓

CCSS Focus

1.NBT.B.2 Understand that the two digits of a two-digit number represent amounts of tens and ones. Understand the following special cases:
  a. 10 can be thought of as a bundle of ten ones—called a "ten."
  c. the numbers 10, 20, 30, 40, 50, 60, 70, 80, and 90 refer to one, two, three, four, five, six, seven, eight, or nine tens (and 0 ones).

STANDARDS FOR MATHEMATICAL PRACTICE: *SMP 2, 3, 5, 6, 7, 8 (see page A9 for full text)*

Opening Activity: Counting with Tens

Objective: Explore the many ways to count and represent two-digit numbers.	**Materials** For each child: • 45 connecting cubes • white boards

Overview

Children count a set of cubes by combining groups of ten and counting the remaining cubes.

Step by Step (20–25 minutes)

1 Set the stage.

- Ask children to guess the number of cubes they have. Discuss the many ways they might count the cubes, e.g., by ones, twos, fives, tens. Remind them of previous lessons where they made bars of ten.

2 Pose the problem.

- Explain that children will count their cubes by making different numbers of tens.

- First they make 1 bar of 10 cubes, count the tens, and then count the ones that remain. Ask children to record the number of tens and ones they counted on their white boards.

- Have children continue the activity by next making 2 bars of 10 cubes, and finally 3 bars of 10 cubes. Each time, they record the number of tens and ones they count.

3 Share work.

- Invite volunteers to share the different numbers of tens and ones they counted. Discuss how making tens helps them count the cubes.

- Write "32 cubes" on the board. Under it write the headings "Tens" and "Ones." In the tens column write 0. Ask children how many cubes they have if they make no bars of ten. Record 32 in the ones place.

- Now record a 1 in the tens column and ask children how many extra ones there are if they make 1 ten. Record 22 in the ones column. Repeat with 2 and 3 tens.

- Discuss how these can all be ways to show 32 cubes. Lead children to notice that each time you add 1 to the Tens column, you take 10 from the Ones column. Ask: *Which of these ways makes it easiest to count all the cubes? Why?*

Check for Understanding

Provide the children with the following problem:

Boom has 4 tens and 5 ones; Buzz has 3 tens and 15 ones. Draw a picture to show how Boom and Buzz could have the same number of cubes.

Allow children to model with cubes, if necessary. Some children may be able to model this situation with cubes, but may struggle to draw a picture. The lesson provides many opportunities to further develop this understanding.

STEP BY STEP

- Ask volunteers to share their drawings from the Opening Activity and explain their reasoning. Listen to their explanations, helping them articulate using the terms tens and ones.

- Read the question at the top of the page and ask children how the base-ten blocks remind them of the Opening Activity. Have them circle groups of ten in the single ones to recognize that the number of blocks in each group is the same; they are just organized differently.

- Read Think with children and ask them to describe the difference between the base-ten blocks on the left and on the right. Guide them to recognize that these show the same number of cubes with different numbers of bundled tens. Have children circle all the groups of 10 that they see and then ask the Mathematical Discourse question.

- For Talk About It, children should be able to use what they have learned in the Opening Activity and on this page to find that 37 is 3 tens 7 ones, 2 tens 17 ones, and 1 ten 27 ones.

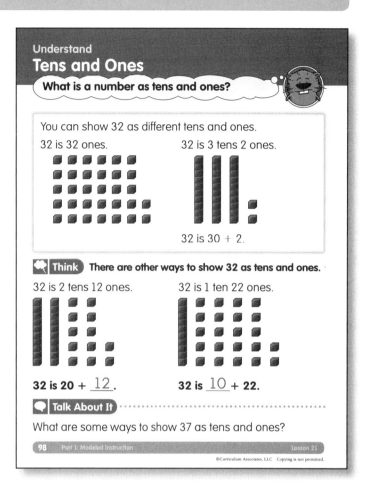

Hands-On Activity

Materials For each child: Hundreds Chart (Activity Sheet 19), connecting cubes

- Instruct children to count out 32 cubes placing one in each box of the chart from 1 to 32.

- Discuss how children can find groups of ten within the chart. Have them identify one group of ten, then two groups of ten and finally three groups of ten. As a class, count the total number of cubes, counting tens first then counting on the ones.

- Tell children to connect the top row of cubes to show a group of ten and set it along the top row. Ask: *How many bars of ten do you have? How many single cubes are left?* Again, count the extra cubes by tens and ones. Have children connect another set of ten and finally the last set of ten, counting the tens and remaining cubes after each bar is made.

Mathematical Discourse

- *How do you know that all these groups of blocks show 32 cubes?*

  Some children may respond that they counted them all. Others may notice that each group has a total of 3 tens and 2 extra ones.

SMP Tip: Children look for and make use of structure as they repeatedly count 10 objects and bundle them into one group of ten. The Hands-On Activity presents an opportunity for doing this. Allow children to also use connecting cubes as they discuss the Talk About It question and whenever the opportunity arises throughout the lesson. (*SMP 7*)

STEP BY STEP

Materials For each child: base-ten blocks

- Have children model 23 with the base-ten blocks on a piece of paper, showing 2 tens and 3 ones. Tell them to write the number of tens and ones on the piece of paper.

- Next have children trade 1 ten for ten ones and count the tens and ones in this model. Ask them to write this number of tens and ones on the paper.

- Work through Problems 1 and 2 with children. Write 45 and 54 on the board. Ask: *How are these numbers the same? How are they different?* Model 45 and 54 with blocks and discuss the meaning of the 5 in each number. Emphasize that in the number 54, the 5 refers to 5 groups of ten. Ask the first Mathematical Discourse question.

- Present the Talk About It question, revisiting the many ways children decomposed 32 on the previous page. Have them work in pairs to find as many ways as possible to represent 45 and 54. Allow them to use blocks for support. Record their findings on the board and ask the second Mathematical Discourse question.

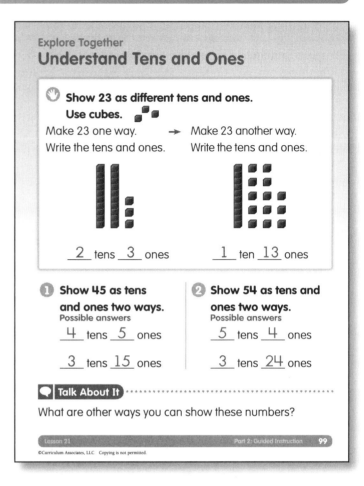

Visual Model

Fold 4 pieces of paper in half and write the numbers 20, 30, 40, and 50 on them as shown.

2	0

Cut 5 other pieces of paper in half and write the numbers 1–9 on them. Cover the 0 on the 20 card with a 3 and display it above a number bond showing 23 in the top box. Show how 23 can be "broken apart" into tens and ones by separating the cards, placing 20 in one part of the bond and 3 in the other part. Connect this model to the tens and ones children wrote on their papers.

Mathematical Discourse

- Can 54 be shown as 4 tens and 5 ones? Explain.

  No. The 5 in 54 means 5 tens not 5 ones. The 4 means 4 ones not 4 tens.

- *Why do you think there are more ways to show 54 than 45?*

  Some children may say that 54 is a bigger number. Others may point out that there are more tens in 54 than in 45, so there are more ways to combine tens and ones.

STEP BY STEP

Materials For each child: base-ten blocks

- Discuss each Connect It problem as a class using the discussion points outlined below.

Draw

- This problem provides children with an opportunity to demonstrate their understanding of the meaning of tens and ones. Remind them that it is like problems they completed on previous pages.

- Allow children to use blocks for support and demonstrate how to draw easy sketches to represent tens and ones.

- Ask children to demonstrate and explain how their drawing shows an equality using questions such as: *Why did you circle these blocks? How is the ten you made like the ones from the group of 36? How can you show that 1 ten is the same as 10 of these blocks?*

Identify

- You may want children to work in pairs, using base-ten blocks to model the choices before deciding which ones represent 76.

- As children work, ask questions such as: *I see a 6 and a 7 in 60 + 7 just like the 6 and 7 in 76, so why didn't you circle 60 + 7? How do you know that 6 tens and 16 ones is the same as 76?*

- You may want to challenge some children to find as many other ways as possible to represent 76 and tell how they found them.

Explain

- A common misconception among children is that each digit in a two-digit number is a separate entity and therefore interchangeable. This problem focuses on this misconception by asking children to analyze the value given to each digit by its label or placement.

- As children explain their reasoning to the class, encourage them to support it with physical and/or visual models. Ensure that they explain what is wrong with the presented reasoning.

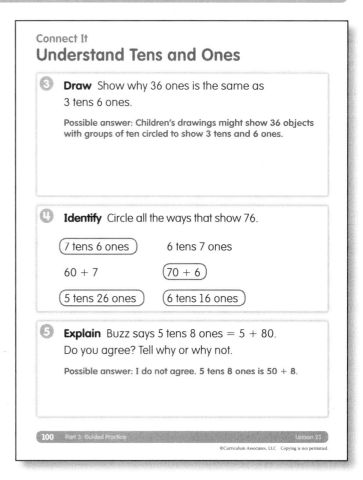

- Rewrite each value as 50 + 8 and 80 + 5 and have children write the two-digit number for each of them. Then write 8 + 50 and 5 + 80 and have them write the two-digit numbers. Model how the order of the addends doesn't affect the number but the order of the digits does.

SMP Tip: Prompt children with questions in order to elicit clear, concise explanations of their actions. Encourage them to use accurate mathematical language in their descriptions and justification for the drawings or choices they made. Lead them to use these explanations and justification to argue why Buzz is or is not correct in his thinking. *(SMP 3 and 6)*

STEP BY STEP

- Read the directions aloud and make sure children understand the task. Encourage them to circle at least 3 tens.

- For Part B, make sure children reverse the order of the digits from the number they made in Part A.

- As children work, support them with questions such as:

  How can you make sure all these ways show the number of blocks you circled?

  Can you think of a different number of tens to use?

  Why did you write this digit as ones in the first part and as tens in the second part?

  Which number can be shown in more ways, the one from Part A or the one from Part B? Why?

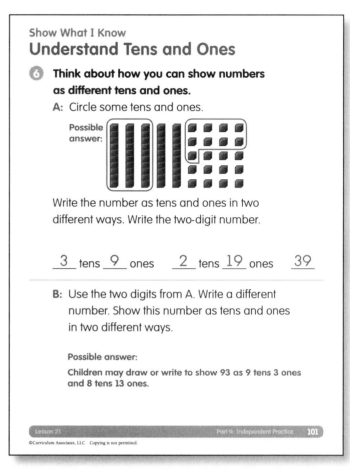

Show What I Know
Understand Tens and Ones

6 **Think about how you can show numbers as different tens and ones.**

A: Circle some tens and ones.

Possible answer:

Write the number as tens and ones in two different ways. Write the two-digit number.

<u>3</u> tens <u>9</u> ones   <u>2</u> tens <u>19</u> ones   <u>39</u>

B: Use the two digits from A. Write a different number. Show this number as tens and ones in two different ways.

Possible answer:
Children may draw or write to show 93 as 9 tens 3 ones and 8 tens 13 ones.

Lesson 21   Part 4: Independent Practice   **101**
©Curriculum Associates, LLC   Copying is not permitted.

SCORING RUBRICS

Expectations for 4–3 Points

Points	Expectations
4	The child: • represents a number of blocks in multiple ways and writes the corresponding number. • reverses the order of the digits and accurately represents the tens and ones.
3	The child: • accurately represents the blocks circled as a group of tens and some ones in one way (e.g., 30 + 4; three tens and 4 ones). • reverses the digits and accurately represents the two-digit number.

Expectations for 2–0 Points

Points	Expectations
2	The child: • represents the blocks circled as a two-digit number, but may not represent it in any other way. • reverses the order of the digits and may use a drawing to represent the value.
1	The child: • may attempt to represent the blocks circled, but that representation may not correspond to the number of blocks that are circled. • writes a number that does not correspond to the blocks circled or to any other number.
0	The child: • does not attempt to represent blocks as tens and ones.

Intervention Activity

Model tens and ones digits.

Materials For each child: 100 connecting cubes, index cards with multiples of ten written on them, (see Visual Model on page 164 for format), Digit Cards (Activity Sheet 25)

- Have children select a multiple of ten card, place it on their desks, and make the appropriate number of tens bars with connecting cubes.

- Children then select a digit card, place it over the zero on the tens card, and place the corresponding number of cubes on the desk. Continue until all cards have been used.

Optional: Have children build some tens and ones, then find the corresponding cards to model the number they built.

On-Level Activity

Cover a hundreds chart.

Materials For each child: Hundreds Chart (Activity Sheet 19), 100 connecting cubes, number cube

- Place children in pairs. Tell them their goal is to fill the chart with connecting cubes.

- Children take turns rolling a number cube and placing the corresponding number of connecting cubes on their hundreds chart, starting with 1 and continuing consecutively. After each turn, the child says: *I have ___ cubes.*

- When a row of ten is filled, the child connects the cubes and lays them across that row. As they accumulate tens, they describe the number of cubes in more than one way, such as: *1 ten and 13 ones, and 2 tens and 3 ones, are each 23 cubes.*

- Play continues until one child fills the chart.

- The game may be expedited by having the children roll two number cubes and use the sum of the numbers to determine how many connecting cubes to place on the hundreds chart.

Challenge Activity

Play guess my number.

Materials For each pair: white boards

- Place children in pairs. One child writes a two-digit number on the white board without revealing it to the partner. He or she gives a clue, such as: *My number has more than 3 tens.* The partner writes a guess on a white board. The first child indicates if the number is correct and if not, provides other clues until the partner writes the correct number on the white board.

- Encourage children to think of many different kinds of clues, such as using "greater than" or "less than" for the digits [the digit in the ones place is greater than the digit in the tens place], using tens and ones [there are more tens than ones; there are three more tens than ones]. Challenge them to use a variety of clues.

- When the number has been guessed, the other partner takes a turn writing a number and giving clues.

- Allow children to play until time has expired.

Optional: You may want to write two-digit numbers on cards for children to randomly select instead of making up their own. Play then continues until all the cards have been used.

Lesson 22 (Student Book pages 102–105)

Compare Numbers

LESSON OBJECTIVES

- Understand the meaning of the symbols $<$ and $>$.
- Compare the value of two two-digit numbers using tens and ones.
- Write the symbols $<$, $>$, and $=$ to compare two two-digit numbers.

PREREQUISITE SKILLS

- Understand concepts of "less than," "more than," and "the same as."
- Understand the equal sign.
- Understand two-digit numbers as tens and ones.

VOCABULARY

$<$: symbol that means "is less than"

$>$: symbol that means "is greater than"

greater than: number with a greater value or quantity

less than: number with a smaller value or quantity

more than: more in quantity or amount

During the lesson you will review the key terms:

compare: to decide if amounts or sizes are greater than, less than, or equal to each other

equal sign ($=$): a symbol that means "is the same as"

fewer: indicating a lesser quantity or amount

more: indicating a greater quantity or amount

THE LEARNING PROGRESSION

In Kindergarten, children use matching or counting strategies to identify the number of objects in a group as less than, equal to, or greater than the number of objects in another group. Children compare two numbers within 10 written as numerals.

In Grade 1, children understand that the two digits in a two-digit number represent tens and ones. They understand 10, 20, 30, 40, 50, 60, 70, 80, 90, and 100 as bundles of tens and zero ones. **In this lesson,** children use models of base-ten blocks to compare the number of tens and ones in two two-digit numbers. They use quick drawings and draw their own representations to compare two two-digit numbers. Children write $<$, $>$, or $=$ to record their comparisons.

In Grade 2, children compare three-digit numbers based on the place-values hundreds, tens, and ones. They use the symbols $<$, $>$, and $=$ to record comparisons.

Ready *Teacher Toolbox* Teacher-Toolbox.com

	Prerequisite Skills	1.NBT.B.3
Ready Lessons	✓ ✓ ✓	✓
Tools for Instruction	✓ ✓	✓
Interactive Tutorials	✓	✓

CCSS Focus

1.NBT.B.3 Compare two two-digit numbers based on meanings of the tens and ones digits, recording the results of comparisons with the symbols $>$, $=$, and $<$.

ADDITIONAL STANDARDS: **1.NBT.B.2a, 1.NBT.B.2b, 1.NBT.B.2c** *(see page A36 for full text)*

STANDARDS FOR MATHEMATICAL PRACTICE: **SMP 3, 4, 6, 7** *(see page A9 for full text)*

Opening Activity: Compare Numbers

Objective: Model to compare two-digit numbers.	**Materials** For each child: • base-ten blocks

Overview

Children use base-ten blocks to model a comparison problem with two-digit numbers. They use phrases such as "more than," "greater than," "less than," and "fewer" to talk about quantities.

Step by Step (10–15 minutes)

1 **Pose the problem.**

- Say: *The class is moving some books to the school library. Jonah and Ryan each made a few trips and carried some books to the library. Jonah carried 24 books in all. Ryan carried 37 books. How can we compare the number of books they carried?*

2 **Model the problem with base-ten blocks.**

- Write the two numbers on the board: 24 and 37.

- Ask: *How can you show 24 using base-ten blocks?* [2 tens and 4 ones] Have children model 24 with their blocks.

- Ask: *How can you show 37 using base-ten blocks?* [3 tens and 7 ones] Have children model 37 with their blocks.

3 **Compare the models.**

- Direct attention to the model for 24. Ask: *How many tens are there?* [2] *How many ones?* [4]

- Now look at the model for 37. Ask: *How many tens are there?* [3] *How many ones?* [7]

- Discuss with children which number has more tens. Guide them to understand that when one number has more tens than another, it is the "bigger" number.

4 **Talk about the models and the problem.**

- Tell children that since 37 has more tens than 24, 37 is greater than 24. Say: *Ryan carried 37 books and Jonah carried 24 books. What can you say about the number of books Ryan carried?* [Ryan carried more books than Jonah.]

- Explain that you can compare two numbers in a different way: 24 is less than 37. Ask: *What can you say about the books Jonah carried?* [Jonah carried fewer books than Ryan.]

- Discuss how the words "fewer" and "less" describe smaller quantities and the words "greater" and "more" describe larger quantities.

- Have children name some words they use when quantities are the same. Look for responses such as "equal," "the same amount," "as many as."

Check for Understanding

Provide children with the following problem: *There are 61 books in one bookcase and 48 books in another bookcase. Compare the number of books.* [61 > 48 and 48 < 61] Note whether children accurately use the words "more," "greater," "less," and "fewer" in their descriptions.

STEP BY STEP

- Begin by asking children what they have learned or remember from the Opening Activity. Ask volunteers to retell the important math ideas they explored.

- Explain that this page is about comparing two amounts to find which is more, just like the Opening Activity. Read the problem aloud.

- Direct children's attention to the base-ten blocks and place-value charts in Model It.

- Remind children they can use what they know about tens and ones to compare 52 and 25. Ask: *Which have a greater value, tens or ones?* [tens]

- Explain that since tens have a greater value, you first look at the tens when comparing two-digit numbers. Have children look at the place value charts that show 25 and 52 Ask: *How many tens are in 52?* [5] *How many tens are in 25?* [2] *Which number has more tens?* [52] Guide children to recognize that if one number has more tens than the other, then there is no need to look at the ones.

- Relate the concept of *more* to the phrase *is greater than* on the page. Tell children you can write the symbol > to mean "is greater than." Write 52 > 25 on the board and point out that the wide end of the symbol points to the greater number.

> **SMP Tip:** When children understand the meanings of symbols used in mathematics and are able to use them to relate quantities appropriately, they recognize that the symbols are a precise and shorter way of recording these relationships. *(SMP 6)*

- Invite children to tell who picked more apples and to explain how they know.

Hands-On Activity

Materials For each child: Place-Value Mat (Activity Sheet 27), base-ten blocks

- Have children model 52 and 25 with base-ten blocks, placing the blocks for each number in the appropriate columns of the place-value mat.

- Ask children to record each number on the place-value mat. Discuss that 52 has more tens and therefore is greater than 25.

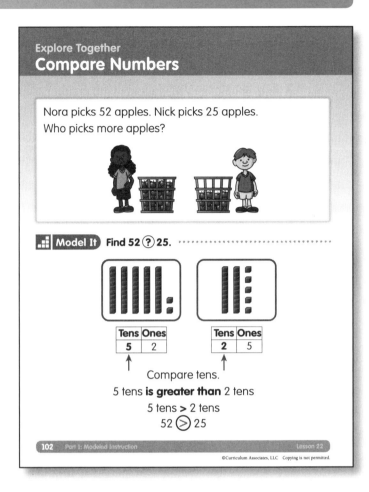

Mathematical Discourse

- *How are the numbers 52 and 25 the same? How are they different?*

  They have the same two digits, 2 and 5. In 52, the 5 is in the tens place; in 25, the 5 is in the ones place. In 52, the 2 is in the ones place; in 25, the 2 is in the tens place.

- *How does changing the position of the 2 change the value of the number?*

  In 25, 2 is in the tens place and has a value of 20. In 52, 2 is in the ones place and has a value of 2. So 2 has a greater value when it is in the tens place than when it is in the ones place.

STEP BY STEP

- Read aloud the problem at the top of the page. Ask children whether they need to find the number that is greater or less. Make the connection between "fewer" and "less than."

- Direct children's attention to the place-value charts in Model It. Challenge children to describe how to use the charts to determine which number is less.

- Read aloud the text on the page. Explain that since both numbers have the same tens, you need to compare the ones.

- Encourage children to describe how they might compare the ones to see which number is less. Lead them to understand that since both numbers have 3 tens, the number with fewer ones is less.

> **SMP Tip:** As children work with tens and ones to compare two-digit numbers, they begin to build general mathematical rules. Using the concept of place-value to compare two numbers deepens their understanding of the structure within the number system. *(SMP 7)*

- Write 35 < 39 on the board. Show that the narrow end of the symbol points to the lesser number. Say: *35 is less than 39; Gabe collects fewer rocks than Rose.*

- Read aloud Talk About It. Children may realize that Fred collects the same number of rocks as Gabe, 35. Ask children what symbol to use to compare the numbers. [the equal sign; 35 = 35]

Fluency

10 More, 10 Less

Materials For each child: 10 More, 10 Less (Activity Sheet 26), base-ten blocks

- Display 2 tens rods and ask: *How many?* [20] *Show another tens rod.* Ask: *How many now?* [30] *What is the addition sentence?* [20 + 10 = 30]

- Remove one tens rod. Ask: *How many now?* [20] *What is the subtraction sentence?* [30 − 10 = 20]

- Continue with other numbers of tens.

- Use the activity sheet for practice with tens.

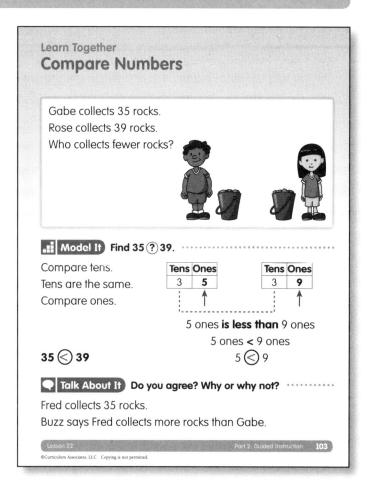

Mathematical Discourse

- *You know that 35 is less than 39. What else do you know about 35 and 39?*

  Children might say that 39 is greater than 35 and that 35 is not equal to 39.

STEP BY STEP

- Read aloud the problem at the top of the page. Ask: *Do you find the number that is greater or less?* [greater] *How do you know?* [The question has the word "more" which relates to a greater number.]

- Direct children's attention to the quick drawing. Explain that a quick drawing is a fast way to show tens and ones. Each line stands for a ten and each circle is a one.

- Invite a volunteer to describe what the quick drawing shows. Ask a different child to explain why 48 is greater than 14.

- Guide children to understand that since 48 is greater than 14, Jen has more coins than Kim. Ask the Mathematical Discourse question to look at this answer in a different way.

- Work together with children to complete Problem 1. Children may quickly recognize that the number of tens and ones are the same in both numbers. Ask children what symbol they write for the phrase "is the same as." [the equal sign, =]

- In Problem 2, children can make their own quick drawings to show that 23 < 27. Invite children to tell what their quick drawings show and how the drawings helped them to compare the numbers.

Visual Model

Materials For each child: 120 Chart (Activity Sheet 23)

Direct attention to the 120 chart as you explain that numbers are greater as you go across each row and then down the next row from top to bottom. Show how to use the chart to verify that 48 is greater than 14. Explain that the row with 48 is closer to the bottom of the chart than the row with 14, so 48 is greater than 14. Allow children to use the chart to check answers to other problems in the lesson.

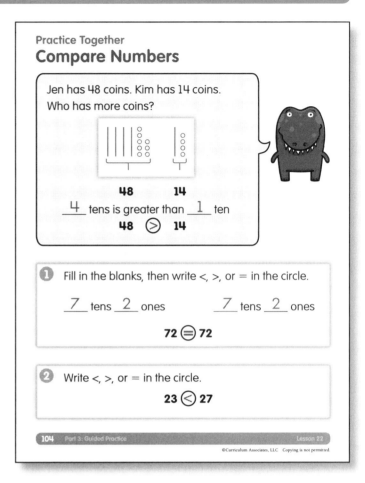

Mathematical Discourse

- *Which girl has fewer coins? How do you know?*

  Since 48 is greater than 14, 14 is less than 48. Since Kim's number of coins is less than Jen's, she has fewer coins.

Part 4: Independent Practice **Lesson 22**

STEP BY STEP

- Have children complete Problems 3 through 5 on their own. Remind them to compare tens first, then ones if the tens are the same.

- In Problem 3, children compare to find 93 > 48. Support is provided for children to write the number of tens and ones in each number.

- In Problem 4, children compare 16 and 60. Children encounter a number with zero ones as they find 16 < 60.

- Supports are removed in Problem 5. Children choose a strategy to use to compare the number pairs.

ELL Support

Provide sentence frames for children to refer to as they work. Write the sentence frames on the board or on index cards:

___ is greater than ___

___ is less than ___

___ is equal to ___

As children gain familiarity with the language, they may discontinue using the frames.

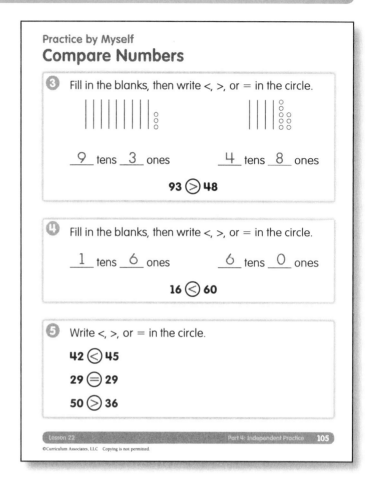

Mathematical Discourse

- *In Problem 3, you found 93 > 48. How could you use the digits 9 and 3 to make a two-digit number that is less than 48? Explain your thinking.*

  If you put 3 in the tens place and 9 in the ones place, you get a number that has 3 tens. Since 3 tens is less than 4 tens, 39 is less than 48.

L22: Compare Numbers **173**
©Curriculum Associates, LLC   Copying is not permitted.

Assessment and Remediation

- Ask children to tell which number is greater, 54 or 38. [54]

- For children who are still struggling, use the chart below to guide remediation.

- After providing remediation, check children's understanding using the following problem: Which number is greater, 46 or 62? [62]

If the error is . . .	Children may . . .	To remediate . . .
38	have compared the digits in the ones place (8 > 4) instead of the digits in the tens place (5 > 3).	provide children with base-ten blocks and a place-value mat to model 54 and 38 as tens and ones. Have them compare the number of tens to find 54 > 38.
38	have compared the digits in the tens place and incorrectly found 3 > 5.	provide children with a number path from 1 to 10 that they can use to see the order of numbers from least to greatest (3 < 5 and 5 > 3).
38	have confused the meaning of greater and lesser.	remind children of the relationship among "is greater than," "more," and > and among "is less than," "fewer," and <. Have them use base-ten blocks to model 54 and 38 and try again to answer the question.

Hands-On Activity

Model a two-digit number that is <, >, or = a given number.

Materials For each pair: Digit Cards (Activity Sheet 25), base-ten blocks

- Use the activity sheet to make two sets of number cards for each pair: 0–9 and 1–9.

- Partners place the number cards facedown in two stacks; 1–9 for tens digits and 0–9 for ones digits. The symbol cards >, <, and = go in a separate facedown stack.

- Partner A turns over a number from each stack and models the two-digit number with blocks.

- Partner B turns over a symbol card and places it next to Partner A's two-digit number. Partner B uses base-ten blocks to model a number that makes a true comparison.

- Partners record the number sentence and repeat the activity, switching roles.

Challenge Activity

Order two-digit numbers from least to greatest and greatest to least.

Materials For each child: Hundreds Chart (Activity Sheet 19)

- Cut the hundreds chart to make number cards 1–100. Have children mix up the cards and place them facedown on the desk.

- Children turn over three cards from the stack and place them in order from least to greatest. Students record their work, e.g., 35 < 49 < 82.

- Children then reorder their cards from greatest to least and record their work, e.g, 82 > 49 > 35.

- Have students continue with other sets of three cards, ordering the numbers and recording their work.

Lesson 23 (Student Book pages 106–109)

Add Tens to Any Number

LESSON OBJECTIVES

- Add multiples of ten to any two-digit number.
- Apply strategies to addition of two-digit numbers.
- Model addition involving tens.

PREREQUISITE SKILLS

- Find 10 more and 10 less than a given number.
- Distinguish between the tens and ones place in a two-digit number.

VOCABULARY

During the lesson you will review the key terms:

ones: single units or objects

tens: groups of ten ones

THE LEARNING PROGRESSION

In Kindergarten, children decompose teen numbers into a ten and some ones, understanding that 10 ones can be seen as a group of ten.

In Grade 1, children further their work in the base-ten system by computing sums within 100. Concrete and visual models support their understanding of place value and help them make a connection between the visual tens and the digit that represents a group of tens. **In this lesson,** children build on prior work with finding 10 more and 10 less by adding or subtracting multiples of ten to a given two-digit number. They become increasingly flexible in their use of strategies, representing sums and differences in many forms and justifying them with physical and visual models.

In Grade 2, children expand their work in the base-ten system. They add and subtract multi-digit numbers, building on their understanding of place value and the strategies they developed in Grade 1.

■ **Ready** *Teacher Toolbox*		Teacher-Toolbox.com
	Prerequisite Skills	*1.NBT.C.4*
Ready Lessons	✓ ✓ ✓	✓
Tools for Instruction	✓ ✓	✓
Interactive Tutorials	✓ ✓	✓ ✓

CCSS Focus

1.NBT.C.4 Add within 100, including adding a two-digit number and a one-digit number, and adding a two-digit number and a multiple of 10, using concrete models or drawings and strategies based on place value, properties of operations, and/or the relationship between addition and subtraction; relate the strategy to a written method and explain the reasoning used. Understand that in adding two-digit numbers, one adds tens and tens, ones and ones; and sometimes it is necessary to compose a ten.

ADDITIONAL STANDARDS: *1.NBT.B.2a, 1.NBT.B.2c, 1.NBT.B.3* (see page A36 for full text)

STANDARDS FOR MATHEMATICAL PRACTICE: *SMP 2, 3, 4, 6, 7, 8* (see page A9 for full text)

Opening Activity: Add Multiples of Ten

Objective: Relate adding a multiple of ten to finding 10 more.	**Materials** For each child: • connecting cubes, base-ten blocks; counters, 120 Chart (Activity Sheet 23)

Overview

Children solve a problem and recognize how their strategies lead to adding a 10.

Step by Step (20–25 minutes)

1 **Pose the problem.**

- Say: *Maria has 17 shells in her sea shell collection. One day on the beach, Maria collects 20 more shells. How many are in her collection now?*

2 **Solve the problem.**

- Tell children they may use counters, base-ten blocks, 120 charts, or drawings to help solve the problem.

- Observe as children work to see if they apply what they know about 10 more to find 20 more.

- Some children may add 20 counters and recount. Others may count on by tens or by ones from 37, while some children may recognize that adding 2 tens increases the tens digit by 2.

3 **Share strategies.**

- Have children present their solutions and strategies to the class. Use your observations of their work to help guide the discussion as children share their reasoning.

- Encourage multiple children to share, ensuring that the strategies presented are representative of the different ways children solved the problem.

4 **Explore the concept.**

- Have children model 17 as tens and ones with connecting cubes or base-ten blocks.

- Write "17 + 20" on the board and discuss how this addition represents the problem. Show two additional ten blocks and ask: *When I add 1 ten to 17, how many tens are there? When I add a second ten, how many tens are there then?*

- Relate adding 20 to adding 10 (or finding 10 more than a number). Help children count on by tens from 17, saying "27" when 1 ten is added, then "37" when 1 more ten is added.

Check for Understanding

Provide the children with the following problem: *Jordan has 13 toy cars and 10 toy trucks. How many toy vehicles does he have?* [23]

Help children write a number sentence to represent the problem. Ask them to show the strategy they used to solve the problem.

Look for the ways in which children solve the problem without expectation that all children will be successful. Use the Hands-On Activity on page 177 and the Visual Model on page 178 as additional support for those children who struggle with the concept of adding tens to a number.

Allowing children to model the addition in multiple ways will help them connect the model to the problem and number sentence.

STEP BY STEP

- Read the problem aloud. Discuss how this problem is similar to the one they solved in the Opening Activity. Ask children how adding 10 is like finding 10 more than a number.

- Complete the Hands-On Activity to reinforce the concept of adding tens and adding ones.

- Draw attention to the Model It. Compare the process shown to how children used blocks to add in the Hands-On Activity. Discuss with children how the blocks and the number sentences below them are related.

- Remind children that there are many ways to think about finding a sum. Ask the Mathematical Discourse question to engage children in utilizing and sharing mental strategies.

SMP Tip: Consistently emphasizing the structure of the base-ten system of numeration helps children gradually internalize that structure. This enables them to use this understanding to add tens and ones in two-digit numbers, and later as they explore addition and subtraction involving composing and decomposing a ten. (*SMP 7*)

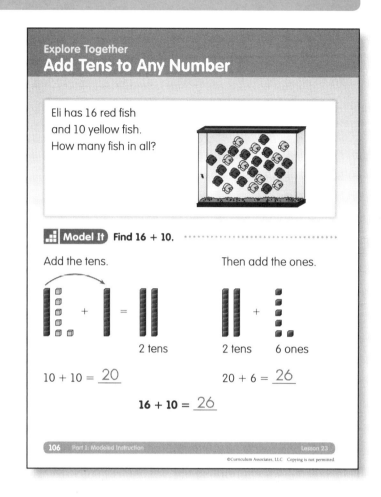

Hands-On Activity

Materials For each child: connecting cubes or base-ten blocks, Place-Value Mat (Activity Sheet 27), Digit Cards (Activity Sheet 25)

- Have children model 16 on a place-value mat with cubes or base-ten blocks. Then have them place the corresponding digit card under each place to indicate how many tens and ones there are.

- Tell children to add ten more ones blocks. Ask: *How are adding 1 ten and adding 10 ones alike?* Reinforce that when 10 ones are added, the ones must be composed into a ten. By adding a tens block, the composing is already completed.

- Have children place digit cards to represent the number in each place. Discuss that adding 10 increases the tens place by 1 ten, so the digit increases by one. There were no additional ones added, so the ones digit does not change.

Mathematical Discourse

- *What are some ways you can add 16 + 10 in your head?*

   Some children may respond that it is like finding 10 more so you just make the tens in 16 one more. Others may remember using a 120 chart and "see" 26 right below 16.

STEP BY STEP

- Read the problem aloud. Ask the first Mathematical Discourse question.

- Engage children in sharing strategies they could use to solve this problem. Listen for ideas expressed that are explored in the Visual Model, then use the Visual Model activity to validate the strategies and to provide children a way to "see" the strategies discussed.

- Direct children's attention to the Model It. Discuss how decomposing 13 in the number bond is like breaking it apart in the number sentence addition.

- **Error Alert** Allow children to discuss the Talk About It with a partner before discussing it as a class. Encourage children to clearly describe the error and justify a correct solution strategy.

Visual Model

Materials For each child: 1 counter, 120 Chart (Activity Sheet 23)

Have children place a counter on the number 13 in the 120 chart. Tell them to move their finger to show 10 more. Write:

$$\overset{+10}{\underset{13 \quad 23}{\frown}}$$

Have children move their fingers to show 10 more, continuing to add to the model and repeating until 5 tens are added.

$$\overset{+10}{\underset{13 \; 23}{\frown}} \quad \overset{+10}{\underset{23 \; 33}{\frown}} \quad \overset{+10}{\underset{33 \; 43}{\frown}} \quad \overset{+10}{\underset{43 \; 53}{\frown}} \quad \overset{+10}{\underset{53 \; 63}{\frown}}$$

Discuss how adding 5 tens is like adding 1 ten five times. Recognizing the repeated reasoning involved provides children with a mental strategy for adding multiples of ten to any number. You may wish to repeat, using a different number sentence.

Have children place a counter on the number 50 in their charts. Lead them to explore ways to add 13. Ask the second Mathematical Discourse question. Write 13 + 50 = 63 and 50 + 13 = 63 on the board. Help children recognize that the commutative property applies to multi-digit numbers just as it does to single-digit numbers.

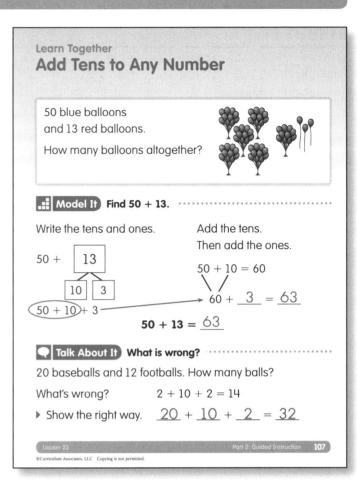

Mathematical Discourse

- *How is this problem the same and how is it different from 16 + 10?*

  Children should notice that a teen number is an addend in both number sentences, however the other addend in this problem is greater than ten.

- *Do you think it is easier to start at 50 and count on 13, or start at 13 and count on 50? Why?*

  Some children may respond that it is easier to count on starting at 50 because only 1 ten needs to be added and then add 3 ones. Others may prefer to start at 13 feeling that they only have to count on 5 tens without having to add the extra ones at the end.

STEP BY STEP

- Read the sample problem aloud. Ask children which number sentence the quick drawing represents. After sharing their ideas, ask children how to change the quick drawing to show 20 + 9.

- Read Problem 1 and discuss the way 32 is decomposed in the number bond. Reinforce the commutative property by asking: *Would the sum be different if we added 32 to 20? Explain.* Ask the Mathematical Discourse question to support previous work adding multiples of ten.

- Present Problem 2 and engage children in describing the strategies and/or models that help them solve the problem. Ask each child to draw a picture of the way they thought about the problem.

> **SMP Tip:** Relating the models explored to each other and to the problem they model and then connecting a number sentence to the physical/visual models facilitates children's ability to independently model a problem situation. *(SMP 4)*

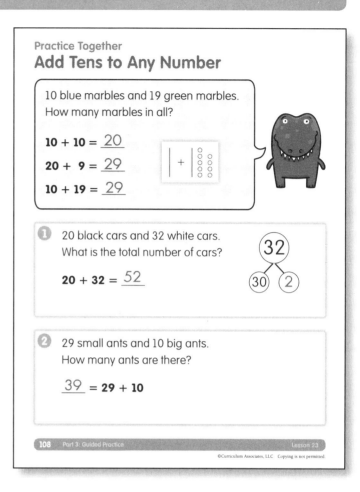

Concept Extension

Explore patterns involved in adding multiples of ten.

Write the additions vertically on the board:

24	34	44		
+ 10	+ 10	+ 10	+ ___	+ ___

Have children solve the first two and then challenge them to find the missing numbers for the other sentences. Lead them to see the patterns that evolve when 10 is added repeatedly.

Extend this pattern to adding multiples of 10:

24	24	24		
+ 10	+ 20	+ 30	+ ___	+ ___

Compare the two models discussing similarities and differences. Refer to adding tens on a 120 chart, reinforcing the concept that adding one ten 2, 3, 4, . . . times is like adding 2, 3, 4, . . . tens to a number.

Mathematical Discourse

- *How does knowing how to add 30 + 20 help you add 32 + 20?*

  Some children may recall how adding 3 + 2 = 5 so 30 + 20 is 50. Since there are a number of ones in 32, they must then be added.

Fluency Practice

Materials For each child: Practice Adding Tens (Activity Sheet 28); Optional: connecting cubes, base-ten blocks, place-value mats, number bond mats, counters, 120 charts

Provide children with the Add Tens worksheet for practice in adding multiples of ten. Encourage the use of individual strategies. Make connecting cubes, base-ten blocks and place-value mats, number bond mats, counters, and 120 charts available for children to use, if needed. Remind children to show their thinking in the box provided on the worksheet or draw a picture showing how they modeled the problem.

STEP BY STEP

- Before children begin work on this page, review the models used in this lesson. Emphasize that children are free to use whatever way helps them solve the problems.

- Read each problem aloud, pointing out that these problems are similar to the ones children solved on previous pages.

- You may wish to build on previous discussions about equality by discussing the position of the totals in the number sentences in each of the problems. Ask children to explain why it is all right to show the totals these two ways.

- Have children work independently to solve each problem, offering support when necessary.

- For Problem 4, observe to see if any children record the total as 605. Support those children by asking how 60 and 5 more would look as a quick drawing or how it would look in a 120 chart.

- Ask children who solve Problem 5 without showing their work to explain the strategy they used.

ELL Support

Reinforce the vocabulary used for the models shown on this page by replicating the quick drawings from Problem 3 on the board and writing the words "quick drawings" above it. Then draw the number bond in Problem 4 on the board and write "number bond" above it.

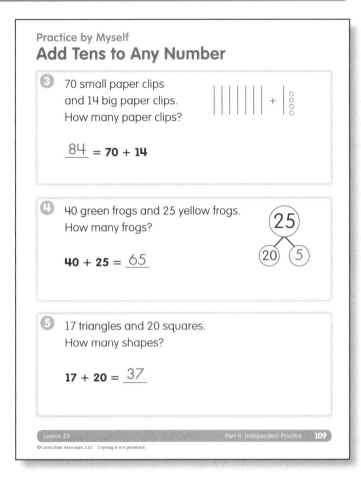

Practice by Myself
Add Tens to Any Number

3 70 small paper clips and 14 big paper clips. How many paper clips?

$\underline{84} = 70 + 14$

4 40 green frogs and 25 yellow frogs. How many frogs?

$40 + 25 = \underline{65}$

25
20 5

5 17 triangles and 20 squares. How many shapes?

$17 + 20 = \underline{37}$

Mathematical Discourse

- *What are some different ways to add 17 + 20?*

  Children might suggest adding 1 ten, 2 tens, and 7 ones to get 37. Others might count on by tens: 17, 27, 37. Another possible strategy is to decompose 17: $10 + 7 + 20 = 37$.

Assessment and Remediation

- Ask children to show the sum and strategy they used for finding 46 + 30. [76]

- For children who are still struggling, use the chart below to guide remediation.

- After providing remediation, check children's understanding using the following problem: find 50 + 37. [87]

If the error is . . .	Children may . . .	To remediate . . .
706	have combined 70 and 6 without attending to place value.	Have children model the problem with blocks in a place-value chart. Remove the ones and ask children how many tens and ones there are. Place a 7 and 0 in the proper place-value locations. Add the 6 ones and ask how many ones there are. Place the digit 6 in the ones place. Help children see that 70 + 6 = 76 since 0 + 6 = 6.
49	have added 30 as 3 ones rather than as 3 tens.	Have children model the addition using a 120 chart, breaking 30 into 10 + 10 + 10. Help children see that 3 groups of ten, not ones are added.

Hands-On Activity

Model addition sentences.

Materials For each pair: base-ten blocks, Digit Cards (Activity Sheet 25), place-value mat, Tens Cards (Activity Sheet 24), and a set of cards containing varied two-digit numbers

- Set the tens cards and the two-digit cards face down next to each other. Have one child pick a number from one pile, model it in the mat, and place digit cards under each place to show the number. The partner chooses a card from the other pile and adds blocks to the mat to model it.

- Together, children adjust the digit cards to show the sum. If a sum is greater than 100, allow children to attempt the challenge, or place the card under the pile and draw again. Repeat switching the starting partner until all cards have been used.

- Optional: Have children record the additions on a white board or paper.

Challenge Activity

Explore patterns.

Challenge children to expand on the Concept Extension activity on page 179, in which they explored the patterns when multiples of ten are added to a number.

Have children find as many different patterns as they can, such as: consistently adding 20 (or 30, 40, etc.); what the pattern looks like using numbers in the hundreds; finding patterns when multiples of 100 are added, etc.

Encourage children to be creative in finding patterns and have them record the patterns they discover.

Lesson 24 (Student Book pages 110–113)

Add Tens and Add Ones

LESSON OBJECTIVES

- Model addition of two-digit numbers.
- Add two-digit numbers without regrouping.

PREREQUISITE SKILLS

- Add ten to any number.
- Model a two-digit number as tens and ones.

VOCABULARY

During the lesson you will review the key terms:

ones: single units or objects

tens: groups of ten ones

THE LEARNING PROGRESSION

In Kindergarten, children decompose teen numbers into 10 ones and some additional ones, laying the foundation for using tens and ones.

In Grade 1, children fluently add within 10 and then 20 using concrete models, drawings, and strategies. They apply addition skills to problem solving situations. **In this lesson,** children compute sums within 100 with attention to place value and the base-ten system of numeration. Adding tens and ones separately reinforces previous work with place value and prepares children for finding sums of any two-digit numbers. Strategies used for single-digit computations and for adding tens to any number support the methods children use for two-digit addition and provide a basis for understanding adding tens and adding ones.

In Grade 2, children work toward fluency with addition and subtraction within 100 and extend this work to addition and subtraction within 1,000, including situations where composing or decomposing a ten is required.

◼ Ready *Teacher Toolbox*   *Teacher-Toolbox.com*

	Prerequisite Skills	1.NBT.C.4
Ready Lessons	✓ ✓ ✓	✓
Tools for Instruction	✓ ✓	✓
Interactive Tutorials	✓	✓ ✓

CCSS Focus

1.NBT.C.4 Add within 100, including adding a two-digit number and a one-digit number, and adding a two-digit number and a multiple of 10, using concrete models or drawings and strategies based on place value, properties of operations, and/or the relationship between addition and subtraction; relate the strategy to a written method and explain the reasoning used. Understand that in adding two-digit numbers, one adds tens and tens, ones and ones; sometimes it is necessary to compose a ten.

ADDITIONAL STANDARDS: *1.OA.A.2* (*see page A36 for full text*)

STANDARDS FOR MATHEMATICAL PRACTICE: *SMP 2, 4, 6, 7, 8* (*see page A9 for full text*)

Opening Activity: How Many Counters?

Objective: Apply known strategies to add two-digit numbers.	**Materials** For each child: • bag containing 20–50 counters

Overview

Children solve a problem, share strategies and compare the problem to previous ones.

Step by Step (15–20 minutes)

1 **Pose the problem.**

Tell children that this activity involves:

1) finding the number of counters in their bag and recording it on a white board.

2) combining their counters with those of a partner.

3) finding the total number of counters in both bags.

2 **Solve the problem.**

• As children complete the activity, observe the strategies they use. Do they count individual counters or group them into tens and ones? Do they combine both sets of counters and recount? Do they recount using tens and ones or count all the counters? Do they add the numbers from each bag rather than count the counters?

• Make observations without giving suggestions, allowing children to use their own methods of counting and finding totals. Use your observations to question groups during class discussion.

3 **Share solution strategies.**

• Invite partners to share the ways they counted the number of counters in their bags. Discuss the advantages of grouping them in tens and ones.

• Have children share strategies they used to find the total of all counters in both bags, recording those that involve writing a number sentence and finding the total. Compare the various strategies, discussing the similar elements of each one.

4 **Compare addends in addition problems.**

• Examine the number sentences on the board. Make sure children notice that each is an addition sentence.

• Compare the number sentences and strategies to the problems children solved when adding tens to any number. Point out that in these problems, both addends have ones. Discuss how with all of these problems, you add the tens, and then add the ones.

Check for Understanding

Take away or add a few counters to children's bags to create a situation that is different from the problem they solved during the activity. Ask them to write the number sentence and find the total.

Scan the room as children work, taking note of those who add numerically and those who count all counters. Be prepared to support children who need additional help in seeing and combining tens and ones.

STEP BY STEP

- Ask children to describe strategies they remember from the Opening Activity.

- Read the problem aloud and direct attention to the 26 + 32 in Model It. Have children solve the problem using any strategy they want.

- Invite volunteers to share solutions and strategies. Prompt children with questions such as: *Why did you choose that strategy? Where did those extra ones you added come from?* Engage the class to ask questions of or challenge peers to justify a strategy.

- Draw attention to Model It. Point out that the base-ten blocks model how to break the two-digit numbers into tens and ones, so the tens can be added together and the ones can be added together.

- Show children how the vertical addition sentence helps group tens together and ones together. Ask them to solve the problem by writing "5 tens 8 ones" as a number.

Visual Model

Materials For each child: Hundreds Chart (Activity Sheet 19), 3 counters

Present the strategy of using a hundreds chart to count on. Display 26 + 32 and 32 = 3 tens 2 ones.

Have children place a marker on the 26 in the chart. Model on the board counting on the 3 tens in 32. Children use a second counter to show the same jumps on the hundreds chart.

26　36　46　56

Then count on 2 more and record:

56　57　58

Repeat with other addition problems.

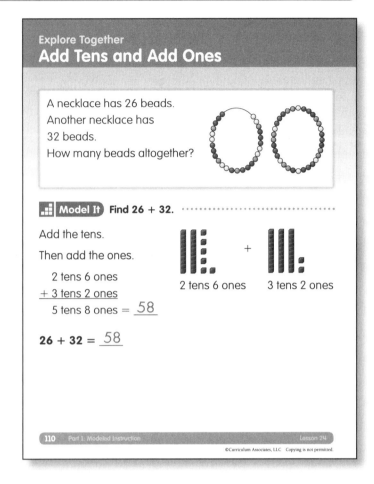

Mathematical Discourse

- *How is adding tens and adding ones like adding tens to any number? How is it different?*

  In both types of problems you add tens, then ones. When you add tens to any number, one of the addends has 0 ones. When you add tens and add ones, both addends have 1 or more ones. These ones have to be added together before adding to the tens.

SMP Tip: As children explore different models for addition, they begin to see repeatedly that when tens and ones are present, tens are added to tens and ones are added to ones. As they work on problems in the lesson, emphasize the reasoning that when tens are added to tens the result is a greater number of tens; and that the same applies to the ones. *(SMP 8)*

STEP BY STEP

Materials Optional: base-ten blocks

- Read the problem aloud and ask children to model it with a number sentence. Discuss the reason for using addition, and use children's number sentences to emphasize that you can add in any order.

- Project the number bonds shown in Model It. Ask how the number bonds are like the base-ten blocks on the previous page. Emphasize that both models show ways to break numbers into tens and ones. You may want to invite a volunteer to model the numbers from the problem with base-ten blocks.

- Ask children to compare the vertical addition sentence on this page with the one on the previous page. Guide them to recognize that both show adding tens and adding ones. On the previous page, the words "tens" and "ones" are used. This page uses numbers that show the value of the tens and ones.

- Have children fill in the blanks with the totals.

- **Misconception Alert** Allow children to discuss Talk About It with a partner before sharing ideas with the class. Guide the class to conclude that both Buzz and Boom are correct. Address misconceptions that there is only one correct way to show adding tens and adding ones.

> **SMP Tip:** Help children see how closely the different representations are related to reinforce the universal nature of the structure of mathematics and build a strong sense of number. (*SMP 7*)

Visual Model

Help children build a visual strategy for adding.

Write the addition sentence 13 + 14 on the board. Ask children to look at the number bonds on the student page, tell what parts are added together, and explain why. Model on the board:

13 + 14

Ask: *When you add the two ones digits, what are you really adding? Why? Would it make sense to add a one to the 4? Explain.*

Write several other addition problems and have children model adding tens, then adding ones.

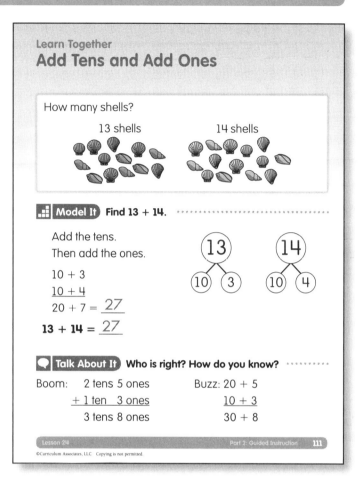

Learn Together
Add Tens and Add Ones

How many shells?

13 shells   14 shells

Model It Find 13 + 14.

Add the tens.
Then add the ones.

$10 + 3$
$\underline{10 + 4}$
$20 + 7 = \underline{27}$

13 + 14 = _27_

Talk About It Who is right? How do you know?

Boom: 2 tens 5 ones   Buzz: 20 + 5
         + 1 ten   3 ones   10 + 3
         3 tens 8 ones   30 + 8

Mathematical Discourse

- *What way makes it easiest for you to add? Why?*

  Listen for sound reasoning in the choices children make. If they respond that "it is easier" press them to explain what makes it easier than the other methods. Make sure their choices demonstrate an understanding of addition within place values.

STEP BY STEP

- Read the example problem aloud. Ask children how the 34 beads are modeled. Lead them to see that 34 is modeled as 30 + 4 and with a quick drawing. Repeat for 55.

> **SMP Tip:** Reinforce the importance of adding sticks to sticks and circles to circles (tens to tens and ones to ones). As children internalize that 1 stick + 2 circles results in 12 and not 3, they develop the abstract reasoning about adding like terms, such as denominators of fractions and variables in number sentences. (*SMP 2*)

- Read Problem 1, pointing out that this model is like the number sentence in the example problem with some numbers missing. Discuss what numbers belong in the blanks, making sure children record 1 ten as 10.

- Have children complete the number bonds in Problem 2 and ask them to describe ways they can use the bonds to find the total.

- Remind children that they are free to use models or strategies not shown on this page that help them think about addition of two-digit numbers.

- If children struggle to get started, suggest that they make quick drawings to picture the tens and ones in each number.

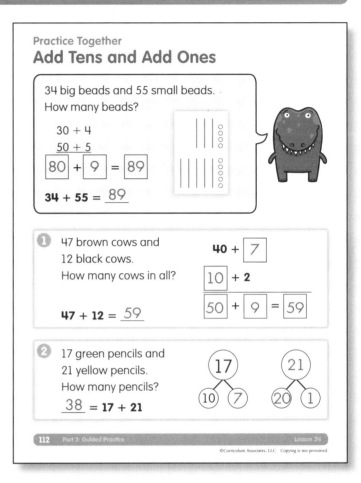

Mathematical Discourse

- *How do picture models help you think about an addition?*

  Children may respond that the picture helps them "see" the parts that need to be added. Some may say that the sticks help them think of the digit for the tens place. Others may like the way the arrows show jumps when they count on.

Fluency Practice

Materials For each child: Practice Adding Tens and Ones (Activity Worksheet 29)

Distribute the activity sheet and tell children that they are free to use any of the models from this or other lessons to help them solve the additions.

STEP BY STEP

Materials Optional: base-ten blocks, connecting cubes

- Before children work on this page, review the models used in this lesson. Emphasize that children are free to use whatever way helps them solve the problems. Discuss with them that by completing the model shown in each problem they are demonstrating that they know how to solve in many ways.

- Read each problem aloud, then have children work independently to solve.

- Watch children to ensure they are recording 5 tens and 8 tens as 50 and 80, respectively, in Problem 3. Prompt them with questions such as: *What is another way to write 5 tens?*

- For children who struggle with the concept of decomposing a number into tens and ones numerically in Problem 4, suggest they use base-ten blocks or connecting cubes to decompose each two-digit number and record numbers for each place value in the number bonds.

- Encourage children to show the model or explain the strategy they used to solve Problem 5.

Hands-On Activity

Materials For each child: base-ten blocks

- Have children use base-ten blocks to add 43 + 17. First, ask them to identify the tens and ones in each number, then model the tens and ones with base-ten blocks. [4 tens 3 ones and 1 ten 7 ones]

- Ask children to combine the tens and tell how many there are in all. [5 tens]

- Then have children combine the ones. Guide them to realize that the ones make an additional ten for a total of 6 tens, or 60.

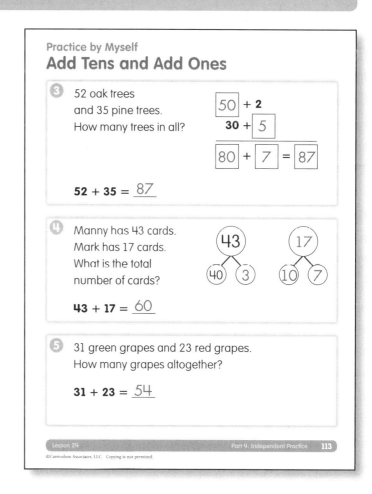

Mathematical Discourse

- *What is another way to find the total in Problem 3?*

  Children might describe writing 52 as 5 tens 2 ones and 35 as 3 tens 5 ones, then adding tens and adding ones to get 8 tens 7 ones, or 87. Others may see that the sum of the tens digits is 8 and the sum of the ones digits is 7, and instinctively know that this represents 87.

Assessment and Remediation

- Ask children to find the sum 27 + 62 and show or describe the model or strategy they used. [Possible answer: 20 + 7 + 60 + 2 = 80 + 9, or 89]

- For children who are still struggling, use the chart below to guide remediation.

- After providing remediation, check children's understanding using the following problem: Find the sum 43 + 32. [75]

If the error is . . .	Children may . . .	To remediate . . .
87 or 82	have added 2 tens but failed to add the additional ones.	Compare the model or strategy children used to the number sentence. Check to see that both addends are modeled correctly and lead them to see that both groups of ones must be added.
17	have counted 8 tens and 9 ones and added 8 + 9.	Have children model the addends with connecting cubes, break one ten into individual ones and count them. Reinforce the concept that each ten equals 10 ones therefore 8 tens equals 80 ones not 8 ones.
Any other number	have miscounted.	Have children check their work using a different model or strategy to identify the error.

Hands-On Activity

Model two-digit addition problems.

Materials For each pair: Place-Value Mat (Activity Sheet 27), Hundreds Chart (Activity Sheet 19), Number Bond Mat (Activity Sheet 3), base-ten blocks or connecting cubes, 10 cards containing two-digit addition number sentences

- Children place the number sentence cards facedown. One child draws a card, places it face up, models the addition and finds the sum.

- The partner solves the problem using a different model. Compare answers. If they are the same, a new card is drawn and the number sentence is modeled in two different ways.

- If the sums are different, partners exchange models, work the problem again, and determine which sum is correct and where the error was made.

Challenge Activity

Explore the effects of rearranging digits in addends.

- Write the expressions "24 + 53" and "23 + 54" and have children find the sums. Guide them to recognize that the sum is the same for both problems. Ask children how the number sentences are the same and how they are different.

- Tell children that their challenge is to find out if the sums will ALWAYS be the same when the digits in the ones place are switched around and if it works when the digits in the tens place are switched. Encourage them to justify their conclusion using words and pictures.

- Challenge them further to determine if this works when the ones and tens digits are switched in each number and justify why or why not (for example: 24 + 53 and 42 + 35).

Lesson 25 (Student Book pages 114–117)

Add and Regroup

LESSON OBJECTIVES

- Add two-digit numbers with regrouping.
- Compose a ten when adding ones.
- Relate two-digit addition with regrouping to two-digit addition without regrouping and to the "make a ten" strategy.

PREREQUISITE SKILLS

- Add two-digit numbers without regrouping.
- Utilize the making a ten strategy.

VOCABULARY

make a ten: a strategy that uses combinations of numbers that add to ten when finding totals greater than 10

THE LEARNING PROGRESSION

In Kindergarten, children find number partners to make a ten and decompose teen numbers into ten ones and some more ones.

In Grade 1, children develop concepts related to the base ten system as they make a ten when adding two numbers whose sum is greater than ten and as they add tens to tens and ones to ones in double-digit addition. **In this lesson,** children expand on prior work with two-digit addition by recognizing that when adding ones to ones the sum may be greater than ten. Children apply models and strategies explored in previous lessons to addition with regrouping, developing an understanding of the process of making a ten from the sum of the ones digits to add to the existing tens.

In Grade 2, children continue work with two-digit addition and subtraction and extend base ten computations to three-digit numbers.

▣ **Ready** *Teacher Toolbox*		*Teacher-Toolbox.com*
	Prerequisite Skills	*1.NBT.C.4*
Ready Lessons	✓ ✓ ✓	✓
Tools for Instruction		✓
Interactive Tutorials	✓	✓ ✓

CCSS Focus

1.NBT.C.4 Add within 100, including adding a two-digit number and a one-digit number, and adding a two-digit number and a multiple of 10, using concrete models or drawings and strategies based on place value, properties of operations, and/or the relationship between addition and subtraction; relate the strategy to a written method and explain the reasoning used. Understand that in adding two-digit numbers, one adds tens and tens, ones and ones; and sometimes it is necessary to compose a ten.

STANDARDS FOR MATHEMATICAL PRACTICE: **SMP 1, 2, 3, 4, 6, 7, 8** *(see page A9 for full text)*

Opening Activity: Explore Addition Strategies

Objective: Build the concept of regrouping with addition.	**Materials** For each child: • Hundreds Chart (Activity Sheet 19) • base-ten blocks or connecting cubes • counters

Overview

Children explore, justify, and apply strategies for addition involving composing a ten in the ones place.

Step by Step (20–25 minutes)

1 **Pose the problem.**

- Tell children that Buzz and Boom both solved the problem "16 + 8" in different ways.
- Project each strategy, reading them one at a time and allowing children time to think about it before reading the next one.
- Buzz said he added 16 + 4 to make 20 and then added 4 more.
- Boom said he broke 16 into 10 and 6. He added 6 + 4 to make ten, added 4 more, and then added the other 10.

2 **Model strategies.**

- Have children work with a partner to model each strategy using blocks, hundreds charts, or other tools of their choice. Ask children if both strategies led to the same answer. [yes, 24]
- Ask each pair to decide which strategy they think was easier to use or which they like better. Ask several groups to explain their decisions.

3 **Justify strategies.**

- Invite volunteers to justify each strategy by demonstrating it with a model. Ask children to explain why each strategy works.
- Compare the two strategies, asking children to tell how they are different and how they are alike.

4 **Apply strategies.**

- Discuss with children how adding these numbers is like or different from the addition problems they have done in previous lessons. Focus on the fact that in this problem, the total of the digits in the ones place is greater than 10.
- Encourage children to work with a partner to find a different way to solve the problem and share it with the class. Make sure the strategies are mathematically accurate, and lead children to alter the ones that are flawed.

Check for Understanding

Provide the children with the following problem:

Tell children to draw a picture showing how to add 16 + 8.

Some children might be able to make quick drawings that represent taking 4 ones from 8 ones and adding it to the 6 ones in 16 in order to make 2 tens. Others may make a drawing and count all. Support the latter group by allowing them to work with connecting cubes to physically create a 10 with the ones from both numbers.

STEP BY STEP

Materials For display: 7 red and 18 blue counters or cubes

- Read the problem aloud. Ask children to relate this situation to the Opening Activity by discussing ways to organize the erasers in a way that makes it easier to find the total.

- Use the Hands-On Activity to prepare children for the diagram shown in Model It.

> **SMP Tip:** Display 18 blue counters and 7 red counters. Move two of the red counters into the blue group to demonstrate the viability of reorganizing addends to make a ten and to reinforce the application of the associative property of addition. *(SMP 7)*

- Draw attention to the diagram shown in Model It. Relate the diagram to the Hands-On Activity with questions such as: *How are the pictures shown like the 10-frames you filled? What is the arrow telling you to do? Why is it helpful to move two of the seven ones over to the group of 18?*

- Connect the process shown here to the making a ten strategy by asking the Mathematical Discourse question.

Hands-On Activity

Materials For each child: two copies of 10-Frame (Activity Sheet 11), 7 red and 18 blue counters or cubes

Have children model 18 with blue counters on two 10-frames and 7 using red counters on a third 10-frame. Ask them to reorganize the counters to make it easier to count the total. Guide children to take 2 counters from 7 and place them with 8 to complete another frame of 10. Remind children that the total in addition is not affected by moving the parts being added.

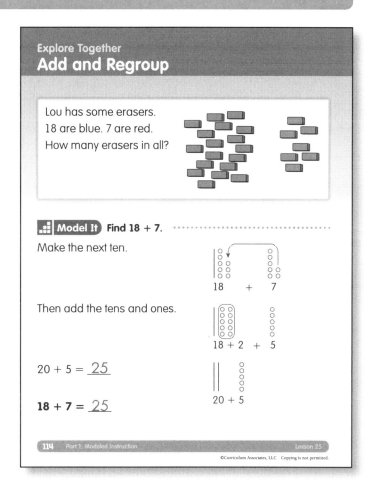

Mathematical Discourse

- *How is adding 18 + 7 like using the "make a ten" strategy?*

  Children should notice that in adding 8 ones and 7 ones, the total is greater than 10, so composing a ten helps find the sum. In this problem, there is another ten to add so the sum has 2 tens, not one.

Visual Model

Demonstrate the use of a quick number bond to help children see the numbers involved in making a ten.

$$18 + 7 =$$
$$\overset{\wedge}{10 \quad 8}$$

STEP BY STEP

- Read the problem aloud and compare it to the problem from the Model It on page 110 of the student book. Guide children to recognize that this addition problem involves two two-digit numbers.

- Use the Hands-On Activity to allow children to explore different strategies. Justify all reasonable methods, emphasizing that there are many ways to find the sum.

- Explore the model shown in Model It, helping children relate it to other models and strategies they have used. Point out that the sum of the ones digits is decomposed into a ten and some ones, so you can add all tens, then add ones.

- **Error Alert** Read Talk About It. Have children work with a partner to find 25 + 16. Allow some pairs to present their work and tell who is right. After children understand that Buzz did the problem correctly, ask children to describe what they think Boom did wrong.

Hands-On Activity

Materials For each child: Hundreds Chart (Activity Sheet 19), crayons, counters

- Have children model 35 in the hundreds chart by shading in the rows of ten and then adding 5 more counters. Ask them to add 27 to the chart in whatever way makes it easiest for them to count the total.

- Discuss the strategies children use to find the total. Listen for strategies such as: coloring 2 more rows and adding 7 counters; coloring 2 rows, filling the row of 5 counters with 5 more and adding the other 2 at the end; counting on 2 tens from 35 and then adding 7 ones, etc.

- Encourage children to find many different ways to calculate the sum and then demonstrate/explain their strategies to the class. Pose questions such as: *How is your strategy like . . . ? Why can you put 5 of the 7 counters next to the other 5?*

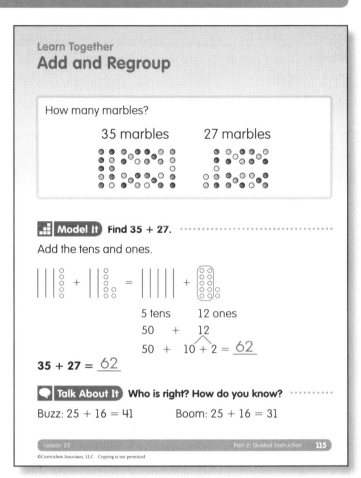

Mathematical Discourse

- *How is adding 35 + 27 like adding 35 + 23? How is it different?*

  In both problems, you add tens to tens and ones to ones. When you add 35 and 27, the total of the ones is greater than 10. When you add 35 and 23, the total of the ones is less than 10.

Visual Model

Reinforce the addition of tens to tens and ones to ones by showing 35 and 27 in number bonds:

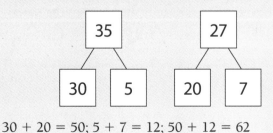

30 + 20 = 50; 5 + 7 = 12; 50 + 12 = 62

STEP BY STEP

- Read the sample problem aloud. Ask children to describe the strategy that is used to add 27 and 64.

- Encourage children to describe or demonstrate other strategies that might be used to solve the example problem.

- Some children may suggest counting on by tens and then adding the ones. Reinforce the concept of the commutative property by asking: *Is it easier to start with 27 or 64 when counting on? Why? Why doesn't it matter which number you start with?*

- Have children use the model shown for Problem 1 as a guide, but encourage them to try whatever strategies or models they prefer to show the addition. Allow pairs to compare strategies they used.

> **SMP Tip:** Draw attention to the tens and ones shown in Problem 2. Ask children if it would make sense to write the answer for 3 tens and 15 ones as 315 and why or why not. This allows children to apply the structure they have learned with the base ten system. *(SMP 7)*

- Use the Mathematical Discourse question to engage children in describing strategies and models. Stress the importance of each child utilizing a strategy that is comfortable and effective for that individual. Make sure children understand that for any problem, the strategy they find most effective may be different from what other people choose, and that's okay. Remind children that in the Opening Activity, Buzz and Boom used different strategies to get the same answer.

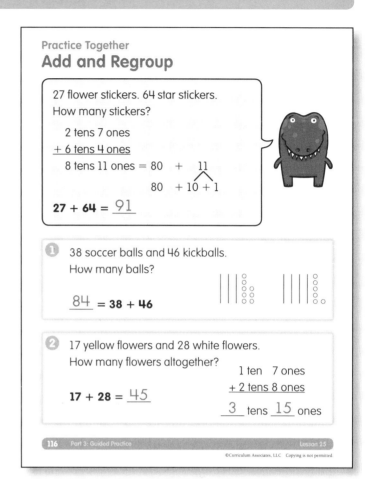

Mathematical Discourse

- *What strategy or model makes it easiest for you to add with regrouping? Why?*

    Listen to children's responses, encouraging them to justify specifically rather than saying, "It's easier." Responses should refer to combining tens and ones and accounting for composing and regrouping a ten.

Fluency Practice

Materials For each child: Practice Regrouping to Add (Activity Sheet 30)

Distribute the activity sheets. Instruct children to find the total for each addition problem. Tell them to show their work using drawings, number bonds, or numbers and words.

STEP BY STEP

- Before children work on this page, review the models used in this lesson. Emphasize that children are free to use whatever way helps them solve the problems. Tell them that they may use a different strategy for each problem if they choose.

- Read each problem aloud, then have children work independently to solve.

- Observe children as they complete Problem 3, paying attention to the methods children use to find the sum. Do they combine the ones, compose a ten, and count all the tens? Do they count all the blocks individually? Do they count all the tens and then count on all the ones? Do they ignore the model and mentally find the sum? Use these observations to provide each child the appropriate tools or support he or she needs to be successful.

- Watch for children who fail to interpret 7 tens as 70 in Problem 4. Encourage them to use base-ten blocks to model the problem and check their answer.

- Remind children to show the strategy they used in Problem 5 with a drawing or other type of model, or by describing the strategy.

- Use the second Mathematical Discourse question to start a discussion about the different strategies children used to solve the problems on this page.

ELL Support

Some English language learners may need support with the vocabulary in Problem 4. Write the word *Shapes* on the board and invite children to draw or write the names of shapes that they know. Reinforce the idea that circles and squares (and others) are all kinds of shapes.

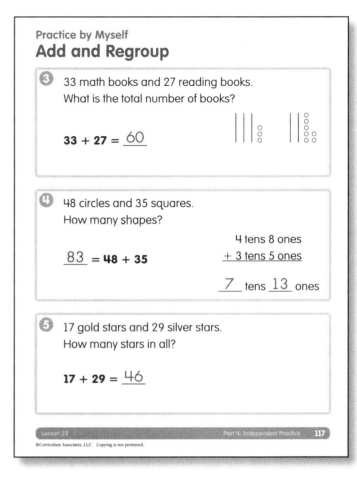

Mathematical Discourse

- *How are the models shown in Problems 3 and 4 alike? How are they different?*

  Both models show breaking up the addends into tens and ones. Problem 3 does this with drawings of tens and ones. Problem 4 does this with numbers and words.

- *How did you choose a strategy for each problem? Did you use the same strategy for all the problems?*

  Allow children to describe and justify the strategies they used. Discuss why some strategies might make more sense for certain problems (for example, making a ten in Problem 3 leaves no leftover ones to add). Encourage children to find a balance between choosing a strategy they are comfortable with and a strategy that "works well" for a specific problem.

Assessment and Remediation

- Ask children to find the sum and show their work: 27 + 58 = . [85]

- For children who are still struggling, use the chart below to guide remediation.

- After providing remediation, check children's understanding using the following problem: 15 + 49 = . [64]

If the error is . . .	Children may . . .	To remediate . . .
715	have recorded 7 tens and 15 ones as 715.	Have children model the problem with blocks. Write 7 tens as 70 and 15 as 10 + 5. Ask children how they would add 70 + 10 + 5 and compare it to their answer. Discuss which answer is correct and why. Encourage them to recognize the error they made by having them tell what is wrong with the original answer.
75	have failed to add the composed ten to the 7 tens.	Isolate the ones digits and have children calculate. Ask them to write 15 as tens and ones. Lead children to see that the 10 from 15 needs to be combined with the other tens to find the sum.
any other sum	have miscalculated.	Tell children to check their answers using a physical model.

Hands-On Activity

Build and solve problems involving regrouping.

Materials For each pair: 2 number cubes (1–6 and 4–9), white boards or paper, base-ten blocks

- Place children in pairs. One partner rolls the number cubes and forms a two-digit number using the numbers rolled as digits. The number is recorded on a white board or paper. The other partner rolls the number cubes and forms a two-digit number to add to the first number.

- Partners work together to find the sum, then check using base-ten blocks. If their sum is not correct, they must find their error before rolling again.

- If the addition requires regrouping, the partners earn a point. The activity ends when the partners have earned 5 points or when time expires.

Challenge Activity

Explore strategies involving subtraction.

Materials For each child: Hundreds Chart (Activity Sheet 19), base-ten blocks

- Remind children of the strategies they used during this lesson. Tell them that you thought of another strategy for adding 18 + 7: Add ten to 18 and then subtract 3.

- Challenge children to:

  - try the strategy with at least 10 different addition problems involving a two-digit and a one-digit number.

  - justify why this strategy works.

  - determine if it will work for adding other numbers.

- Allow children to share their work.

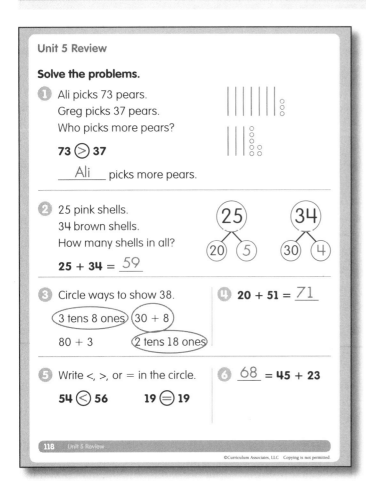

Unit 5 Review

Solve the problems.

1. Ali picks 73 pears.
   Greg picks 37 pears.
   Who picks more pears?

   73 ⊙ 37

   _____Ali_____ picks more pears.

2. 25 pink shells.
   34 brown shells.
   How many shells in all?

   25 + 34 = _59_

3. Circle ways to show 38.

   (3 tens 8 ones)   (30 + 8)
   80 + 3   (2 tens 18 ones)

4. **20 + 51 = _71_**

5. Write <, >, or = in the circle.

   54 ⊙ 56   **19 ⊜ 19**

6. **_68_ = 45 + 23**

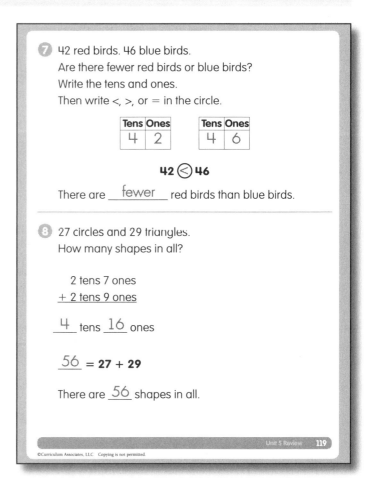

7. 42 red birds. 46 blue birds.
   Are there fewer red birds or blue birds?
   Write the tens and ones.
   Then write <, >, or = in the circle.

Tens	Ones
4	2

Tens	Ones
4	6

   42 ⊙ 46

   There are ___fewer___ red birds than blue birds.

8. 27 circles and 29 triangles.
   How many shapes in all?

     2 tens 7 ones
   + 2 tens 9 ones

   _4_ tens _16_ ones

   _56_ = 27 + 29

   There are _56_ shapes in all.

STEP BY STEP

- Have children solve the problems individually and show their work. Emphasize that children are free to use whatever way helps them solve the problems.

- Monitor children's comfort and ability to move flexibly between different representations of tens and ones—visual model of base ten blocks, tens and ones chart, number bond, words, and mathematical expressions.

- Some models refer to a number of tens, while others represent tens numerically (as 20 or 30, for example). Children should be able to explain the meaning of a ten [10 ones] and use their knowledge of tens and ones to add two-digit numbers.

- For Problems 7 and 8, children need to apply knowledge of tens and ones to a context and use their understanding of numbers in base ten to solve problems.

- If children struggle with the representation in Problem 8, have them relate it to the charts shown in Problem 7. Then guide them to add the tens and add the ones. Finally, elicit that the tens and ones must be written as a number. You may wish to have some children use base ten blocks or a visual representation of base ten blocks.

STEP BY STEP

- On this page, children write a two-digit number and set up an addition problem involving regrouping. They add, using any approach that makes sense to them.

- Direct children to complete the Put It Together on their own.

- Read the directions and task aloud. Make sure children understand what they need to do to complete the task.

- As children work on their own, observe their progress and understanding. Respond to their questions and provide additional support as needed.

- Have children share their problem and solution with the class. Ask them to explain the strategy they used.

- Have the class ask questions about each child's work. Encourage children to justify their work and tell how they added and regrouped.

Put It Together

9 Add two numbers.

Use the digits 5 and 7 to write a number.
Add your number to 28.
Show your work.

> Children write either 57 or 75. They might make a quick drawing to show their number and 28.
>
> Possible answer:
>
>   5 tens 7 ones
>   + 2 tens 8 ones
>   7 tens 15 ones = 8 tens 5 ones
>
>   57 + 28 = 85

120 Unit 5 Review

©Curriculum Associates, LLC   Copying is not permitted.

SCORING RUBRICS

Expectations for 4–3 Points

Points	Expectations
4	The child: • writes 57 or 75. • uses an appropriate strategy to add either 57 or 75 to 28; all work is accurate.
3	The child: • writes 57 or 75. • uses an appropriate strategy to add either 57 or 75 to 28; work might have minor errors.

Expectations for 2–0 Points

Points	Expectations
2	The child: • writes 57 or 75. • shows work with some indication of a strategy for adding either 57 or 75 to 28 that contains some computational errors.
1	The child: • may write a number other than 57 or 75, for example just 7 or 5. • shows work with no clear strategy for adding either 57 or 75 to 28 that is inaccurate and/or incomplete.
0	The child: • does not attempt to complete the task.

Unit 6: Geometry—Shapes

Which lessons are students building upon?

Kindergarten, Lesson 29
See Position and Shape
G.A.1 (and K.CC.4d for NY)

Kindergarten, Lesson 30
Name Shapes
K.G.A.2, K.G.A.3

Kindergarten, Lesson 31
Compare Shapes
K.G.B.4

Kindergarten, Lesson 30
Name Shapes
K.G.A.2, K.G.A.3

Kindergarten, Lesson 31
Compare Shapes
K.G.B.4

Kindergarten, Lesson 32
Build Shapes
K.G.B.5, K.G.B.6

Kindergarten, Lesson 30
Name Shapes
K.G.A.2, K.G.A.3

Kindergarten, Lesson 31
Compare Shapes
K.G.B.4

Kindergarten, Lesson 32
Build Shapes
K.G.B.5, K.G.B.6

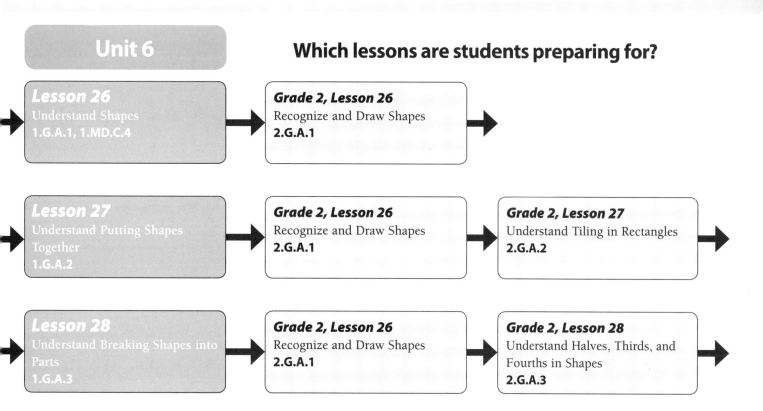

Unit 6

Which lessons are students preparing for?

Lesson 26
Understand Shapes
1.G.A.1, 1.MD.C.4

→ **Grade 2, Lesson 26**
Recognize and Draw Shapes
2.G.A.1

Lesson 27
Understand Putting Shapes Together
1.G.A.2

→ **Grade 2, Lesson 26**
Recognize and Draw Shapes
2.G.A.1

→ **Grade 2, Lesson 27**
Understand Tiling in Rectangles
2.G.A.2

Lesson 28
Understand Breaking Shapes into Parts
1.G.A.3

→ **Grade 2, Lesson 26**
Recognize and Draw Shapes
2.G.A.1

→ **Grade 2, Lesson 28**
Understand Halves, Thirds, and Fourths in Shapes
2.G.A.3

Lesson 26 (Student Book pages 122–125)

Understand Shapes

LESSON OBJECTIVES

- Identify the defining attributes of a shape.
- Distinguish between defining and non-defining attributes.
- Classify a shape based on its defining attributes.

PREREQUISITE SKILLS

- Recognize and name basic shapes.
- Recognize similarities and differences among shapes.
- Draw basic shapes.

VOCABULARY

corner: a point where two or more lines meet

hexagon: a shape with 6 sides and 6 corners

rectangle: a shape with 4 sides and 4 square corners that has opposite sides the same length

rhombus: a shape with 4 sides and 4 corners that has all sides the same length

side: a line segment that is part of a shape

square: a shape with 4 sides and 4 square corners that has all sides the same length

triangle: a shape with 3 sides and 3 corners

THE LEARNING PROGRESSION

In Kindergarten, children explore basic shapes in their world by naming and describing them by their visible attributes.

In Grade 1, children build on the concept of shapes by classifying, composing, and partitioning them. **In this lesson,** children analyze shapes based on defining attributes and recognize attributes that do not affect the shape—non-defining attributes. They recognize that some quadrilaterals are named by attributes other than the number of sides and corners and utilize those attributes in classifying them.

In Grade 2, children extend their understanding of shapes to include pentagons and draw shapes based on specific attributes.

📦 Ready *Teacher Toolbox*   *Teacher-Toolbox.com*

	Prerequisite Skills	1.G.A.1
Ready Lessons	✓ ✓ ✓	✓
Tools for Instruction	✓ ✓	✓
Interactive Tutorials	✓ ✓	✓ ✓

CCSS Focus

1.G.A.1 Distinguish between defining attributes (e.g., triangles are closed and three-sided) versus non-defining attributes (e.g., color, orientation, overall size); build and draw shapes to possess defining attributes.

ADDITIONAL STANDARDS: **1.MD.C.4** *(see page A36 for full text)*

STANDARDS FOR MATHEMATICAL PRACTICE: **SMP 2, 3, 6, 7** *(see page A9 for full text)*

Opening Activity: What Belongs?

Objective: Build the concept of defining attributes.	**Materials** For each pair: • Shapes 1 (Activity Sheet 31)

Overview

Children find a common attribute among shapes and determine whether other shapes belong in the same group.

Step by Step (20–25 minutes)

1 **Sort closed figures.**

- Display two cards with closed shapes. Include one shape that has only straight sides and one that has both straight and curved sides.

- Tell children that these shapes belong together in a special way. Give them time to think about this and then display a card containing an open shape.

- Explain that this shape does not belong with the others. Have children talk to a partner about what makes it different.

- Discuss that the first two shapes are "closed." Relate these shapes to fenced areas, explaining that there is no opening for anyone to get in or out. The other shape is open (or not closed) so anyone could get in or out.

- Display several other shapes, both open and closed, having children determine whether or not each one belongs to the group of "closed" shapes.

2 **Sort shapes with straight sides.**

- Repeat the activity above, first displaying two polygons, then two shapes with curved sides. Challenge children to explain why the polygons belong together.

- Emphasize that in the first two shapes, all sides are straight, and that a shape with any curved sides does not belong to the group.

- As you display other shapes, have children tell whether they belong to the group "straight sides."

3 **Sort by attribute.**

- Give each pair of children a set of shape cards.

- Draw a large circle on the board. Write the word "closed" above it. Tell children that only shapes that are closed belong in the circle.

- Have pairs determine which of their shapes belong in the circle. Invite them one at a time to put a shape in the circle. Allow the class to agree or disagree and then come to a consensus.

- Repeat for shapes with straight sides.

4 **Evaluate defining attributes.**

- Scatter all the shapes on the floor or display them on the board. Have children identify and justify the shapes that belong to the groups "closed" and "straight sides." You may want to identify all these shapes as polygons, but don't expect mastery of the term.

- Ask children to describe other ways that the shapes are alike and different. Discuss that the shapes are different sizes and colors. Encourage children to think about whether shapes of different size and color can still belong to the groups "closed" and "straight sides."

Check for Understanding

To check children's understanding of the defining attributes of a polygon, ask them to draw 3 shapes that are closed and have straight sides.

STEP BY STEP

- Begin by having volunteers share the shapes they drew from the Opening Activity. Ask them to justify that their shapes belong to both groups.

- Explain to children that there are many different kinds of shapes, but in this lesson they will only be working with shapes that are closed and have straight sides.

- Draw a few triangles on the board. Ask children what is the same about all these shapes. Then draw a square with the group of triangles and ask if it belongs and why. Help children focus on the fact that triangles have 3 sides and 3 corners.

- To emphasize that color is not a defining attribute, point out the red triangle, rectangle, and hexagon. Discuss that they are all the same color but not the same shape.

- Discuss the Talk About It question. Guide children to recognize that all the shapes are closed and have straight sides. Triangles, rectangles, and hexagons have different numbers of sides and corners. Use the Mathematical Discourse question to extend this discussion.

> **SMP Tip:** As children describe shapes, provide prompts that encourage them to communicate precisely about defining attributes. *(SMP 6)*

Concept Extension

Explore the concept of non-defining attributes.

- Use colored chalk to draw several triangles of different size, color, and orientation. Ask children to describe the differences in the shapes.

- Make a dot in one corner of each shape to use as a starting point. Slide a pointer along each side of a triangle as you count the sides. Then touch each corner, counting each one.

- Guide children to understand that a change in the color, orientation, or size doesn't affect the shape. In this case, the number of sides and corners is what defines the shape.

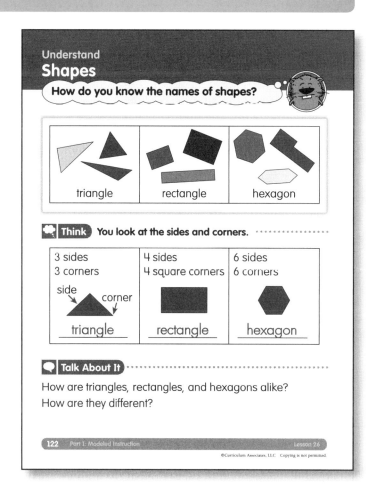

Understand
Shapes

How do you know the names of shapes?

triangle rectangle hexagon

Think You look at the sides and corners.

3 sides 3 corners	4 sides 4 square corners	6 sides 6 corners
side corner triangle	rectangle	hexagon

Talk About It

How are triangles, rectangles, and hexagons alike? How are they different?

122 Part 1: Modeled Instruction Lesson 26

©Curriculum Associates, LLC Copying is not permitted.

Mathematical Discourse

- *Boom says the pink shape in the hexagon box can't be a hexagon because it has square corners and the other ones don't. What do you think?*

  The kind of corners doesn't make a difference. If a shape has 6 sides and 6 corners it is considered a hexagon.

Misconception Alert Some children may associate the name of a shape with a particular figure they have seen repeatedly, such as the hexagon, trapezoid, and triangle found in a set of pattern blocks. Exposing children to a variety of shapes that belong to a category allows them to examine them analytically rather than depend on visual recognition.

STEP BY STEP

Materials For each child: index card

- Begin by having children examine the shapes shown on the page. Ask the Mathematical Discourse question.

- Explain to the children that shapes with 4 sides and 4 corners have many different names. Each group of shapes has common attributes that make them belong together.

- Provide each child with an index card. As they complete the activity on this page, model for them how to use the card to check for square corners and to mark it with a pencil to compare side lengths.

- Read the directions aloud. Walk through the completed example. Invite volunteers to explain why there is an *X* next to the first attribute and dots next to the others.

- Make sure children understand that they need to decide whether each of the attributes fit with a square and then with a rectangle.

- Discuss the Talk About It questions. Guide children to recognize that if the same attribute has a dot for both the rectangle and square, both shapes have this attribute in common. The *X* indicates a difference.

SMP Tip: Children focus on defining attributes and reason abstractly by discussing questions similar to those in Talk About It. Expand the discussion by asking: *How is a square like a rhombus? How is it different? How is a rectangle like a rhombus? How is it different?* (SMP 2)

ELL Support

Materials For display: square piece of paper

Hold up the square paper. Explain that a "square corner" is any corner that looks like the corners of a square. Then tape the paper to the board and point out the "opposite" sides. Ask children to identify square corners and opposite sides in the shapes on the student page.

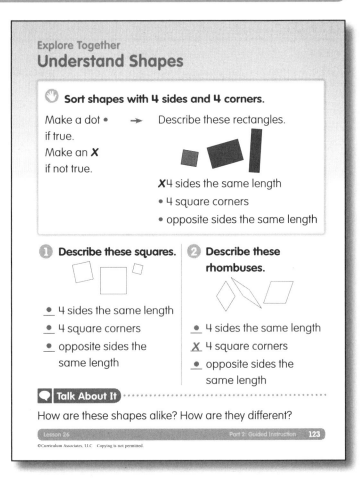

Mathematical Discourse

- *What is the same about all the shapes on this page? What is different about them?*

   All the shapes have 4 sides and 4 corners, but some of the sides are different lengths. Some of the corners are square corners and some are not.

STEP BY STEP

- Discuss each Connect It problem as a class using the discussion points outlined below.

Classify:

- You may want to place children in pairs to talk about the shapes. Remind them that some shapes may not belong to any of the groups listed.

- Display a copy of the shapes shown on the page and invite volunteers to point out the shapes they colored red and ask for justification. Encourage children to articulate the defining attributes. Repeat with the remaining shapes.

- Ask children to identify the shapes that they did not color and explain why.

Create:

- Allow children to work with a partner to describe each shape and provide support to those who struggle to connect a name with its shape. After the discussion, each child draws shapes independently.

- Encourage children to draw their shapes as carefully as possible. Do not expect precision in their drawings; however, allow children who are concerned about precision to use a straight edge.

- Invite a volunteer to display the shapes they drew and justify them. Ask others to display shapes that are different in some way from those already shown.

- Discuss how some attributes may be different, such as the size of the entire shape or lengths of some sides, yet all the shapes within each category have defining attributes that put them in the group. The one common attribute among them all is that they each have 4 sides and 4 corners.

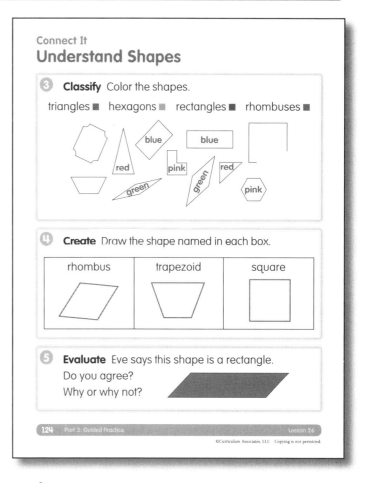

Evaluate:

- Discuss the questions as a group. Encourage children to focus on attributes, prompting them with questions such as: *Why do you think Eve might have thought this is a rectangle? Why is it important to know all the things that give a shape its name?*

- Emphasize the fact that for a shape to be given a specific name it must possess all the attributes of the shape, not just one or two.

- Stimulate further evaluation of the attributes of shapes by asking: *Boom says this shape looks like a rhombus because it is slanted. What do you think?*

- You may want to extend this concept by having children evaluate other shapes. For example, draw a square in the box labeled "rhombus" or a rectangle in the box labeled "trapezoid" and ask children if they think it belongs there and why.

STEP BY STEP

- Read the directions aloud. Make sure children understand that they must draw shapes that all have the name they selected.

- In Part A, make sure children understand that they can choose any shape on the list. They draw three different examples of that shape.

- In Part B, children compare and contrast the shapes they drew.

- As children work, prompt them with the following questions:

  What are some things you could do to make each shape a little different from the others?

  Can you find more than one way to make your shapes different from each other?

  What makes your shape different from the other shapes listed?

  How can you make sure all your shapes have the same name?

Show What I Know
Understand Shapes

6 **Make the same shape in different ways.**

A: Choose a shape to draw. Circle its name.

hexagon (triangle) rectangle
rhombus   square   trapezoid

Draw 3 of your shapes. Make each one different in some way.

Possible answer:

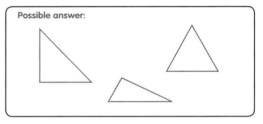

B: How are your shapes different? How are they alike?

Possible answer: They all have 3 sides and 3 corners. The sides are different lengths. One has a square corner. The rest have no square corners.

Lesson 26   Part 4: Independent Practice **125**
©Curriculum Associates, LLC   Copying is not permitted.

SCORING RUBRICS

Expectations for 4–3 Points

Points	Expectations
4	The child: • draws three shapes that have the defining attribute of the shape selected and alters each one with varied non-defining attributes. • identifies all non-defining attributes as the differences and all defining attributes as the similarities.
3	The child: • draws three shapes that have the defining attributes of the shape selected; however, the non-defining attribute may be the same for each shape (e.g., all are different sizes). • describes similarities using some defining attributes and describes differences based on the one non-defining attribute.

Expectations for 2–0 Points

Points	Expectations
2	The child: • draws three basic shapes, some of which may not be different from the others. • may describe similarities in a general way such as "all the same shape" and differences as "all different."
1	The child: • may draw shapes that do not all match the circled name. • may identify similarities and differences as either "all different" or "all the same."
0	The child: • does not attempt to draw shapes or answer the questions.

Intervention Activity

Match shapes and attributes.

Materials For each child: Shapes 1 (Activity Sheet 31)

- Have children place an attribute card at the top of their desks. They then examine each shape card and compare it to each of the attributes.

- If the shape fits all attributes, the shape card is kept face up under the attribute card. Unused shape cards are placed in a pile.

- Repeat with each of the other attribute cards.

On-Level Activity

Classify shapes by name.

Materials For each pair: Shapes 1 (Activity Sheet 31), a 3-foot length of yarn or string

- Place children in pairs and show them how to form a circle with the string. Have them lay out the shape cards face up and stack the attribute cards face down.

- Children turn up an attribute card, set it next to the circle, and take turns selecting a shape card. If the shape matches the attribute card, it goes in the circle.

- When all the shapes are placed, children discuss why they all belong in the circle. Then they remove the shapes, select a different attribute card, and repeat the activity.

Challenge Activity

Classify shapes that belong to multiple groups.

Materials For each group: Shapes 1 (Activity Sheet 31), two 3-foot lengths of yarn or string

- Allow children to work in groups of 2 to 4. Show them how to make two overlapping circles with the yarn, creating an intersection. Model the activity by placing the attribute cards for rectangle and square above each circle. Discuss how the intersection means that a shape could belong to both groups, square and rectangle.

- Select some shape cards and place them in the proper section of the overlapping circles. Point out that some shapes do not belong to either group, so they go outside the circles. Discuss why the squares are in the intersection.

- After modeling the activity, tell children to place their attribute cards face down and divide the shape cards among themselves. They randomly choose two attribute cards and place them above each circle. Then they take turns placing one of their shape cards in an appropriate section of the circles (or outside), justifying the placement.

- The group decides if the shape is placed correctly and either keeps it there or removes it. Then the next child has a turn. Continue until all shapes are placed.

- Children can redistribute the shape cards, select two different attribute cards, and repeat the activity.

Lesson 27 (Student Book pages 126–129)

Understand Putting Shapes Together

LESSON OBJECTIVES

• Compose two-dimensional shapes to create composite shapes and then compose new shapes from the composite shape.

PREREQUISITE SKILLS

• Identify and describe squares, circles, triangles, rectangles, hexagons, trapezoids, and rhombuses.

VOCABULARY

circle: a figure with no sides and no corners

compose: to combine two or more shapes to create a new shape

composite shape: a figure that is made up of two or more shapes

decompose: to break apart a shape into smaller shapes

half-circle: one of two equal parts of a circle

quarter-circle: one of four equal parts of a circle

During the lesson you will review the vocabulary from Lesson 26.

THE LEARNING PROGRESSION

In Kindergarten, children compose shapes to build pictures and designs.

In Grade 1, children compose and decompose different shapes, building an understanding of part-whole relationships. **In this lesson,** children put together two or more shapes to create a composite shape. They learn to perceive a combination of shapes as a single new shape. As a result of this work, children begin to notice shapes within an already existing shape. These ideas are extended in the next lesson in which children break circles and squares into two or four equal parts.

In Grade 2, children continue to partition circles and squares into 2 and 4 equal parts, extending the concept to rectangles and 3 equal parts.

■ **Ready** *Teacher Toolbox*

Teacher-Toolbox.com

	Prerequisite Skills	*1.G.A.2*
Ready Lessons	✓ ✓ ✓	✓
Tools for Instruction	✓ ✓	✓
Interactive Tutorials	✓	✓

1.G.A.2 Compose two-dimensional shapes (rectangles, squares, trapezoids, triangles, half-circles, and quarter-circles) or three-dimensional shapes (cubes, right rectangular prisms, right circular cones, and right circular cylinders) to create a composite shape, and compose new shapes from the composite shape.

STANDARDS FOR MATHEMATICAL PRACTICE: SMP 2, 3, 4, 5, 6, 7 (*see page A9 for full text*)

Opening Activity: Make New Shapes

Objective: Explore ways to put together shapes to make other known shapes.	**Materials** For each child: • pattern blocks or Pattern Blocks (Activity Sheet 33)

Overview

Children explore putting together shapes to make new shapes by placing different pattern blocks together to form the shape of another pattern block.

Step by Step (10–15 minutes)

1 **Introduce the activity.**

• Distribute pattern blocks to children. Hold up the different shapes and have children identify the shape names. Have children use triangles to make a rhombus, a trapezoid, and a hexagon. Then tell children that they will investigate ways to put shapes together to make other shapes.

2 **Combine two shapes to make a new shape.**

• Ask children to put together two triangles so that one side of each shape is touching. Then invite children to find a block shape that is the same shape as the new shape. Children should see that two triangle shapes form a rhombus.

• You may wish to have children place the triangles on top of the rhombus to see that the two shapes match.

• Ask children to put together two trapezoids so that they form one of the other block shapes. Guide children to join corresponding sides of the trapezoids and find the block that it matches. Children should see that two trapezoids are combined to make a hexagon.

3 **Combine like shapes to make new shapes.**

• Tell children that they can put together more than two blocks to create other block shapes. Invite children to use only triangles to make a trapezoid. Ask: *How many triangles did you use to make a trapezoid?* [3]

• Examine different ways to make a hexagon. Ask: *How many trapezoids did you use to make a hexagon?* [2] *If three triangles make a trapezoid, how many triangles are needed to make a hexagon?* [6] Allow children to combine triangles to make a hexagon and verify their answers.

• Ask children how they might put together rhombuses to make a hexagon. Encourage children to place a rhombus block on top of a hexagon block, aligning two sides. Then have children place a second rhombus block. Ask: *How can you make a hexagon using only rhombuses?* [put together 3 rhombuses]

Check for Understanding

Challenge children to use three different block shapes to make a hexagon shape. Look for understanding that a triangle and rhombus can be combined to make a trapezoid and that two trapezoids combine to make a hexagon. Children will have opportunities to develop understanding as they work through the activities of the lesson.

STEP BY STEP

Materials For each child: pattern blocks or Pattern Blocks (Activity Sheet 33)

- Introduce the question at the top of the page. Discuss with children why they think it is important to know about putting shapes together.

- Direct attention to the shapes shown at the top of the page. Invite children to describe how the pictures remind them of what they did in the Opening Activity.

- Ask children to identify the shapes that have been put together to make the new shape. Then have children name each new shape. Point out that triangles are used to make all three shapes.

- Read Think with children. Direct attention to the hexagon on the left and have children identify the blue shape as a rhombus. Tell children to draw other shapes they can add to the rhombus to make a hexagon. Then challenge them to show another way to make a hexagon that is different from the two ways shown on the page.

- Present the Talk About It question. Encourage children to share the different ways they put together shapes. Use the Mathematical Discourse question to extend the discussion.

Visual Model

Draw 3 regular hexagons on the board. As you complete the activity, use different colors to represent the different shapes that you draw. Start with a hexagon that shows six triangles. Then ask children what shape can be made with 2 triangles. In the second drawing, replace 2 triangles with 1 rhombus. Continue the process until the second hexagon shows three rhombuses. Refer children back to the hexagon with six triangles. Ask them what shape can be made with 3 triangles. In the third hexagon, show how 2 trapezoids can be put together to make a hexagon.

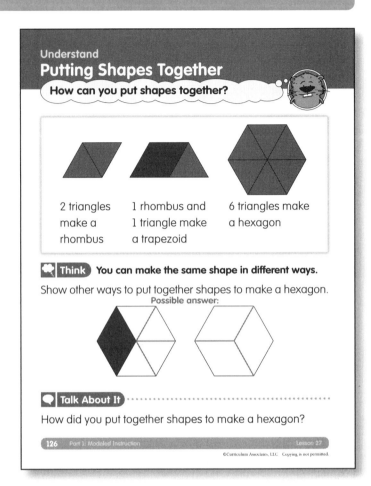

Mathematical Discourse

- *How did you decide what shapes to show in your hexagon drawings?*

  Look for an understanding of which pattern block shapes were used to represent hexagons on the page and which shapes can be combined to make a trapezoid, which is essentially half of a hexagon.

STEP BY STEP

Materials For each child: Shapes 2 (Activity Sheet 32)

- Review the directions at the top of the page. Explain to children that they will put together shapes to make a new shape, and then they will use that new shape to make another new shape.

- Distribute shapes to children. Lead them through the steps of the model at the top of the page, tracing the lines within the rectangle to show the shapes that were put together.

- Have children put together shapes to make the half-circle shown in Problem 1. Tell them to draw the shapes they used.

- Then have them use the shape made in Problem 1 to make the shape in Problem 2, drawing the shapes that were put together to make the circle. Talk about how many quarter-circles were used to make the half-circle and circle.

- Read aloud the Talk About It question. Allow children to use all the shape pieces to see what other composite shapes they can make. Encourage them to describe the shapes they create.

> **SMP Tip:** As children compose shapes, they are building understanding of patterns and iterating units. Encourage children to see not just the composite shape, but the shapes that form the composite shape. Take advantage of opportunities to point out shapes, asking children to describe how that shape might be combined with other shapes to form a new shape or what shapes can be combined to form that shape. *(SMP 7)*

Concept Extension

Put Together 3-Dimensional Shapes

Materials For display: connecting cubes

Display a connecting cube and have children name its shape. Put together several cubes to create two different larger cubes. Ask: *What shapes did I put together to make another shape?* [cubes] Then make several rectangular prisms. Show children how to combine those rectangular prisms to create a cube. Discuss the idea that 3-dimensional shapes can be put together to make other 3-dimensional shapes.

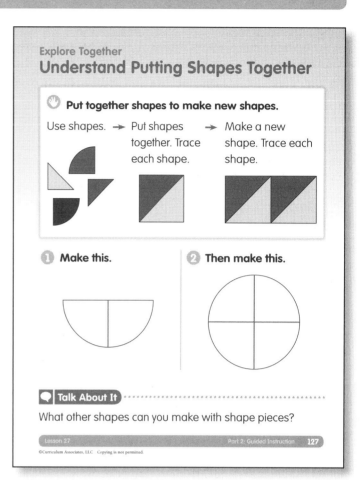

Mathematical Discourse

- *Where in your home might someone have put together shapes to make new shapes?*

  Children might suggest tile in bathrooms or kitchens, brickwork on a pathway, or fabric pieces to make a quilt.

STEP BY STEP

Materials For each child: Shapes 2 (Activity Sheet 32)

Discuss each Connect It problem as a class using the discussion points outlined below.

Analyze:

- Tell children that each of the rectangles is formed by several triangles, but they will have to combine these triangles at times to decompose each shape into the given number of shapes. You may want to demonstrate one of the shapes with the class.

- Suggest that children use different colors to show each smaller shape. Encourage them to outline the shapes before coloring to clearly see the sides of the individual shapes used to make the composite shape.

- If children have difficulty starting the activity, remind them of ways in which they combined shapes previously in the lesson.

- Invite children to describe the ways that they decomposed each rectangle. Encourage children to share different solutions.

> **SMP Tip:** Allowing children to use shape pieces of different colors to compose rectangles enables them to view situations in which tools can help solve a problem. Encourage children to continue to use concrete models to solve other geometry problems. (*SMP 5*)

Create:

- One way to approach Problem 4 is to rearrange the smaller shapes from the rectangles in Problem 3 to create a trapezoid.

- Invite children to share their drawings. Encourage all to comment on the drawings and explanations.

- Ask children to explain how they solved this problem. Some children may start with the rectangle and move the two outside triangles. Others may start with the triangles and put them together in different ways until they form the trapezoid.

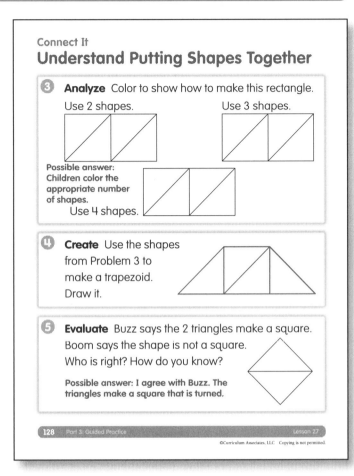

Evaluate:

- **Misconception Alert** This problem focuses on a common misconception that children have about shapes in different positions.

- Ask children to talk with a partner about the problem. After a few minutes, start a class discussion about the shape.

- Hold up a square pattern block and have children identify it as a square. Rotate the square so that it is oriented like the shape on the student page. Guide children to see that the shape is still a square.

STEP BY STEP

Materials For each child: pattern blocks or Pattern Blocks (Activity Sheet 33)

- Tell children that they will complete this page independently.

- Read the directions aloud, making sure children understand what they are expected to do. Allow children to use pattern blocks as they work independently to solve the problems.

- In Part A, children use four or more small shapes to make and draw two different composite shapes.

- In Part B, children identify and count the smaller shapes that were used in one of the composite shapes they drew.

- Observe children as they work. Ask questions, such as the following to encourage thinking and problem-solving strategies:

  How do you know that you have followed the directions?

  How can you easily show the different shapes that you used in each new shape?

  How can you tell that you have recorded all the shapes in Part B?

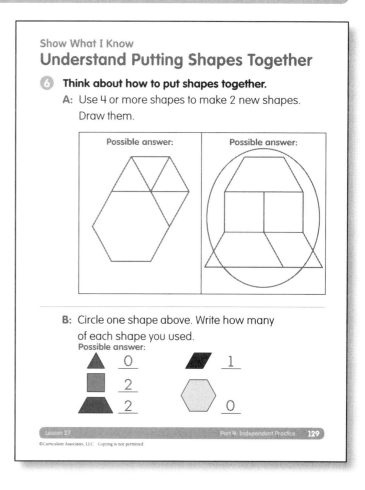

SCORING RUBRICS

Expectations for 4–3 Points

Points	Expectations
4	The child: • accurately uses four or more shapes to make two new shapes and draws the small shapes that were used. • circles one shape, and accurately counts and identifies the number of smaller shapes in the composite shape.
3	The child: • may make two new shapes, but may not use four or more smaller shapes for each composite shape or does not indicate the smaller shapes in the composite shape. • may identify the shapes used in the composite shape, but may identify some shapes incorrectly or miscount the number of smaller shapes used.

Expectations for 2–0 Points

Points	Expectations
2	The child: • may make a composite shape, but does not use four or more smaller shapes or does not make two composite shapes. • identifies only a few of the shapes used in the composite shape.
1	The child: • attempts to make two different composite shapes, but there is no evidence of understanding either problem.
0	The child: • does not attempt to solve the problems.

Intervention Activity

Match shapes to outlines.

Materials: Pattern Blocks (Activity Sheet 33), pattern blocks

- Have children place actual pattern blocks within each shape on the activity sheet, naming the shapes and the number of sides.

- Have children remove the pattern blocks. Point to the rhombus. Instruct children to make the rhombus shape with pattern blocks other than the rhombus. Allow children time to experiment with different shapes until they find a combination that works.

- Guide children to continue working through the shapes, placing different pattern blocks within the outlines to see which pattern blocks can be combined to create each shape on the activity sheet.

On-Level Activity

Use Shapes to Make New Shapes

Materials: pattern blocks or Pattern Blocks (Activity Sheet 33)

- Guide children to put together two triangle pieces to make a new shape. Have children name the new shape.

- Ask children to add another triangle to the new shape to make another new shape. Have them name that new shape.

- Challenge children to add more shapes until they have formed a hexagon. Encourage some children to try to make a hexagon that looks different than the pattern block hexagon.

- Invite children to share the work they did and name all the shapes they used to make the hexagon.

Challenge Activity

Make pictures with shapes.

Materials: 7 tangram pieces, tangram pictures, paper, pencil

- Display pictures made from tangram pieces. Challenge children to make their own tangram puzzles or pictures.

- Encourage children to use all seven pieces in their pictures. Have children make their pictures on a sheet of paper. Once the picture is made, children trace around their pictures to make an outline.

- Allow children to trade papers. See if another child can recreate the picture by placing the tangram pieces within the outline.

Lesson 28 (Student Book pages 130–133)

Understand Breaking Shapes into Parts

LESSON OBJECTIVES

- Divide circles and rectangles into two and four equal parts.
- Identify the number of equal parts in a divided shape.
- Name the parts as halves, fourths, and quarters.
- Understand that if a whole is divided into more parts, the parts get smaller.

PREREQUISITE SKILLS

- Identify circles, squares, and rectangles.
- Compose and decompose shapes.
- Draw shapes.

VOCABULARY

equal parts: parts that cover an equal amount of space

fourths, fourth: four equal parts; one of four parts of a whole

halves, half: two equal parts; one of two equal parts of a whole

quarters, quarter: four equal parts; one of four parts of a whole

unequal parts: parts of a whole that are not the same size

whole: all of an object, a group of objects, shape, or quantity

THE LEARNING PROGRESSION

In Kindergarten, children discuss shape and orientation. They also put shapes together to compose other shapes.

In Grade 1, children develop competencies about shapes, including understanding defining and non-defining attributes and composing and decomposing shapes. **In this lesson,** children decompose simple shapes into equal shares of halves and fourths. They describe the relationships between the equal shares and the whole, and between the halves and fourths. This lesson is a foundational building block of fractions, which will be extended in future grades.

In Grade 2, children partition circles and rectangles into two, three, or four equal shares and recognize that equal shares of identical wholes need not have the same shape.

Ready *Teacher Toolbox*   *Teacher-Toolbox.com*

	Prerequisite Skills	I.G.A.3
Ready Lessons	✓ ✓ ✓	✓
Tools for Instruction	✓	✓
Interactive Tutorials	✓	✓

CCSS Focus

1.G.A.3 Partition circles and rectangles into two and four equal shares, describe the shares using the words *halves, fourths,* and *quarters,* and use the phrases *half of, fourth of,* and *quarter of.* Describe the whole as two of, or four of the shares. Understand for these examples that decomposing into more equal shares creates smaller shares.

STANDARDS FOR MATHEMATICAL PRACTICE: **SMP 2, 3, 4, 6, 7** *(see page A9 for full text)*

Opening Activity: Fold Paper into Equal Parts

Objective: Explore equal shares and identify the parts as halves and fourths.

Materials For each child:
- rectangular sheet of paper
- Shapes 2 (Activity Sheet 32)

Overview

Children explore equal shares by folding paper rectangles and circles into halves and fourths. Children observe the change in size of the parts as more parts are made.

Step by Step (10–15 minutes)

1 Pose the problem.
- Invite two children to come to the front of the class. Hold up a large sheet of paper. Say: *These two friends want to share a sheet of paper so that they each have the same amount of paper. How can they share the paper?*

2 Explore halves.
- Distribute sheets of paper to pairs of children. Have them determine how to share the paper so that each person has an equal part.
- After a few minutes, allow pairs to share their strategies. Some children may fold the paper in half, matching sides and corners. Others may simply draw a line down what they approximate to be the middle of the paper.
- Discuss with the class how to determine if the parts are equal. Encourage partners to see if the two parts match exactly.

3 Explore fourths.
- Pose a similar problem. Say: *Four friends want to share a sheet of paper. How can they share the paper?*
- Distribute another sheet of paper to each pair of children. Guide them to use the strategy of folding and aligning the sides of the paper to make the parts equal.
- Again, have children share their strategies and compare their equal parts. Look for partners who divided the paper differently and discuss how the equal parts can look different but still be equal parts of the whole piece of paper.

4 Compare halves and fourths.
- Ask children to compare their two sheets of paper. Note that one sheet shows two equal parts while the other sheet shows four equal parts.
- Have children observe and discuss the size of one part on each sheet of paper. Guide children to see that the sheet with more parts has smaller parts.

Check for Understanding

Use the activity sheets to cut out and distribute paper circles to each child. Tell them that the circle represents a pie. Ask children to show how four friends can equally share the pie.

If children struggle with completing the task or showing fourths, they will have opportunities to develop understanding as they work through the activities of the lesson.

STEP BY STEP

- Introduce the question at the top of the page. Then direct attention to the circles. Invite children to describe how the pictures remind them of what they did in the Opening Activity.

- Discuss how a shape that shows two equal parts shows "halves" and one part is "half of" the whole. Then help children make the connection between the number "four" and the word "fourths" as you discuss one of four equal parts being a "fourth of" the whole.

- Read Think with children. Have them imagine that the squares on the page are pieces of paper or sandwiches that are being shared. Guide children to compare the squares. Ask: *How do you know the parts are not equal?* [They do not cover an equal amount of the shape.]

> **SMP Tip:** Solving real-life problems with models helps make children develop mathematical proficiency. Ask children to routinely interpret their mathematical results in the context of a situation and see if the results make sense. *(SMP 4)*

- Present the Talk About It question. Encourage discussion by asking questions, such as: *How can you tell if the parts shown at the top of the page are equal? Does someone have a different way to tell if the parts are equal?* Allow children to share their ideas.

Hands-On Activity

Show equal parts on a geoboard.

Materials For each pair: geoboard and rubber bands

Have partners stretch a rubber band on the geoboard to form a square and then use another rubber band to break the square into two equal parts. Encourage children to use the pegs on the geoboard to help them find the middle of one side of the shape. Guide them to anchor the rubber band on that peg and stretch it to the opposite side of the square. Then have children suggest how to divide the square into four equal parts. As children share their work, discuss whether they have made equal parts.

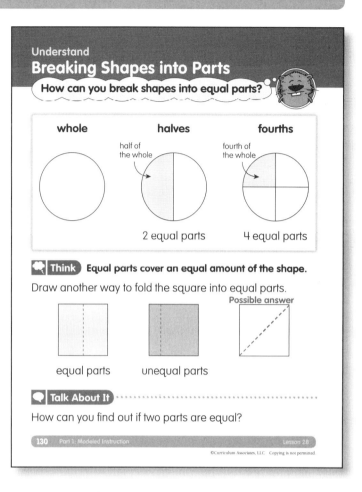

Mathematical Discourse

- *If you can't fold a shape in half, how can you be sure that you are breaking it into equal parts?*

  Look for responses that include using what they know about the attributes of a shape, or knowing the smaller shapes that can be put together to create a larger shape.

ELL Support

Some languages do not include the "th" sound. When you introduce "fourth" and "fourths," emphasize the "th" ending and contrast the words "four" and "fourth." Allow children to practice pronouncing the words and hearing the difference.

STEP BY STEP

Materials For each child: Shapes 2 (Activity Sheet 32)

- Cut out the large circle and square from the activity sheets and distribute to each child. Review the directions at the top of the page.

- Have children follow the model by folding the paper circle to show two equal parts. Help them make the connection between the fold line and the line in the second circle that makes equal parts. Ask children why the word "halves" is circled.

- Allow children time to complete Problems 1 and 2. Check that they fold the paper correctly to show equal parts. Encourage children to replicate the fold lines by drawing lines in the shapes on the page.

- Remind children to circle the word that describes the parts. When children get to Problem 2, review that "quarters" is another word that is used to describe four equal parts and means the same thing as "fourths."

- Read aloud the Talk About It question. Encourage children to justify their answers. Ask the Mathematical Discourse question.

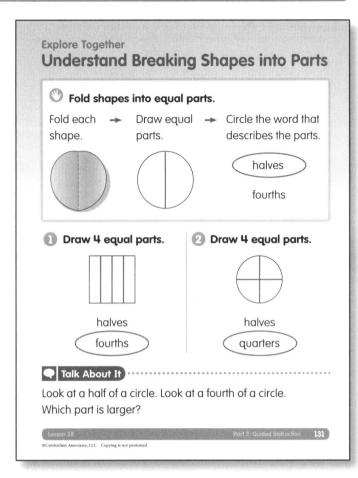

Concept Extension

Fold other shapes into equal parts.

Materials For each child: paper shapes (triangles, rectangles, trapezoids, and hexagons)

Distribute the paper shapes. Have children fold the shapes into two equal parts. Then ask children to try to divide each shape into four equal parts. Discuss the results. Children should discover that not all of the shapes can be divided into four equal parts.

Mathematical Discourse

- *How did you decide if a half of a circle or a fourth of a circle is larger?*

  Some children might have used the parts of the folded shapes, while others may have used the pictured halves and fourths on the page. Encourage several children to share their strategies.

STEP BY STEP

Discuss each Connect It problem as a class using the discussion points outlined below.

Explain:

- This problem focuses on the understanding that decomposing into more equal parts creates smaller parts.

- Suggest that children refer to other places in the lesson where they have divided circles into equal parts.

- Ask questions such as: *How can you tell whose pizza has smaller pieces? How does the size of a part change when there are more parts?*

> **SMP Tip:** Asking children to show how they found an answer provides an opportunity for children to construct a viable argument. Encourage children to use concrete referents, such as drawings or diagrams, to make their arguments. *(SMP 3)*

Identify:

- In previous problems, the number of equal parts is given. This problem focuses on children's ability to describe the number of equal parts in the whole.

- Suggest that children mark each part as they count the number of equal parts. They might also label each part with a consecutive counting number.

- Ask children what each of the equal parts of this shape is called. [a fourth or a quarter]

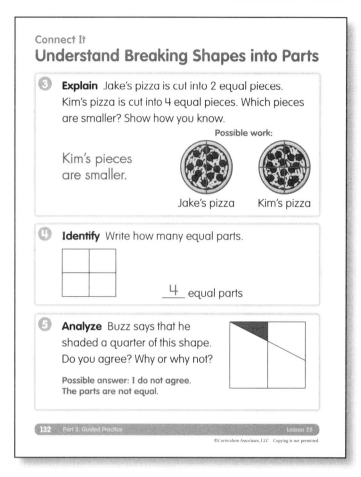

Analyze:

- This problem features the meaning of a "quarter" as well as the importance of dividing into equal parts when showing a quarter.

- Ask children to talk with a partner about the problem. After a few minutes, start a class discussion about how to know what a quarter of a shape is.

- Ask questions, such as: *How many parts do you make to divide a shape into quarters? How can you tell if the shape is divided correctly?*

- After children share their answers, you may want to draw similar rectangles on the board and invite volunteers to show how to correctly divide the shape into quarters.

STEP BY STEP

- Tell children that they will complete this page independently.

- Read the directions aloud, making sure children understand what they are expected to do.

- In Part A, 5 cookies need to be shared equally between 2 friends. Children identify that each friend will get some whole cookies and an equal part of one cookie.

- In Part B, 5 cookies need to be shared equally among 4 friends. Children identify that each friend will get a whole cookie and an equal part of one cookie.

- Observe children as they work. Ask questions such as the following to encourage thinking and problem-solving strategies:

When Ben shares the cookies with one friend, how many equal shares will there be?

How many whole cookies will Ben and his friend each get?

How can Ben and his friend equally share the remaining cookie?

When Ben shares the cookies with three friends, how many equal shares will there be?

If each friend gets one whole cookie, how can they share the remaining cookie?

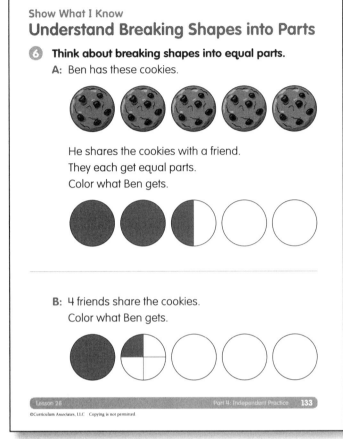

Show What I Know
Understand Breaking Shapes into Parts

6 **Think about breaking shapes into equal parts.**

A: Ben has these cookies.

He shares the cookies with a friend.
They each get equal parts.
Color what Ben gets.

B: 4 friends share the cookies.
Color what Ben gets.

Lesson 28   Part 4: Independent Practice   **133**
©Curriculum Associates, LLC   Copying is not permitted.

SCORING RUBRICS

Expectations for 4–0 Points

Points	Expectations
4	The child: • accurately shades Ben's share of the cookies in each situation.
3	The child: • may shade the whole cookies in each situation, but does not shade the partial cookie.
2	The child: • may shade more than one cookie in each situation, but does not accurately shade all wholes or parts.
1	The child: • may shade some of the cookies, but there is no evidence of understanding of the problems.
0	The child: • does not attempt to solve the problems.

Intervention Activity

Match and make halves and fourths.

Materials For each child: 4 sheets of paper, marker or crayon, scissors

- Cut one sheet of paper into two equal parts and label each part with the word "half." Cut a second sheet into four equal parts and label each part with the word "fourth."

- Have children match the fractional puzzle pieces to a whole rectangular piece of paper, placing them on top of the paper to check that they match.

- Have children fold, cut, and label the unmarked sheets of paper to show halves and fourths.

- You may want to follow up with a discussion about the idea that fourths of the same shape are smaller than halves.

On-Level Activity

Show halves and fourths.

Materials For each child: 2 sheets of paper, 2 paper plates, marker or crayon

- Distribute the materials to each child. Have children fold one sheet of paper to show two equal parts. Then have children label each part with the word "half."

- Have children fold the other sheet of paper to show four equal parts. Have children label each part with the word "fourth." Discuss with children that the word "quarter" can also be used to describe each part.

- Invite children to repeat the process with the paper plates, showing both halves and fourths.

Challenge Activity

Make more equal parts

Materials For each child: 3 or 4 pieces of paper

Distribute paper. Challenge children to fold each piece of paper to show a different number of equal parts. Tell them to try to make more than four equal parts with each piece of paper. Have children share their results with the class. You may wish to identify the various numbers of equal parts and ask children to suggest what these parts might be called.

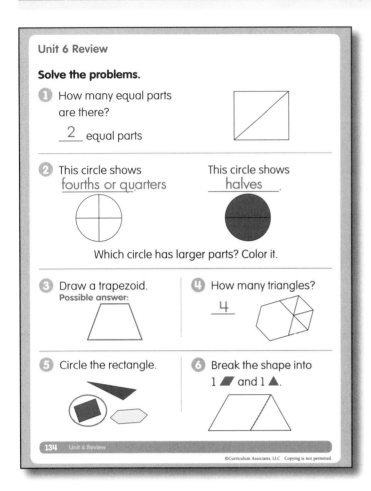

Unit 6 Review

Solve the problems.

1. How many equal parts are there?

   __2__ equal parts

2. This circle shows __fourths or quarters__.

   This circle shows __halves__.

   Which circle has larger parts? Color it.

3. Draw a trapezoid.
   Possible answer:

4. How many triangles?

   __4__

5. Circle the rectangle.

6. Break the shape into 1 ▰ and 1 ▲.

134   Unit 6 Review

©Curriculum Associates, LLC   Copying is not permitted.

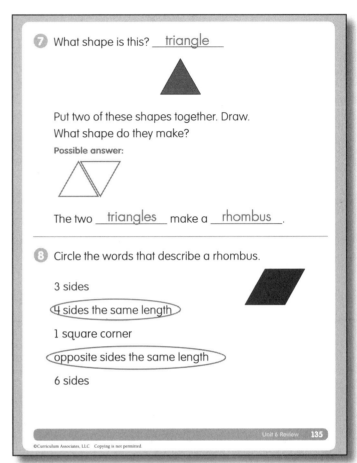

7. What shape is this? __triangle__

   Put two of these shapes together. Draw. What shape do they make?
   Possible answer:

   The two __triangles__ make a __rhombus__.

8. Circle the words that describe a rhombus.

   3 sides

   (4 sides the same length)

   1 square corner

   (opposite sides the same length)

   6 sides

©Curriculum Associates, LLC   Copying is not permitted.

Unit 6 Review   135

STEP BY STEP

Materials For each child: Shapes 2 (Activity Sheet 32), Pattern Blocks (Activity Sheet 33)

- Have children solve the problems individually and show their work. Emphasize that children are free to use whatever way helps them solve the problems.

- Circulate and observe children as they work. Children should be able to identify shapes and their distinguishing attributes such as number of sides.

- You may want to distribute cutout shapes (from the activity sheets) or pattern blocks for children to use as templates for tracing or as models for drawing shapes. The distinguishing attributes should be visible in the shapes that the children draw.

STEP BY STEP

- On this page, children draw a shape that is made up of two or four triangles. Then they use this to create a new composite shape. They name the composite shape and identify the equal parts.

- Direct children to complete the Put It Together on their own.

- Read the directions and task aloud. Make sure children understand what they need to do to complete the task.

- As children work on their own, observe their progress and understanding. Respond to their questions and provide additional support as needed.

- Have children share their finished drawing with the class. Ask them to name the number of parts their first shape is divided into. [2 or 4].

- Have children point to and identify the shapes they used to make the second composite shape.

Put It Together

9 **Make shapes.**

Put together 2 or 4 triangles like this ◣.

Make a shape with 4 sides. Describe the shape.

The shape is a ___rectangle___ .   **Possible answer:**
It has __4__ equal parts.

Circle the word that describes
the equal parts.

halves   (fourths)

Use the shape you made.
Add some other shapes   **Possible answer:**
to make a new shape.

Draw the new shape.

136   Unit 6 Review

©Curriculum Associates, LLC   Copying is not permitted.

SCORING RUBRICS

Expectations for 4–3 Points

Points	Expectations
4	The child: • draws a composite shape using two or four triangles. • identifies the number of equal parts and the fractional name. • identifies all the shapes in the composite shape.
3	The child: • draws a composite shape using two or four triangles. • identifies the number of equal parts and/or the fractional name. • identifies most of the shapes in the composite shape.

Expectations for 2–0 Points

Points	Expectations
2	The child: • may use two or four triangles, but the drawing does not align corresponding sides. • identifies the number of equal parts or the fractional name, but not both. • identifies some of the shapes in the composite shape.
1	The child: • may not use the correct number of triangles and the drawing does not align corresponding sides. • incorrectly identifies the number of equal parts and/or the fractional name. • incorrectly identifies most or all of the shapes in the composite shape.
0	The child: • does not attempt to complete the task.

Unit 7: Measurement and Data—How Many? How Much? How Long?

Which lessons are students building upon?

Kindergarten, Lesson 26
Compare Lengths
K.MD.A.1, K.MD.A.2

Kindergarten, Lesson 27
Compare Weight
K.MD.A.1, K.MD.A.2

Kindergarten, Lesson 28
Sort Objects
K.MD.B.3

Kindergarten, Lesson 26
Compare Lengths
K.MD.A.1, K.MD.A.2

Kindergarten, Lesson 27
Compare Weight
K.MD.A.1, K.MD.A.2

Kindergarten, Lesson 26
Compare Lengths
K.MD.A.1, K.MD.A.2

Kindergarten, Lesson 26
Compare Lengths
K.MD.A.1, K.MD.A.2

Unit 7

Which lessons are students preparing for?

Lesson 29
Sort and Count
1.MD.C.4, 1.G.A.1, 1.G.A.2

→ **Grade 2, Lesson 23**
Draw and Use Bar Graphs and Pictographs
2.MD.D.10

Lesson 30
Compare Data
1.MD.C.4, 1.OA.A.1, 1.OA.C.6

→ **Grade 2, Lesson 20**
Compare Lengths
2.MD.A.4

→ **Grade 2, Lesson 23**
Draw and Use Bar Graphs and Pictographs
2.MD.D.10

Lesson 31
Order Objects by Length
1.MD.A.1

→ **Grade 2, Lesson 16**
Understand Length and Measurement Tools
2.MD.A.1

→ **Grade 2, Lesson 17**
Measure Length
2.MD.A.1

Lesson 32
Compare Lengths
1.MD.A.1

→ **Grade 2, Lesson 17**
Measure Length
2.MD.A.1

→ **Grade 2, Lesson 20**
Compare Lengths
2.MD.A.4

Lesson 33
Understand Length Measurement
1.MD.A.2

→ **Grade 2, Lesson 19**
Understand Estimating Length
2.MD.A.3

→ **Grade 2, Lesson 20**
Compare Lengths
2.MD.A.4

Lesson 34
Tell Time
1.MD.B.3

→ **Grade 2, Lesson 24**
Tell and Write Time
2.MD.C.7, 2.NBT.A.2

Unit 7: Measurement and Data—How Many? How Much? How Long?

225

Lesson 29 (Student Book pages 138–141)

Sort and Count

LESSON OBJECTIVES

- Define meaningful categories for a given set of objects and sort the objects according to the categories.

- Count to find the number of objects in each category.

- Represent categorical data using tally charts, charts with numbers, and picture graphs.

PREREQUISITE SKILLS

- Count up to 20 objects.

- Identify geometric shapes.

VOCABULARY

data: numerical information about a set of objects, usually gathered through observation, surveys, or measurement

picture graph: a data display in which pictures are used to represent the number of data in each category

sort: to group or organize objects by shared attributes

tally chart: a data display in which tally marks are used to represent the number of data in each category

tally marks: marks used to show pieces of data being counted

THE LEARNING PROGRESSION

In Kindergarten, children classify objects into categories. They count collections of objects and compare sets of objects.

In Grade 1, children begin to organize and represent categorical data in various ways. They ask and answer questions about data, using what they know about addition and subtraction. **In this lesson,** children sort objects into categories and begin to understand the benefits of organizing and representing such data. They represent categorical data in tally charts, in charts with numbers, and in picture graphs. They count the objects in each category and begin to explore categorical information.

In Grade 2, children make picture graphs and bar graphs to represent data sets with up to four categories. They solve simple put-together, take-apart, and compare problems using information presented in the graphs. Children's work with categorical data in early grades prepares them for later work with bivariate categorical data—data that are categorized according to two attributes.

■ **Ready** *Teacher Toolbox*   *Teacher-Toolbox.com*

	Prerequisite Skills	1.MD.C.4
Ready Lessons	✓ ✓ ✓	✓
Tools for Instruction	✓ ✓	
Interactive Tutorials	✓ ✓	

CCSS Focus

1.MD.C.4 Organize, represent, and interpret data with up to three categories; ask and answer questions about the total number of data points, how many in each category, and how many more or less are in one category than in another.

ADDITIONAL STANDARDS: *1.G.A.1, 1.G.A.2* (see page A36 for full text)

STANDARDS FOR MATHEMATICAL PRACTICE: *SMP 2, 3, 4, 6* (see page A9 for full text)

Opening Activity: Understanding Sorting and Counting

Objective: Identify the rule, or attribute, for a given sorting procedure.	**Materials** For each child: • writing utensils, such as pen, pencil, marker, crayon, and chalk

Overview

Children explore the concept of organizing, or sorting, data by categories as they try to determine the rule and predict how each item will be sorted.

Step by Step (5–10 minutes)

1 Pose the problem.

• Explain to children that you are going to sort them into two groups and it is their job to figure out the sorting rule.

2 Sort the children.

• Decide on a sorting rule—striped clothing, for example—but do not share with the class.

• Have children come up to the front of the room one by one, and guide them to the left (striped) or right (not striped).

• After several children have been sorted, ask the class to predict which side the next child will go to.

• Continue sorting, and asking children to predict which group the children belong to.

3 Identify the rule.

• After several predictions, have children state what they think the sorting rule is. Keep a list of ideas to discourage repeats.

• If children are unable to figure out the rule, provide some hints. For example: *What do you notice that is the same about everyone in this group?* Or get more specific, such as: *What is the same about everyone's clothing in this group?*

• Once the rule is identified, have children sort a few more classmates. Then discuss their observations about the two groups.

4 Talk about sorting rules.

• Ask: *What other sorting rules could you use?* Elicit the idea that there are many different ways to sort a group, for example by hair color or gender. Challenge children to look around the room and suggest other sorting rules for different classroom objects.

• Display the writing utensils. Ask: *What would happen if I sorted all the objects that are used to write into one group and all the objects that are not used to write into another group?* [You'd have only one group.]

Check for Understanding

As children give their ideas for the sorting rule, listen for evidence that they understand the purpose of sorting: to differentiate objects according to their attributes. Be alert for children who think there is only one way to sort a group.

Part 1: Modeled Instruction

STEP BY STEP

- Read the questions at the top of the page.

- Explain that to answer these questions, you have to sort the shapes. That means to make groups that include all the same shapes. Use the Hands-On Activity to introduce the sorting process or provide practice.

- Read Model It with children. Point out that the tally chart uses tally marks to represent each object that fits the sorting category. Guide children to identify the sorting categories as triangle, square, and trapezoid.

- Have children count the triangles, making sure that they track each one. Ask the Mathematical Discourse question to emphasize the importance of organization and tracking.

- Compare children's counts with the number of tally marks in the triangle row.

- Tell children to complete the tally chart by counting the squares and then the trapezoids. As they count and track each shape above, children make a tally mark in the chart below.

- Ask children to verify that the tallies are correct for each shape. Then ask them to complete the second chart with the appropriate numbers for each category.

Hands-On Activity

Materials For each pair: pattern blocks

Have children work in pairs. Give them about 10–12 pattern blocks with three different shapes. Have children sort the blocks into groups and explain their sorts to the class. Ask how many pattern blocks are in each category.

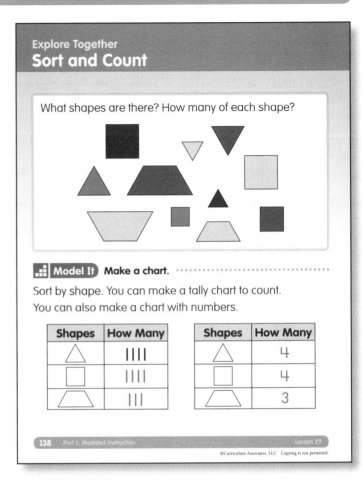

Mathematical Discourse

- *How can you keep track of the objects as you count them?*

  Some children may cover the shapes with their fingers. Others might make a mark on each as they count. Children should be able to explain their method and show that there is a one-to-one correspondence between tally marks and the actual number of items in any category.

STEP BY STEP

Materials For each pair: colored strips of paper in different lengths to match the pencils in the problem.

- You may want to give children colored strips of paper to allow them to do a physical sort.

- Read the questions at the top of the page. Be sure children understand that they need to sort by color.

- Have children work with a partner to verify the number of yellow pencils. One child counts and marks the yellow pencils while the other counts the tally marks. Guide children to recognize that the number of tally marks in each row matches the number of circles in the picture graph.

- Instruct partners to complete the tally chart and picture graph in a similar manner, taking turns counting and making tally marks and circles. Encourage them to check their work.

- **Error Alert** Read Talk About It. Discuss that the pencils are different lengths and can also be sorted into groups of short pencils and long pencils. Clear up the misconception that there is only one way to sort a group of objects. Then present the Concept Extension to extend this discussion.

> **SMP Tip:** As children experiment with organizing and representing data—sorting, counting, making picture graphs, etc.—they begin to make connections between the different models. To support this emerging understanding, ask children to explain how a tally chart or picture graph helps them understand the information or see patterns in the data. (*SMP 4*)

Concept Extension

Sort by two attributes.

Review that the pencils can be sorted by color or by length. Then explain that they can be sorted by both color and length. Ask: *How many pencils are both yellow and short?* [2] *How many are yellow and long?* [2] Continue with the other colors. After counting the pencils that belong in each of these groups, ask children to find the total number of pencils and verify that it is the same as in the sorting by color.

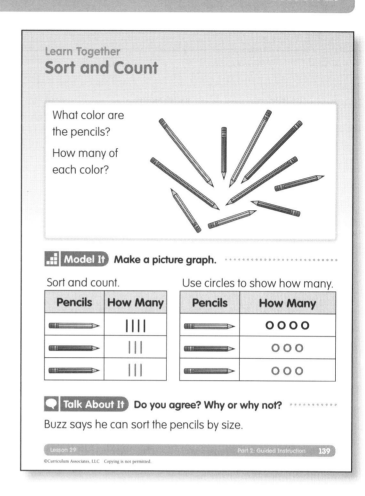

Mathematical Discourse

- *How are the tally chart and picture graph alike? How are they different?*

  Children should understand that both the tally chart and the picture graph show how many of each color pencil there are. The tally chart uses tally marks to stand for each pencil and the picture graph uses circles.

STEP BY STEP

- Direct attention to the picture of the balls at the top of the page. Tell children that they will sort the balls into groups of footballs, kickballs, and soccer balls. Then they will make a tally chart and picture graph to show how many of each kind of ball there are.

- You may want to make copies of the picture and cut out the individual balls so children can use them to complete the sorting process.

- Put children in pairs to complete the tally chart. One partner can count the balls while the other makes tally marks. Together, partners check their work and make sure their tally charts are complete.

> **SMP Tip:** Children attend to precision as they communicate with each other to carefully count and precisely record each piece of data. When they check their work, children make sense of the symbols (tally marks) they used to record the data. (SMP 6)

- Direct attention to Problem 2. Guide children to see that the column headings and the categories match those in the tally chart. Have children complete the picture graph independently.

- Compare completed graphs as a class and allow children to make corrections as needed.

Concept Extension

Discuss how graphs can be used.

- Discuss with children how graphs display data that has been counted and sorted. This allows people who were not involved in the sorting and counting to see what the results are.

- Explain that graphs can be used to ask and answer questions about the data. Ask questions, such as the following, and have children explain how the graph can be used to find the answer: *What kind of balls are there the most of? The fewest? How many more soccer balls than footballs are there? How many balls are there in all?*

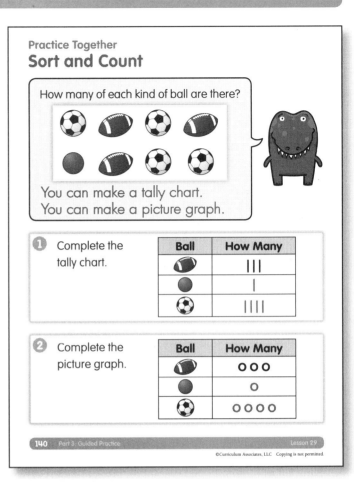

Mathematical Discourse

- *What pictures are used in the picture graph to show how many of the different kinds of balls there are? Why do you think these pictures are used?*

  Children might recognize that the pictures of circles resemble the shape of the balls and realize that circles are easy to draw.

STEP BY STEP

Materials For each child: Data Cards (Activity Sheet 34)

- Read each problem aloud, then have children work independently to solve.

- Cut the data cards from copies of the activity sheet and distribute a set to each child.

- Pose a data collection situation. Say: *A teacher has cards with pictures of apples, pears, and bananas. She asks some children to pick the card that shows the fruit that they like best. She collects the cards they pick. The picture at the top of the page and the cards that you have show their choices.*

- Tell children that they need to sort the fruit cards and make a tally chart, a chart with numbers, and a picture graph. Make sure children understand that the same data is used for each of the displays.

- Observe children as they work to make sure they are sorting correctly. Suggest that they choose a picture that is easy to draw to make the picture graph.

- Ask the Mathematical Discourse questions to check that children understand the process used for collecting and displaying data.

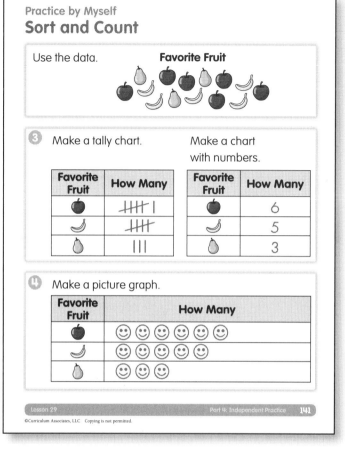

Fluency Practice

Materials For display: 120 Chart (Activity Sheet 23)

Display the 120 chart. Have the class count on by 1, 2, and 5, using examples like the following.

- count by 1:
  start at 22 and end at 40
  start at 46 and end at 60

- count by 2:
  start at 12 and end at 40
  start at 68 and end at 90

- count by 5:
  start at 25 and end at 120
  start at 55 and end at 100

Mathematical Discourse

- *Why do you think you were asked to make a tally chart first? Which chart or graph do you think shows the data best?*

  Children might recognize that they first have to sort and count the data and that the tally chart helps with the counting process. Some children may prefer the chart with numbers as a data display since there is no need to count. Others might prefer the picture graph since it is more illustrative and concrete.

Assessment and Remediation

- Show children a tally chart containing information about favorite colors: 5 blue, 6 green, 4 yellow. Have them make a picture graph to display the data.

- For children who are still struggling, use the chart below to guide remediation.

- After providing remediation, check children's understanding by changing the numbers and/or colors used in the chart, asking children to create a picture graph using the new data.

If the error is ...	Children may ...	To remediate ...
the pictures do not correspond to the number of people	not understand how to count tally marks.	Explain that each line stands for one person who picked that color. Point out that a diagonal line is used to make a group of 5. Ask children to count the tallies again and fix their graphs.
labels are missing or inaccurate	not recognize the importance of appropriate labels or know how to write them.	Ask children to describe in words what the categories represent. Have children write their description in the appropriate position on the graph. Discuss how someone who hasn't studied the data would not know what the pictures mean if they are not labeled.

Hands-On Activity

Build a tally chart one category at a time.

Materials For each pair: Chart Template (Activity Sheet 35), 12–15 connecting cubes in 3 colors

- Give pairs of children a few connecting cubes that are all the same color and the chart template. Have them write the color in the first column and write tally marks in the second column as they count the cubes. Discuss.

- Collect the connecting cubes. Give pairs 2 colors of connecting cubes and another blank chart. Elicit that they need to sort the cubes before counting and writing tally marks. Have children complete the task.

- Collect the connecting cubes. Give pairs 3 colors of connecting cubes and a third chart. Have children describe what they need to do: sort, count, tally. Have them complete the task and then verify their tallies.

Challenge Activity

Create pattern block pictures and make a tally chart.

Materials For each child: pattern blocks, paper, pencil

- Have children create a picture using at least a dozen of the pattern block shapes. Encourage them to combine multiple pieces together so that the picture is made up of pattern block shapes touching. You may want to model an example.

- Once the children have created their pictures, have them trace one shape at a time before removing it from the design. Then have the children create a tally chart of the shapes they used.

- Children may wish to swap tally charts with a partner and gather the blocks that the tally chart specifies. Then each child can attempt to follow the traced diagram to make their partner's pattern block picture.

Lesson 30 (Student Book pages 142–145)

Compare Data

LESSON OBJECTIVES

- Answer questions about data in charts and graphs.
- Compare quantities represented in charts and graphs.

PREREQUISITE SKILLS

- Read a tally chart or picture graph.
- Compare quantities within 20.

VOCABULARY

There is no new vocabulary. During the lesson you will review the key terms:

compare: to decide if amounts or sizes are greater than, less than, or equal to each other

data: numerical information about a set of objects, usually gathered through observation, surveys, or measurement

picture graph: a data display in which pictures are used to represent the number of data in each category

tally chart: a data display in which tally marks are used to represent the number of data in each category

tally marks: marks used to show pieces of data being counted

THE LEARNING PROGRESSION

In Kindergarten, children classify objects into categories. They work with data using counting and order relations.

In Grade 1, children sort and count to organize and represent categorical data in various ways. They work with up to three categories. **In this lesson,** children build their repertoire of analytical skills through comparing categorical data in charts and graphs. They ask and answer questions about data, using what they know about addition, subtraction, and comparison. Using categorical data builds skills with real-world problem solving.

In Grade 2, children draw picture graphs and bar graphs to represent data sets with up to four categories. They solve simple put-together, take-apart, and compare problems using information presented in the graphs. Children's work with categorical data in early grades prepares them for later work with bivariate categorical data—data that are categorized according to two attributes.

⬛ Ready *Teacher Toolbox*   *Teacher-Toolbox.com*

	Prerequisite Skills	1.MD.C.4
Ready Lessons	✓ ✓	✓
Tools for Instruction	✓ ✓	✓
Interactive Tutorials	✓ ✓	✓ ✓

CCSS Focus

1.MD.C.4 Organize, represent, and interpret data with up to three categories; ask and answer questions about the total number of data points, how many in each category, and how many more or less are in one category than in another.

ADDITIONAL STANDARDS: *1.OA.A.1, 1.OA.C.6* (see page A36 for full text)

STANDARDS FOR MATHEMATICAL PRACTICE: *SMP 1, 2, 4, 5, 7* (see page A9 for full text)

233

Opening Activity: Compare Data

Objective: Collect and display categorical data, and describe features of the data set.	**Materials** For each child: • 1 square sticky note

Overview

Children collect and use categorical data to answer a question. They describe the data, noting particular aspects such as total number of answers and which categories have the most/least responses.

Step by Step (15–20 minutes)

1 Pose the problem.

- Pose an interesting question to the class involving categorical data, such as: *How many pockets do first graders have in their clothing?* Ask children to discuss reasons why someone might want to know this information. Reasons may include "simple curiosity."

2 Organize a data display.

- Draw the outline of a picture graph on the board. Include the column headings "How Many Pockets" and "Number of Children."

- Enlist children's help in determining the number of pockets to show in each row. Do not skip numbers. Start with 0, because some children may have no pockets. Ask children to predict what the greatest number of pockets will be and draw rows accordingly.

3 Gather and display the data.

- Group children in pairs. Each child counts the number of pockets in their clothing. The partner watches and records the result on the sticky side of a sticky note. Children may work alone if they prefer.

- Invite each child to come up and place their sticky note in the appropriate row for their number of pockets. Tell them to place each sticky note right next to any others that are already in the row, without overlapping. This creates a picture graph of squares, with one square for each child.

4 Describe the data.

- When the graph is complete, tell children that they are now ready to describe the data. Give children a minute to study the graph.

- Ask: *How many answers are there in all? How can you find out?* Children may add the number of squares in each row or count all.

- Ask which category has the most responses and which has the fewest. Encourage children to ask and answer other questions they can think of about the graph.

- Have children look for interesting differences/similarities between the categories and offer explanations for why they think the data came out this way.

Check for Understanding

Have children work in small groups to prepare a report that summarizes the information they have found. Reports might explain how they gathered data and summarize the key features of the data.

STEP BY STEP

- Begin by asking children what they have learned or remember from the Opening Activity. Explain that picture graphs are one way to organize and display data so others can understand what it is about.

- Read the description at the top of the page and go over the parts of the picture graph: the title, the categories, the pictures.

- Ask: *What are you trying to find out?* [How many have dogs or cats.] Use the Mathematical Discourse questions to discuss the meaning of the data.

- Explain that the Model It shows one way to answer the question. Read the information. Have children point to each picture and count it. Ask: *Why don't you just count everything together?* [We are not looking for the total number of children.] Ask: *Why do you start at "1" for each row?* [Each row tells the number of children who have one kind of pet.]

- Have children tap each smile face and count them out loud for dogs and cats.

- Have children complete the addition statement and answer the question.

> **SMP Tip:** Show children how picture graphs are a tool for solving data problems. Present the data shown in the picture graphs as scattered words on the board. Discuss how the graph organizes the data and makes it much easier to answer questions, like those in the Mathematical Discourse. *(SMP 5)*

Fluency Practice

Materials For each child: Practice Adding Three Numbers (Activity Sheet 36)

Distribute the activity sheet, explaining that children need to add each group of numbers and show their work. Have children work independently.

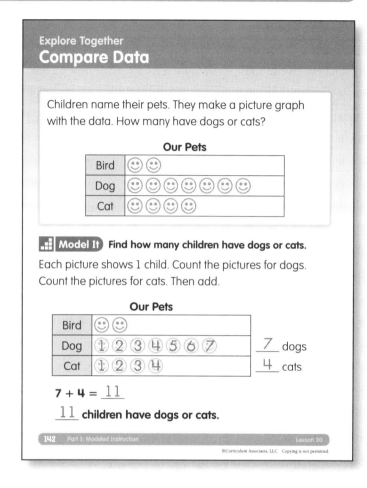

Mathematical Discourse

- *What information does this picture graph give us? What do the pictures stand for?*

  Children should be able to recognize that the picture graph tells what pets a group of children have. Each picture represents one child who has a pet.

- *What other questions could you ask and answer about this data?*

  Children might suggest questions that involve comparisons, such as the most, the fewest, or how many more. Other questions might ask about the total number of data items in two or all three of the categories.

STEP BY STEP

- Read the question aloud. Discuss the difference between the table shown here and the picture graph on the previous page; the table shows numeric values rather than pictorial representations of quantities.

- Discuss the meaning of the table and that each number represents how many people chose that fruit as their favorite. Ask: *Why might someone want to compare favorite fruits?*

- Have children examine Model It. Point out that the number paths are another way to show how many of each kind of fruit. Discuss this as a method for comparing quantities. Use the Mathematical Discourse question to relate to other ways of comparing.

- Have children complete the comparison and discuss.

- Ask children to discuss the Talk About It questions with a partner. Encourage each pair to ask and answer two questions about the data. Circulate to monitor discussions.

> **SMP Tip:** While children are discussing these Talk About It questions, they are making use of the structure provided by the displays of data and building a foundation for future data representations. Ask them which representations best help them answer their questions and why. (*SMP 7*)

Hands-On Activity

Build a data set from information in a table.

Materials For each group: connecting cubes in 3 colors

Mention that, in the past, the class has sorted and counted objects to make charts or graphs. This time, they will use the information in the table to make a collection of objects. Have children choose one color of connecting cubes to represent each fruit. Children work in groups of three to assemble "fruit bars" with connecting cubes to represent the numbers shown in the table. Each child makes a bar for one fruit.

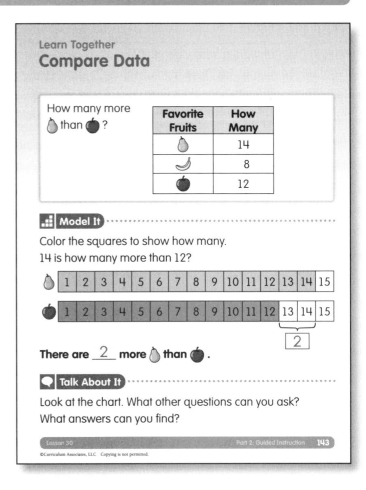

Mathematical Discourse

- *What are some other ways you can compare?*

  Children might mention various methods they have used, such as comparing actual objects, using bar models, matching one-to-one, counting on, etc.

ELL Support

Discuss the use of the word "table." Explain that when information is organized into rows and columns, that is often called a table. This is not a tally chart, because it does not have tally marks, and it is not a picture graph because it does not use pictures to represent the data, only numbers. In fact, the tally charts and picture graphs are special kinds of tables. Ask children what other meanings they know for the word "table."

STEP BY STEP

- Read the directions to the example problem. Ask children to describe how the graph shows that more children like grapes than strawberries or apples. Explain that "most" means "more than anything else." Ask the Mathematical Discourse question to encourage children to think about the process used in analyzing data.

- Discuss Problem 1 with children. Have them tell what is being asked. Ask them to describe the table, identify the three kinds of blocks, and tell what the numbers mean. Discuss approaches for solving and have children find the total.

- Discuss Problem 2 with children. Review the convention for grouping tally marks in groups of 5. Have the children describe what the tally chart represents. [how many markers] Elicit that the questions ask for "how many more" and "how many fewer" comparisons. Have children work in pairs to answer the questions and then explain their solutions to the class.

Visual Model

Make a picture graph from tally marks or a data table.

A picture graph is a visual model of data. Have children make their own picture graphs based on the data representations in Problem 1 or Problem 2. Children may work alone or with a partner. For the data in these problems, pictures of smile faces or stick figures don't make sense. Discuss what kinds of pictures, or symbols, would be appropriate. For example, children might use circles or check marks to represent the shapes in Problem 1 and might use simple illustrations of a marker or perhaps rectangles to represent the markers in Problem 2.

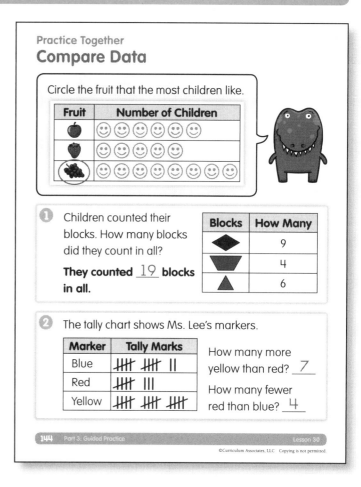

Mathematical Discourse

- *When you look at data in a table, chart, or graph, what do you look for first, and why?*

    Children can learn from listening to each other's strategies for making sense of data. Listen for those who may be focusing on peripheral attributes of the display rather than the important parts. Also listen for indications that children are seeking the meaning in a data display rather than just seeing an assemblage of pictures or numbers.

STEP BY STEP

- Before children work on this page, review the different data displays presented in this lesson.

- Read each problem aloud, then have children work independently to solve.

- For Problem 3, observe to see if children are able to connect the context—liking something best—to the tally chart. They then have to find the object that "most" children like "best."

- Problem 4 asks children to make comparisons based on the data in Problem 3. Observe to ensure that children understand the meaning of "more" and "fewer." Ask children to explain the strategies they used to solve.

- Ask the Mathematical Discourse question to show the connection between data analysis and problem solving.

Concept Extension

Write a number sentence to compare.

Display the tally chart and solution to Problem 3. Write the following statement on the board to compare boots and slippers: "4 more children like boots best than like slippers best." Say: *This is a word sentence that compares the data. Let's write a number sentence.* Point out that 8 children like slippers best and 12 like boots best. Ask: *Which is greater?* [12] *How can you tell?* [There are more tally marks for boots than for slippers.] Say: *You know that 8 plus some more is equal to 12.* Write "8 + ___ = 12" and ask for a volunteer to solve. Next, write the following to compare sneakers and boots: "6 fewer children like boots best than like sneakers best." Point out that this time the question is "how many fewer." Have children describe how to write a missing addend number sentence and solve.

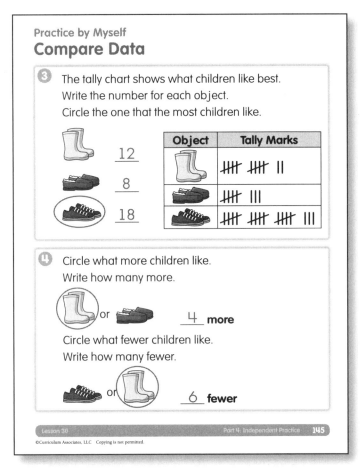

Mathematical Discourse

- *How can you check your work when you compare data?*

    Listen for multiple strategies for solving problems and verifying that the answers are correct. Encourage children to solve a problem one way and then check it using a different approach. For example, if a child uses subtraction to determine that 4 more children like boots than slippers, they might line up counters to verify their answer.

Assessment and Remediation

- Ask children to look at a picture graph showing number of rainy (3), cloudy (9), and sunny (13) days and tell how many more days were sunny than rainy. [10]

- For children who are still struggling, use the chart below to guide remediation.

- After providing remediation, check children's understanding using the following problem: Look at a picture graph showing number of rainy (8), cloudy (14), and sunny (11) days and tell which kind of weather occurred on the most days and how they know. [cloudy, because there were 3 more cloudy days than sunny days and 6 more cloudy days than rainy days]

If the error is...	Children may...	To remediate...
3 or 13	not understand how to compare and gave one of the quantities instead.	Explain that this is the number of rainy (or sunny) days. Have children count the pictures for rainy days and for sunny days. Ask if there are more sunny days or more rainy days. [sunny] Have them use the method of their choice to compare the quantities.
16	not understand how to compare and gave the sum instead.	Have children line up connecting cubes to represent the rainy and sunny days. Point out how the cubes and the rows of pictures in the picture graph look similar. Allow children to match the connecting cubes or use another strategy to compare.
6 or 12	be trying to compare rainy and cloudy days.	Have children point to the items they are comparing; correct any misunderstanding.

Hands-On Activity

Make a picture chart.

Materials For each child: Chart Template (Activity Sheet 35), assortment of small objects of 3 kinds (pattern blocks, buttons, dried beans, etc.)

- Give each child a handful of the objects. Have them sort their objects directly onto a blank picture graph template.

- Have children remove their objects one by one, replacing each one with a picture. Ask them to label the rows and count pictures in each row.

- Invite children to display their picture graphs and describe the data, giving at least one comparison.

Challenge Activity

Survey the class and report the results.

- Have children work in pairs or small groups to create a categorical question to ask their classmates. Each group surveys the class and records the data with a tally chart.

- Groups use the tally chart to make either a picture graph or a numeric table. Each group presents their results to the class, along with information about the total number of responses, which categories had the most and fewest responses, and any other information they found interesting.

- Display the results in the classroom.

Lesson 31 (Student Book pages 146–149)

Order Objects by Length

LESSON OBJECTIVES

• Order three objects by length.

PREREQUISITE SKILLS

• Compare quantities within 10.
• Describe measurable attributes of objects, such as length.

VOCABULARY

length: the distance from one point to another

longer: describes the greater length of two objects being compared

longest: greatest in distance

shorter: describes the lesser length or height of two objects being compared

shortest: least in distance

taller: describes the greater height of two objects being compared

tallest: describes the greatest height when ordering three or more objects by height

During the lesson you will review the key term:

compare: to decide if amounts or sizes are greater than, less than, or equal to each other

THE LEARNING PROGRESSION

In Kindergarten, children begin to describe measurable attributes, such as length. They directly compare two objects to see which object is longer or shorter.

In Grade 1, children compare and order objects by length. They use a non-standard reference unit to measure objects by laying multiple copies of a shorter object end to end. They understand that the number of such reference objects is the length measurement of the item being measured. **In this lesson,** children compare the lengths of three objects, lining them up so that one end is aligned, and put the items in order by length. They identify the shortest and longest objects.

In Grade 2, children come to understand the need for standard units of measurement and begin using standard tools to measure objects and compare length.

■ Ready *Teacher Toolbox*   *Teacher-Toolbox.com*

	Prerequisite Skills	1.MD.A.1
Ready Lessons	✓	✓
Tools for Instruction	✓ ✓	
Interactive Tutorials		

CCSS Focus

1.MD.A.1 Order three objects by length; compare the lengths of two objects indirectly by using a third object.

STANDARDS FOR MATHEMATICAL PRACTICE: *SMP 3, 6, 7 (see page A9 for full text)*

Opening Activity: Compare Length and Height

Objective: Compare lengths of three objects.	**Materials** For each child: • pencils of different lengths

Overview

Children develop a process for comparing the lengths of three objects.

Step by Step (5–10 minutes)

1 **Pose the problem.**

• Show children a short pencil and a box of pencils of various lengths and thicknesses. Say: *I got this pencil from a board game. I want to save all our short pencils to use in our classroom games. Let's compare the length of some pencils and find which ones are the shortest.*

2 **Set up the problem.**

• Take 3 pencils from the box and distribute to 3 children who are not sitting near each other.

• Have children stand and hold up their pencils.

• Ask: *Can you tell which is shortest?* [No]

• Ask: *What should you do to compare the lengths of these pencils?* Guide children to recognize that they can lay the pencils side by side.

3 **Solve the problem.**

• Emphasize the importance of aligning one end of the pencils (use the eraser or flat end).

• Have children point out which is longest and shortest. Set aside the shortest pencil for use in classroom games.

4 **Discuss.**

• Ask: *How could you tell which was shortest?* [The other pencils "stick out" farther.]

• Reiterate the importance of aligning one end of the objects.

• Show some pencils that are of various widths. Say: *You could compare the width of these pencils.* Explain that width is the distance across. Ask how you could line up the pencils to compare their widths.

• Call two children of different heights to the front of the room. Explain that you don't say "length" when you measure children or objects that are positioned up and down; you say "height" and "how tall." Say: *Let's compare the height of these two children.* Have the class determine which child is taller and which is shorter.

Check for Understanding

Have children work in pairs to put three pencils in order by length and then explain how they did it. Watch for misalignment of the objects and for children who don't understand that the shortest one is the one that "sticks out" a lesser distance than all the others.

STEP BY STEP

- Begin by asking children what they have learned or remember from the Opening Activity. Review the idea of lining up objects to compare length.

- Read the problem aloud. Discuss with the class how they would compare the length of the collars. Elicit that you can't always tell just by looking.

- Point out that, in Model It, the collars are off the dogs' necks and are stretched out to their full length. Also point out the dashed line that indicates the collars are properly lined up. Ask: *What would happen if one of the collars was bent or twisted?* [We couldn't measure accurately.]

> **SMP Tip:** Encourage children to attend to precision by questioning them about how and why to align the end points of objects. The procedures children learn in this lesson form the foundation for future work with measurement, including assigning an appropriate number to a measurement. (SMP 6)

- Have children run their fingers along each collar and compare them visually. Ask children which collar is longest and tell them to complete the first sentence.

- Repeat with the shortest collar and have children complete the second sentence. Ask: *How do you know?* Ask the Mathematical Discourse question to extend the discussion.

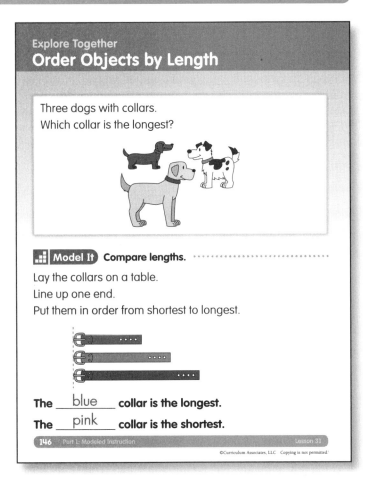

Mathematical Discourse

- *What other measurements could you compare in this picture?*

  Children should use the language of measurement to talk about the height of the dogs and the length of the dogs or their tails. Some may even mention width. Have children clarify how they would compare these dimensions, and address any misconceptions or misuse of terminology.

ELL Support

Help children distinguish among the many terms for measuring and comparing length: "length," "height," "width," "long," "tall," "wide," "short." Discuss the comparative forms such as "longer" and "shorter;" these are used to compare two objects. When comparing three objects, teach children to use the superlative "est" forms—"longest," "tallest," "shortest"—to tell which object is the most long/tall/short of all.

STEP BY STEP

- Read the problem aloud. Ask: *Are you comparing the length, width, or height of the books? How do you know?* [height; you need to measure from the shelf to the top of the book]

- Have children hold up a book and indicate which sides are used to measure its height. Invite a volunteer to describe how you might compare the heights of these books.

- Direct children's attention to Model It. Ask: *How do you know the books are lined up properly?* [They are all on the same shelf.] Point out that they are all aligned the same way as well, with the binding side out.

- Have children mark the books as indicated. Check that they are correctly choosing the shortest and tallest book.

- **Error Alert** Read Talk About It aloud. Have children discuss the problem in pairs. Then discuss as a class. Elicit that only two of the three flowers are aligned on the dashed line. Use the Mathematical Discourse question to continue the discussion.

Hands-On Activity

Compare the widths of books.

Materials For each child: a book

Have children stand their books up to show the direction for measuring the book's height (up and down). Then have them indicate the direction for measuring the book's width (across). Organize children in groups of three. Have them compare the widths of their books, put the books in order from narrowest to widest, and identify the widest book. Circulate to monitor and provide guidance. Ask: *What edge of the books did you line up to compare widths?* [The spine, or possibly the edge opposite the spine. All three books should be aligned along the same edge.]

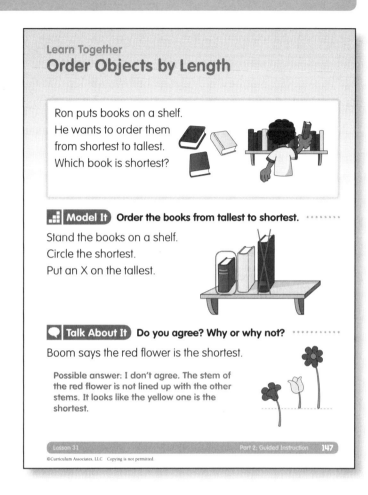

Learn Together
Order Objects by Length

Ron puts books on a shelf.
He wants to order them
from shortest to tallest.
Which book is shortest?

Model It Order the books from tallest to shortest.

Stand the books on a shelf.
Circle the shortest.
Put an X on the tallest.

Talk About It Do you agree? Why or why not?

Boom says the red flower is the shortest.

Possible answer: I don't agree. The stem of the red flower is not lined up with the other stems. It looks like the yellow one is the shortest.

Mathematical Discourse

- *How would you help Boom find the shortest flower?*

  Children's responses should indicate that one end of all three flowers must be aligned before they can compare and find the shortest. Some children may be tempted to guess. Press them to verify their answers; "just knowing" is not enough in math. They need to be able to explain their reasoning.

STEP BY STEP

- Read through the problem with the class. Point out the use of the word shorter to compare the top worm with the bottom worm. Guide children to recognize that all three worms are aligned, so they can easily compare lengths.

- For Problem 1, have children explain how they determined the shortest and the longest pencil.

- Read Problem 2 with the class. Use the Mathematical Discourse question to guide discussion. Elicit children's ideas about how to approach the problem and encourage flexible thinking.

- Reinforce the use of the words "shorter," "longer," "shortest," and "longest" by asking children to compare the lengths of the worms, pencils, and dogs in as many ways as they can.

Fluency Practice

Make a ten with connecting cubes.

Materials For each child: Practice Making a Ten to Add (Activity Sheet 37), connecting cubes in 2 colors

Give children 20 connecting cubes, 10 of each color. Hand out the activity sheet. Children model the addition facts using two colors of connecting cubes. Then they decompose one addend, compose a ten with the other addend, and write the new addition sentence, including the sum. Model the example, problem $5 + 8 = $ ___. Make trains of 5 and 8 connecting cubes. Break apart the 5-cube train and place 2 of the cubes on the 8-cube train to make 10. Relate this action to the number sentences shown in the example problem.

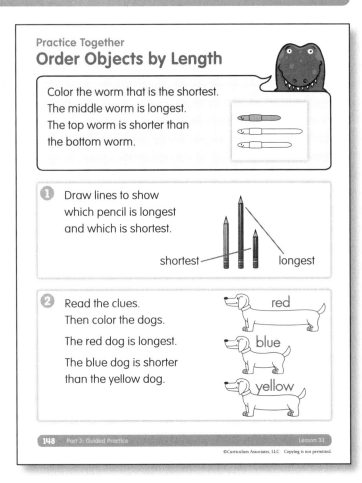

Practice Together

Order Objects by Length

Color the worm that is the shortest.
The middle worm is longest.
The top worm is shorter than the bottom worm.

① Draw lines to show which pencil is longest and which is shortest.

shortest — longest

② Read the clues.
Then color the dogs.
The red dog is longest.
The blue dog is shorter than the yellow dog.

red
blue
yellow

148   Part 3: Guided Practice   Lesson 31
©Curriculum Associates, LLC Copying is not permitted.

Mathematical Discourse

- *How do you know which dog to start with?*

  Listen for evidence of logical reasoning. Since all three dogs are aligned, the first sentence tells you that the first dog should be red. According to the second sentence, you can compare the two remaining dogs and color the shorter one blue.

STEP BY STEP

- Before children work on this page, review the length comparison words used throughout the lesson.

- Read each problem aloud, then have children work independently to solve.

- Problem 3 requires children to use logical reasoning to determine which color to use for each bat.

- Problem 4 has the children identify the attribute of the object rather than look for the object with a given attribute. Ask children how they determined the answer.

- Problem 5 provides an open-ended opportunity for children to draw their own image of something that is taller than the given rectangles. Ask children to describe to you how they know their line is the tallest. Watch that children are comparing height rather than width.

> **SMP Tip:** As children gain practice in making length comparisons, they focus on the measurable attribute of length and gain a better understanding. Encourage children to remember the structure of these problems as they approach new measurement challenges. (SMP 7)

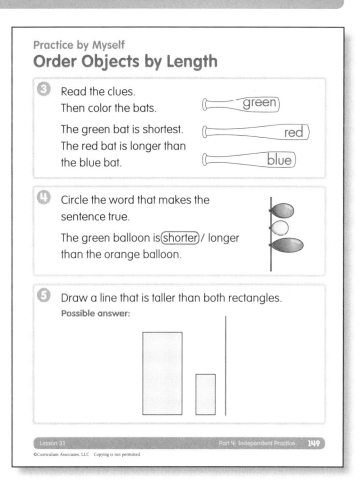

Concept Extension

Order four or five objects by length or height.

Materials For each pair: four or five objects

Give pairs of children four or five objects and have them put the objects in order by length (or height). Have each group describe how they solved the problem and explain their answer.

Assessment and Remediation

- Ask children to put three objects in order from shortest to longest.

- For children who are still struggling, use the chart below to guide remediation.

- After providing remediation, check children's understanding using the following problem: Identify the tallest and shortest item in a set of three objects.

If the error is . . .	Children may . . .	To remediate . . .
reverse order	not understand that the order matters.	Have children point to the shortest and the longest. If these are incorrect, place the shortest object on the left and say: *What comes next?* Continue in this manner.
an order of short, long, medium or long, short, medium	not have aligned one end of each object or compared the other ends incorrectly.	Guide children to align one end of each object. Then have them lightly trace to the end of each object with a finger. Ask: *Which object sticks out the farthest?* Guide children to identify this as the longest object. Ask: *Which one is next longest?* Then elicit that the remaining object is the shortest.
objects jumbled or piled	not understand the task.	Pick up the objects and hold them so that they are almost aligned. Point out that some objects stick up farther than the others. Explain that these are longer. Help children align the objects correctly. Then have them lightly trace each object. Ask: *Which object sticks out the farthest?* Guide children to identify this as the longest object. Ask, *Which one is next longest?* Then elicit that the remaining object is the shortest.

Hands-On Activity

Compare heights of connecting cube towers.

Materials For each group of 3: connecting cubes (a different color and number for each child)

- Group three children together. Have each child build a tower out of connecting cubes, all the same color.

- Tell groups to order the towers from shortest to tallest.

- Tell one child from each group to add 3 cubes to their towers. Allow the group to re-order their towers if needed.

Challenge Activity

Line up from shortest to tallest.

Put children in groups of three or four. Say: *Your task is to line up in order from shortest to tallest, without talking. You may use gestures, but you cannot speak.* Have other children check to see if the group lined up correctly.

Lesson 32 (Student Book pages 150–153)

Compare Lengths

LESSON OBJECTIVES

- Recognize that sometimes it is not possible to compare length directly.

- Compare two objects by comparing their lengths to a third, reference, object.

- Use logical reasoning to indirectly compare the length of objects.

PREREQUISITE SKILLS

- Compare the lengths of two objects.

- Compare and order quantities within 10.

VOCABULARY

There is no new vocabulary. During the lesson you will review the key terms:

compare: to decide if amounts or sizes are greater than, less than, or equal to each other

length: the distance from one point to another

THE LEARNING PROGRESSION

In Kindergarten, children begin to understand the concept of length, which is a core measurement concept. They use direct comparison to compare lengths of two objects.

In Grade 1, children compare and order objects by length. They use a non-standard reference unit to measure objects by laying multiple copies of a shorter object end to end. They understand that the number of such reference objects is the length measurement of the item being measured. **In this lesson,** children develop an understanding of indirect measurement, which underlies the use of standard measuring tools. They reason that if object A is longer than the reference object and object B is shorter than the reference object, then object A is longer than object B.

In Grade 2, children come to understand the need for standard units of measurement and begin using standard tools to measure objects and compare length. They use measurement concepts to create a number line, which is a model used repeatedly in later grades.

Ready *Teacher Toolbox*		*Teacher-Toolbox.com*
	Prerequisite Skills	*1.MD.A.1*
Ready Lessons	✓	✓
Tools for Instruction	✓ ✓	
Interactive Tutorials		

CCSS Focus

1.MD.A.1 Order three objects by length; compare the lengths of two objects indirectly by using a third object.

STANDARDS FOR MATHEMATICAL PRACTICE: *SMP 3, 5, 6, 7 (see page A9 for full text)*

Opening Activity: Compare Lengths

Objective: Use a reference object to sort other objects as "taller" or "shorter."

Materials For each child:
- unsharpened pencil
- assortment of classroom items

Overview

Sort children into "taller" and "shorter" groups by comparing each child to one average-height child.

Step by Step (5–10 minutes)

1 Pose the problem.

- Choose a child who is about the median height for children in the class. Say: *Let's sort out who is taller and who is shorter than [child's name].*

2 Sort the children.

- One by one, invite children to the front of the room and have them stand back-to-back with the first child, who serves as the reference.

- Have shorter children form one group and taller children form another. Children who are the same height as the reference child can return to their seats.

3 Compare the two groups.

- Point to the "shorter" group. Ask: *What can you say about this group?* Guide children to recognize that they are shorter than the reference child and thus shorter than everyone in the "taller" group.

- Point to the "taller" group. Ask: *What can you say about this group?* Elicit that they are taller than the reference child and thus taller than those in the "shorter" group.

- Have one child from each group step forward, along with the reference child. Ask: *Without measuring, tell me whether [child from taller group] is taller or shorter than [child from shorter group]. How do you know?*

- Don't accept responses that "he/she looks taller." Lead children to the understanding that the child from the "taller" group is taller than the reference child, who is taller than everyone in the "shorter" group. So, the child from the "taller" group is taller than the child from the "shorter" group.

4 Compare other items using a reference object.

- Give each child an unsharpened pencil.

- Have them search the room for one object that is longer than the pencil and one that is shorter.

Check for Understanding

As children find shorter and longer objects, ask them to compare the lengths, without measuring, based on their comparison to the pencil. Take note of which children have not yet grasped the idea of indirect comparison.

STEP BY STEP

- Begin by asking children what they have learned or remember from the Opening Activity. Reinforce the idea that they compared each child to the same child and this allowed them to make comparisons among the two groups, "taller" and "shorter."

- Read the problem aloud. Explain that the tables are too big to move next to each other and compare directly. Ask: *What if you had a long piece of string? How could you use it to compare the tables the way you used [child's name] to compare children's heights?* Discuss their ideas.

- Direct attention to Model It, pointing out that the string is laid along the length of each table.

- Ask: *Which table is longer than the string?* [the gray table] *Which table is shorter than the string?* [the brown table] *So, which table is longer?* [the gray table]

- Have children complete the Model It sentences and discuss their conclusions. Discuss the Mathematical Discourse questions. Use the visual model to show logical reasoning about the relationship between the lengths.

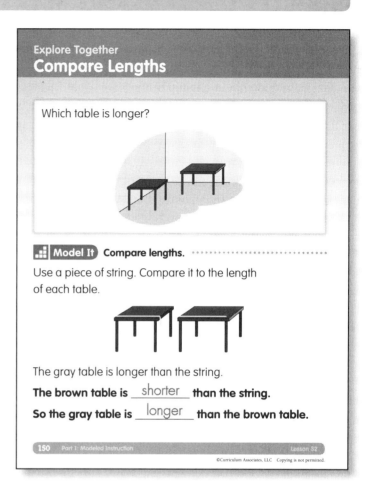

Explore Together
Compare Lengths

Which table is longer?

Model It Compare lengths.

Use a piece of string. Compare it to the length of each table.

The gray table is longer than the string.

The brown table is ___shorter___ **than the string.**

So the gray table is ___longer___ **than the brown table.**

150   Part 1: Modeled Instruction   Lesson 32

©Curriculum Associates, LLC   Copying is not permitted.

Visual Model

Model the logic of indirect comparison.

Draw the following diagram on the board. Discuss with children how it models the problem on the student page.

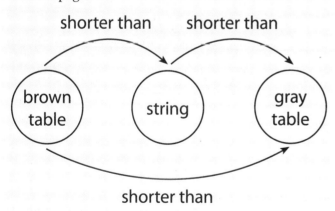

Mathematical Discourse

- *What is the order of these three objects from shortest to longest? How does this help you compare the lengths of the tables?*

  Children should be able to name the objects from shortest to longest: brown table, string, gray table. Children might recognize that the object that was used as the reference object ended up in the middle. This is why the string can be used to indirectly compare the length of the two tables.

STEP BY STEP

Materials For display: strip of paper

- Read the question at the top of the page. Ask: *How can you compare the lengths of the shoe and the spoon?* Introduce the idea of using a strip of paper.

- Show children a strip of paper, and ask how it is like the piece of string used to compare the tables or the pencil that they used in the Opening Activity. Then model how to use the paper to compare the length of two classroom objects.

- Read Model It and ask children which object is longer than the paper and which one is shorter. Then ask them to fill in the blanks.

- Talk About It focuses on reasoning about indirect measurement. Read the problem with the class.

- Have children work in pairs to draw their response. Circulate and monitor their work. Some children may be able to answer without even drawing, but encourage them to make a drawing to justify their conclusions.

- **Error Alert** Invite partners to share their drawings with the class. Ask the Mathematical Discourse question to focus on the error in logic that Boom made. Challenge children to correct Boom and make a true statement.

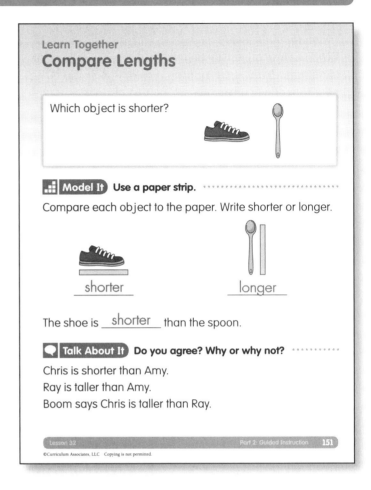

Learn Together
Compare Lengths

Which object is shorter?

Model It Use a paper strip.

Compare each object to the paper. Write shorter or longer.

shorter   longer

The shoe is ___shorter___ than the spoon.

Talk About It Do you agree? Why or why not?

Chris is shorter than Amy.
Ray is taller than Amy.
Boom says Chris is taller than Ray.

Hands-On Activity

Materials For each child: strip of heavy paper

Give each child or pair a strip of heavy paper to use as a reference unit. Have them find at least three objects in the classroom that are the same length as, longer than, and shorter than the reference unit.

Mathematical Discourse

- *How did you decide if Boom is correct?*

  Look for explanations that show evidence of logical reasoning. One person is taller than Amy and the other is shorter. So, logically, Amy is in between and the taller person is taller than the one who is shorter than Amy.

STEP BY STEP

- The example problem guides children to make a superlative comparison: finding the longest snake. Discuss with the class and ask children to explain the conclusion.

- For Problem 1, guide children to compare the heights of the rectangle and the triangle. Then have them complete the problem. Discuss their rationale for their answer. Encourage children to make a variety of comparison statements using all three objects.

- Problem 2 focuses on reasoning related to indirect measurement. Have children discuss this in pairs. Circulate and support their discussion. For those who struggle, remind them of the Visual Model on page 249 or have them draw an illustration of the problem situation.

> **SMP Tip:** Children use transitivity when they indirectly compare lengths of multiple objects. Encourage them to state their logic in an order that makes sense and follows the structure of the problem. For example: "My string is longer than the pencil. My string is shorter than the book. That means the book is longer than the pencil." *(SMP 7)*

- Ask the Mathematical Discourse questions to encourage more in-depth thinking about indirect measurement.

Concept Extension

Materials For display: box of objects of differing lengths, a reference object

Have children sort objects in the box as shorter, same, or longer than the reference object. Then choose one of the "longer" objects as a reference object and have children further sort these as shorter, same, or longer than the new reference object. Discuss how the "longer" group can now be classified as "a little bit longer," "longer," and "a lot longer."

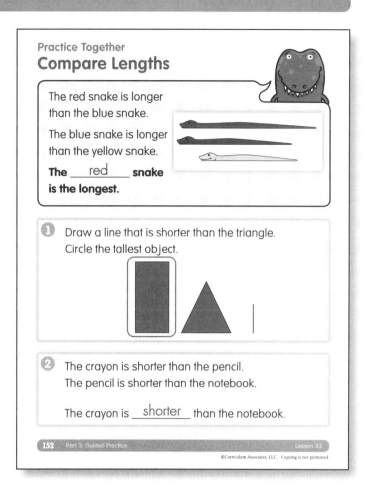

Practice Together
Compare Lengths

The red snake is longer than the blue snake.

The blue snake is longer than the yellow snake.

The ___red___ **snake is the longest.**

1 Draw a line that is shorter than the triangle. Circle the tallest object.

2 The crayon is shorter than the pencil. The pencil is shorter than the notebook.

The crayon is ___shorter___ than the notebook.

Mathematical Discourse

- *Suppose I have two objects and they are both shorter than a third object. Can I tell which one is shorter or longer than the other? Why or why not? What can I do if I really need to compare their lengths but I can't compare them side by side?*

   If both objects are shorter than the reference object, then you cannot compare their lengths using that reference object. It would be necessary to find a different reference object that differentiates the heights of the two objects.

STEP BY STEP

Materials For each child: piece of string that is longer than the picture of the sticky notes but shorter than the picture of the marker, connecting cubes

- Before children work on this page, review the models and tools used in this lesson. Emphasize that children are free to use whatever way helps them solve the problem.

- Read each problem aloud, then have children work independently to solve.

- For Problem 3, you may want to provide children with a piece of string as described in the materials list. You may want to challenge some children to create their own tool or strategy to compare the lengths.

- Monitor children's work on Problem 4 to ensure that they understand the directions. Have them explain their rationale. Elicit that you can't always tell "just by looking."

- For children who still struggle with Problem 5, have them use connecting cubes to model each object. Then discuss the reasoning.

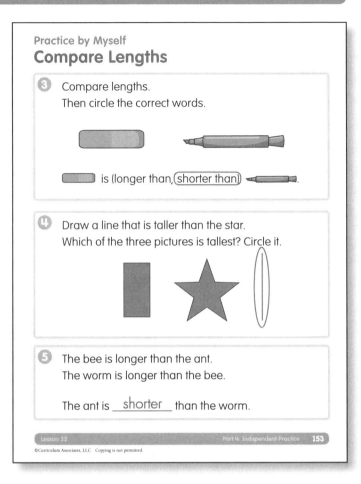

Fluency Practice

Materials For each child or pair: Make Equal Facts (Activity Sheet 38)

Have children work individually or in pairs to complete the activity sheet. Pairs can complete one side of the number sentence for each problem.

Mathematical Discourse

- *In Problem 5, what is the answer if the bee is shorter than the ant and the worm is shorter than the bee? How can you tell?*

  Children should show evidence of logical reasoning in their response. The bee is still the reference object, but the lengths of the other objects have been reversed. Consider providing cards with the names of the objects on them to help children reorganize their thinking.

Assessment and Remediation

- Ask children to put cards with the names of three people in order by height, shortest to tallest, and state who is the shortest. Give the following rules: Pam is taller than Joe. Robin is taller than Pam. [Joe, Pam, Robin; Joe is shortest.]

- For children who are still struggling, use the chart below to guide remediation.

- After providing remediation, check children's understanding using the following problem: Given a strip of paper or a string, use the paper or string to measure two objects and state which of the two objects is longer or shorter than the other. [Answer will vary depending on the objects chosen.]

If the error is . . .	Children may . . .	To remediate . . .
Robin, Joe, Pam	have focused on the first comparison and then placed Robin incorrectly.	Read the first sentence and verify that Joe and Pam are in correct relation to each other. Point to the second sentence and have the children place Robin correctly.
Pam, Robin, Joe	have focused on the second comparison and not used the first comparison.	Read the second sentence and verify that Pam and Robin are in correct relation to each other. Point to the first sentence and have the children place Joe correctly.
Robin, Pam, Joe	have ordered the people from tallest to shortest.	Remind children that the shortest goes on the left. Have children start with Pam. Read the first sentence and place Joe accordingly. Read the second sentence and place Robin accordingly.

Hands-On Activity

Compare lengths of clay snakes to a cube tower.

Materials For each pair: clay, connecting cubes, pieces of paper labeled "longer" and "shorter"

- Children work in pairs to make a cube tower.

- One child takes the paper that says "longer" and the partner takes the paper that says "shorter." Children make clay snakes that are longer or shorter than their cube tower.

- Each child compares his/her snake to the tower. Children make statements such as, "My snake is longer than the cube tower and your snake is shorter than the cube tower. So my snake is longer than your snake."

- Partners switch papers and repeat the activity.

Challenge Activity

Compare lengths of irregular paths, using string.

Materials: masking tape, string

Use masking tape to mark three crooked paths from various spots in the classroom to the door. One path should be longer than a piece of pre-measured string and two should be shorter. Ask children how to determine which path is the shortest. One way is to use the piece of string as a reference object. Give children the piece of string and have them lay it along each path and state whether the string is shorter or longer than the path. Ask: *How can you tell?* [Either the path extends past the end of the string or the string extends past the end of the path.] Ask: *How can you now find the shortest path?* [One way would be to use a shorter string. Another would be to mark on the string itself where each path ends.]

Lesson 33 (Student Book pages 154–157)

Understand Length Measurement

LESSON OBJECTIVES

- Measure a length using non-standard units of measure.
- Understand that the number of iterated units from end to end is a measure.
- Iterate units with no gaps or overlaps.
- Understand that "unit" implies uniformity in length.

PREREQUISITE SKILLS

- Order objects by length.
- Compare lengths of up to three objects.

VOCABULARY

measure: the process of finding a number that shows the size or quantity

unit: that which is used to measure the height or length of an object

During the lesson, you will review the key term:

length: the distance from one point to another

THE LEARNING PROGRESSION

In Kindergarten, children compare lengths of objects and describe them in terms of taller, longer, shorter, more, or less.

In Grade 1, children compare lengths of two objects to a third object, building the concept of measurement as the act of comparing a length to a series of other lengths. **In this lesson,** children iterate non-standard units to equal the length of another object, recognizing that the number of units iterated represents the length of the object. They explore how different-sized units affect the numerical representation of length and analyze the importance of using units of uniform length with no gaps or overlaps in measuring an object.

In Grade 2, children build on the concept of measurement using standard units, describing the measure in terms of the unit name. The concept of unit is further developed as children measure an object using two different units, recognizing that the numerical representation is dependent upon the unit.

Ready *Teacher Toolbox*   *Teacher-Toolbox.com*

	Prerequisite Skills	1.MD.A.2
Ready Lessons		✓
Tools for Instruction	✓ ✓	
Interactive Tutorials		

CCSS Focus

1.MD.A.2 Express the length of an object as a whole number of length units, by laying multiple copies of a shorter object (the length unit) end to end; understand that the length measurement of an object is the number of same-size length units that span it with no gaps or overlaps. *Limit to contexts where the object being measured is spanned by a whole number of length units with no gaps or overlaps.*

STANDARDS FOR MATHEMATICAL PRACTICE: **SMP 2, 3, 5, 6, 7** (see page A9 for full text)

Opening Activity: Measure Me

Objective: Explore the concept of measurement.	**Materials** For each pair: • 12–15 straws, each 4 inches in length

Overview

Children use a non-standard unit to measure each other, describing height in terms of a unit.

Step by Step (25–30 minutes)

1 **Pose the problem.**

- Tell pairs of children they are to find the number of straws that will line up to match each of their heights.

2 **Measure each other.**

- Instruct one of the children in each pair to lay flat on the floor or on a table or row of desks while the partner finds the number of straws tall they are. They record the number and then reverse roles.

- Allow children to measure without intervention. Take note of the way in which children iterate the straws. Do they lay them end to end to iterate or are they oriented in varied ways? Do they overlap or leave gaps between the straws? Use these observations to guide discussion.

3 **Compare measurements.**

- Allow each partner pair to tell the number of straws tall they are. Ask who is taller and who is shorter and how they know. Encourage them to use the number of straws as the means of comparison. This may create confusion for some children who are close but not exactly the same height.

- Have children describe the way in which they measured their partner.

- Ask questions such as: *What did you do if the last straw didn't get all the way to the top of the head or if it was a little longer than the top of the head?*

- Reinforce the concept that measurement is an approximation by having two children of almost the same height stand next to each other. Discuss that the number of straws used was the same even though they are not exactly the same height, so you say they are "about" ___ straws tall.

4 **Explore unit iteration.**

- Address the concept of unit iteration with the questions: *Why did you lay the straws in a straight line? What would happen if you left out some of the straws?*

- Have children of two obviously different heights lay on the floor. Line straws up in a straight line next to the taller child and in a zigzag pattern next to the shorter child so the same number of straws is used for each one. Ask: *Does it make sense that both [child's name] and [child's name] are [number of straws used] straws tall? Why not? Why is it important to line the straws up in a straight line to measure?*

Check for Understanding

- Tell children to use straws to measure another object in the classroom.

- Observe methods children use without expectation of complete accuracy at this time. Take note of children who may need additional assistance during the lesson.

STEP BY STEP

Materials For each child: Measuring Tools (Activity Sheet 39), centimeter cubes, connecting cubes

- Begin by asking children to tell the number of straws needed to measure the object of choice from the Opening Activity. Lead them in a review of the important aspects of measuring explored during the Opening Activity and engage them in determining whether their measure makes sense compared to the measure of other objects.

- Have children use their straws to measure the pencil at the top of the page. Discuss how the straws are not the best object to use since they don't closely match up with the pencil. Tell children that there are many other kinds of objects you can use to measure.

- Tell children to place a strip of tiles on the picture of tiles used to measure the pencil in Think. Discuss how the picture of tiles represents the object. Review the way the tiles are lined up and iterated from end to end.

- Allow children time to discuss Talk About It with a partner. Let children share ideas with the class and then ask them to measure the width of their book with tiles.

- Iterate a combination of centimeter cubes and connecting cubes along the width of the book, telling children your measure. Discuss why your measure is different from theirs, emphasizing the need to measure in same-size units.

- Use the Mathematical Discourse questions to discuss the measurement process in more detail.

Hands-On Activity

Materials For each pair: centimeter cubes, 4-inch straws, varied objects such as crayons, markers, books, pencil boxes, etc.

Put children in pairs to measure 3 or 4 items, using both straws and cubes. Tell children to describe the measure in terms of each one, using "about" for approximate measures. Discuss whether it is easier to measure the items with straws or cubes and why.

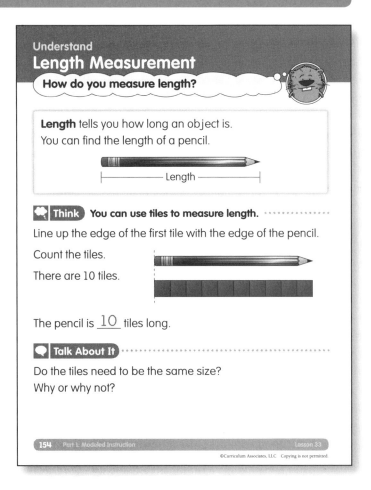

Mathematical Discourse

- *Would it make more sense to measure the length of a table with straws or tiles? Why?*

  Some children may respond that straws are easier to use since the table is big and not as many are needed. Others may respond that by using the tiles, there is a better chance that the tiles will line up along the table.

- *Why is it important to line the first tile up with one end of the object you are measuring?*

  Children should respond that the tiles need to match up with the object so they are the same size. If you don't line up the first tile, you won't be measuring the whole object.

STEP BY STEP

Materials For each child: Measuring Tools (Activity Sheet 39)

- Explain to children that there are many "units" that can be used to measure. Ask them to list things that might be used as a measuring tool. Emphasize that each unit must be the same size.

- Draw attention to the units shown on this page. Have children compare the units and observe the pictures of the measurements.

- Ask: *How is measuring with tiles and paper clips the same? How is it different?* [Both are placed touching end to end from left to right along the entire length of the paintbrush. The units are different sizes.]

- Cut out the tile strips and paper clip strips from the activity sheet and distribute. Read the directions and have children measure the crayon using tiles and then clips. Circulate and help children with the measuring process as necessary.

- Invite children to share their measurements. Discuss and resolve any discrepancies.

- Have children discuss Talk About It in pairs, and then discuss as a class how the size of the unit used affects the numerical measure.

Hands-On Activity

Materials For each child: objects that can be used as units of measure such as unused pencils, toothpicks, craft sticks, etc.

- Have children use each of the "units" to measure objects at their desks, such as the width of the desktop, a book, a piece of paper, etc.

- Discuss the measures, checking to ensure children are iterating from one end of the object to the other and describing their measure numerically with the unit name.

- Ask: *How can your desk have a measure of both ___ and ___ ?* Emphasize that the number represents the number of units, which is determined by the size of the unit used. (SMP 2)

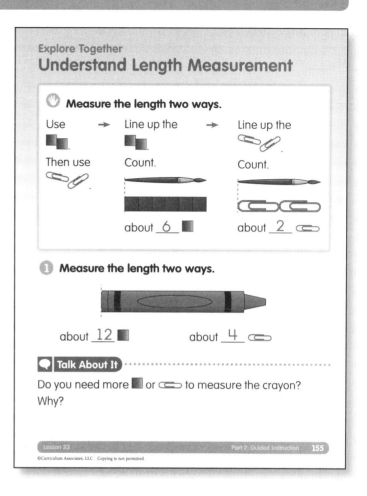

Mathematical Discourse

- *Why is it important to know how to measure something?*

  Children may think of situations such as measuring their foot to buy the right size of shoe, measuring a toy to make sure you have the right size box or bag to store it in, etc. (You may need to make suggestions to jump-start children's ideas.)

STEP BY STEP

Materials For each child: connecting cubes, centimeter cubes, toothpicks

- Discuss each Connect It problem as a class using the discussion points outlined below.

Explain

- Present the problem and have children compare the way the string is measured to the way items were measured on previous pages. Guide them to recognize that two different sizes of paper clips are used.

- Discuss the problems that occur when measuring with different size units. Ask: *Suppose you need a string the same size as the one Buzz has. He tells you it is 8 paper clips long. Do you think you would cut a piece of string the same size as the one Buzz measured? Explain.*

- Have children measure the string using centimeter cubes and then using connecting cubes, recording each measure. Share results, emphasizing the uniformity in the measures.

- Then tell children to use different combinations of the two kinds of cubes and record the number of units used. Children should discover that the numerical measure is not consistent among everyone.

Reason

- Ask children how this way of measuring is similar to the problem Buzz had with the paper clips. Lead them to see that by overlapping the squares, some of the units are smaller than others. It is like measuring with different sizes of units.

- Emphasize that measurement is a comparison of one object to another. Aligning the objects carefully and exactly results in more accurate measures.

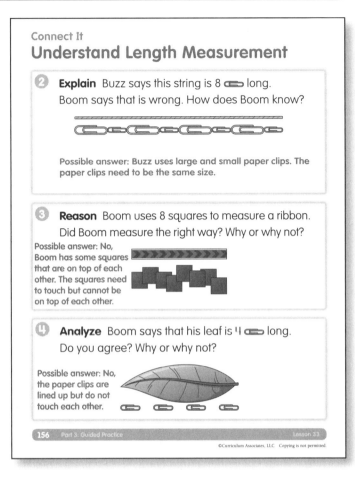

Analyze

- Discuss the reasons Boom may have left gaps between the paper clips as shown.

> **SMP Tip:** Measure an object that is not an exact number of paper clips long. Explain that, even if the last clip doesn't reach the end of the object, they all still must be placed end to end to get the most accurate measure as possible. Emphasize the importance of measuring as accurately as possible. *(SMP 6)*

- Display objects that are non-linear in shape like the leaf. Point out that the length of an object is determined by the longest part of the object. Have the children place toothpicks vertically on each side of the leaf where the paper clips begin and end.

STEP BY STEP

Materials For each child: Measuring Tools (Activity Sheet 39)

- Read the problems aloud and allow children to respond independently.

- Distribute rectangle and square cutouts from the activity sheet.

- As children complete the tasks, support them with the following questions:

  How might the size of the squares and rectangles help you decide which one takes more?

  What does "fewer" mean? How is it different from "more"?

  Where do you think you should begin measuring the pencil you drew? How might toothpicks help you know where to begin and end measuring?

  Think about what Buzz and Boom did wrong when they measured. How can you make sure you are measuring properly?

- As you circulate, ask children to justify the choices they make in Part A.

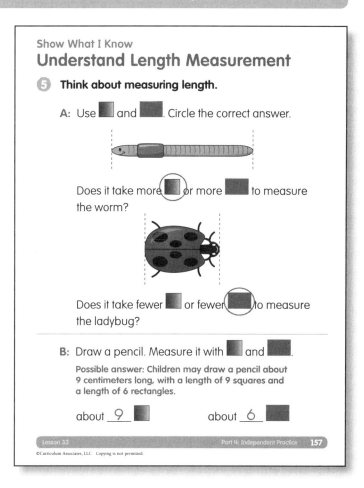

SCORING RUBRICS

Expectations for 4–3 Points

Points	Expectations
4	The child: • selects the unit that answers each question without measuring. • accurately measures the pencil drawn, recording the number of each unit used.
3	The child: • selects the unit that answers each question but needs to measure. • accurately measures the pencil drawn, recording the number of each unit used.

Expectations for 2–0 Points

Points	Expectations
2	The child: • selects the opposing units for each question, justifying that the larger unit represents "more." • measures the pencil drawn but may have minor errors such as small gaps or the unit extended slightly beyond the left side of the figure.
1	The child: • may circle one of the units shown but is unable to give a reason for the choice. • may draw a pencil and attempt to iterate but uses a combination of units with gaps and overlaps and no numerical recording.
0	The child: • does not attempt to answer the questions or measure a pencil.

Intervention Activity

Measure object with cubes.

Materials For each child: classroom objects, centimeter or connecting cubes, toothpicks

- Provide children with several desk-sized objects to measure and a set of centimeter or connecting cubes.

- Place a toothpick vertically on the left side of the item to serve as a guide.

- Instruct children to connect or place cubes side by side from the toothpick to the end of the object. Then have them count cubes and record the measure.

On-Level Activity

Measure around the room.

Materials For each pair: paper divided into 4 sections with varied non-standard unit names in each one, such as centimeter cubes, connecting cubes, toothpicks, straws, paper clips (one size)

- Have children work in pairs to select and measure an object in the classroom. Encourage them to select an object that is easy to measure with each unit listed on their paper.

- After children measure the object with each unit, they record the measure in the appropriate box.

- Discuss which units children needed more of and fewer of to measure the object.

Challenge Activity

Find ways to measure odd-shaped objects.

Materials For each child: string or yarn, classroom objects

Challenge children to find ways of measuring items, such as the distance around a globe/ball or the distance around (perimeter) odd-shaped objects, like their hand or foot, bulletin board letters, etc.

Children must:

- select a method that will help them measure as accurately as possible.

- choose a unit that will give the most accurate measure. (Encourage them to try a variety of units.)

- describe the strategy, unit used, and the number of units needed to measure each item.

Lesson 34 (Student Book pages 158–161)
Tell Time

LESSON OBJECTIVES

- Tell time to the hour and half hour, using analog and digital clocks.

- Write the time to the hour and half hour.

- Understand that 30 minutes is the same as a half-hour.

PREREQUISITE SKILLS

- Understand that when an object is divided into two equal parts, the parts are called halves.

- Count from 1 to 20.

VOCABULARY

analog clock: a clock that uses hour and minute hand positions to show time

digital clock: a clock that uses the number of hours and minutes to show time

half-hour: 30 minutes, or a unit of time that is half as long as one hour

half past: a way of referring to the time that is one half-hour after a given hour (e.g., 3 o'clock and "half past 3")

hour: a unit of time equal to 60 minutes

hour hand: The shorter indicator (or hand) on an analog clock, which shows the hours

minute: a unit of time equal to 60 seconds

minute hand: The longer indicator (or hand) on an analog clock, which shows the minutes

o'clock: literally means "of the clock"; indicates telling time and is used to show that the current time is at or near a particular hour

THE LEARNING PROGRESSION

In Kindergarten, children do not directly address telling time, but teachers often talk about the rhythms of the school day and times to do certain activities.

In Grade 1, children begin reading digital and analog clocks. **In this lesson,** children learn to tell time to the hour and half hour. They relate their concept of "one half" to measuring an intangible item: time. They learn to recognize minutes and hours on analog and digital clocks and to read and write time to the hour and half hour.

In Grade 2, children extend their understanding of how to tell time to include time to the nearest 5 minutes. They also learn the meaning of AM and PM and use them along with the numerical time.

Ready *Teacher Toolbox*   Teacher-Toolbox.com

	Prerequisite Skills	1.MD.B.3
Ready Lessons		✓
Tools for Instruction	✓	✓
Interactive Tutorials		

CCSS Focus

1.MD.B.3 Tell and write time in hours and half-hours using analog and digital clocks.

STANDARDS FOR MATHEMATICAL PRACTICE: *SMP 6, 7 (see page A9 for full text)*

Opening Activity: Tell Time

Objective: Understand how the hour hand and minute hand move on a clock.

Materials For display:
- demonstration clock or
- Clock Face (Activity Sheet 40)
- heavy-stock paper
- round-head fastener
- cardboard

Overview

Children observe and demonstrate the movement of the minute hand completely around the clock as the hour hand moves from one number to the next.

Step by Step (10–15 minutes)

1 Prepare for the activity.

- Display the demonstration clock for the class. If one is not available, you can copy and cut out the Clock Face activity sheet and glue it on heavy-stock paper or cardboard. Punch a hole through the hands and the center of the clock face and attach the hands with a round-head fastener.

2 Investigate the hour hand.

- Explain that telling time includes a number for the hour and a number for the minutes. Tell children that the hour hand points right at the number when it's that hour. Explain that at 12 o'clock, the hour hand points right at 12. Show on the demonstration clock.

- Direct attention to the hour hand on the demonstration clock. Slowly turn the hour hand so that it points to 1, 2, 3, and so on. Have children state the time as it points to each number.

3 Investigate the minute hand.

- Refer again to the demonstration clock, and remind children that clocks have two hands. Discuss how the hands look different.

- Tell children that the minute hand moves completely around the clock in the same time that it takes the hour hand to move from one number to the next.

- Invite a child to move the minute hand around the clock once. As he/she does this, slowly move the hour hand from the 3 to 4.

- Explain that on an actual clock, it would take 60 minutes, or 1 hour for the minute hand to move completely around the clock and for the hour hand to move from one number to the next.

- It may be helpful to provide familiar benchmarks for 60 minutes (1 hour), such as "about how long soccer practice is" or "a little bit longer than math period."

Check for Understanding

Ask several children to tell where the hour hand points for various "on the hour" times. Evaluate their responses for accuracy and understanding. Have several children take turns moving the minute and hour hands and observe.

STEP BY STEP

Materials For display: demonstration clock, For each child: Clock Face (Activity Sheet 40)

- Begin by asking children what they have learned or remember from the Opening Activity. Cut out the hands from the activity sheet, and distribute a clock face to each child.

- Explain that the flat part of an analog clock is called its face. Discuss why it might be called a face. Review the terminology "minute hand" and "hour hand." Have children hold up the minute and hours hands.

- Ask children to describe situations when they might want to know what time it is. Explain that "o'clock" is a word that is used after a number to name the time in hours.

- Show 6 o'clock on the demonstration clock. Explain that the hour hand points directly at 6 and the minute hand points straight up, to 12.

- Read the text at the top of the page, pointing out the hour hand. Explain that this page shows only what the hour hand looks like at different times and that you'll study the minute hand later.

- Direct children's attention to Model It. Ask them to describe the position of the hour hand on the first clock and model it on their clock faces. Elicit that the first clock shows the hour hand pointing exactly to the 2. Explain that this means it's exactly 2 o'clock.

- Ask children to describe the position of the hour hand on the second clock and model it on their clock faces. Guide them to recognize that it points a little past the 2. Remind children that the hour hand moves very slowly, so this clock shows that it's just past 2 o'clock.

- Use the Mathematical Discourse question to discuss the idea of "almost 3 o'clock."

- Have children model and then draw the hour hand at almost 3 o'clock. Discuss.

Fluency Practice

Materials For each child: Facts Practice 1, 2, 3, or 4 (Activity Worksheet 16, 17, 18, or 20) Select one of the Facts Practice activity sheets for children to complete.

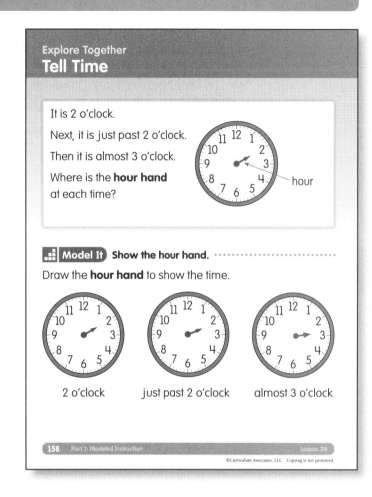

Mathematical Discourse

- *How does the hour hand move on a clock as the time goes from 2 o'clock 3 o'clock? Why?*

  Children should recognize that, over the course of an hour, the hour hand moves very slowly from one number to the next.

- *When the hour hand on an analog clock shows that the time is almost 3 o'clock, what hour does a digital clock show?*

  Make sure children understand that "almost 3 o'clock" means it is still "2 something." The hour on the digital clock won't switch to 3 until it is exactly 3 o'clock.

STEP BY STEP

- Read the question at the top of the page. Discuss the two types of clocks. Point out the hour hand and the part of the digital display that shows the hour. Point out the minute hand and the part of the digital display that shows the minutes.

- Have children look at the hour hand and describe it's position relative to the hours 9 and 10. Guide them to recognize that it's about halfway between 9 and 10.

- Read Model It aloud. Reiterate that the hour hand is halfway between 9 and 10. Relate this to the position of the minute hand, halfway around the clock.

- Ask: *Is it before or after 9 o'clock?* [after] *How can you tell?* [the hour hand is past the 9] Use the first Mathematical Discourse question for further discussion of the minute hand.

- Have children complete Model It on their own. Then discuss. Elicit that the written time, 9:30, looks the same as the time on the digital clock. Show children that times on the hour, such as 4 o'clock and 9 o'clock, include two zeros for minutes as in 4:00 and 9:00.

- Read Talk About It. Discuss with the class. Explain that there are 60 minutes in one hour. Use the second Mathematical Discourse question to explore the idea of "half of 60".

Concept Extension

Relate half hours to half of shapes.

Materials For each child: Clock Face (Activity Sheet 40), markers, paper squares

- Have children draw a line from 12 to 6 and shade the right half of the clock face. Review that the two equal-size parts of a whole circle are halves.

- Ask children to use their fingers to show how the minute hand moves from the 12 to the 6 in a half-hours. Relate the half-hour time period to half of the clock.

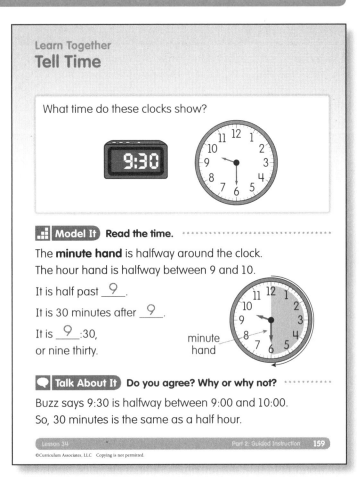

Mathematical Discourse

- *At 9:00 the minute hand was on the 12. How far around the circle did the minute hand travel to get to the 6? How do you know?*

  It may take more prompting, but help children understand that the minute hand traveled halfway around the clock and that's why the hour hand is halfway between 9 and 10.

- *30 + 30 is 60. How does this relate to minutes and hours?*

  Guide children to understand that double 30 is 60, so 30 is half of 60 Since there are 60 minutes in 1 hour, 30 minutes is half of 1 hour. That's why the digital clock shows 30 minutes when the minute hand on the analog clock is face (pointing at 6).

STEP BY STEP

- Read the example problem. Remind children that the minute hand points straight up, toward 12, at the start of the hour. Guide them to recognize that the hour hand points directly at 7, so this clock face shows 7 o'clock.

- Discuss the differences and similarities between the analog and digital clock. Point out the stylized numbers on digital clocks. Use the Hands-On Activity below to familiarize children with SSD (seven-segment display) numbers.

- Read each problem aloud. Then have children complete the problem and discuss.

- In Problem 1, ensure that children recognize the correct placement of the minute hand and the hour hand. Have them say the time out loud, "4 o'clock."

- In Problem 2, have children describe what they have drawn. Listen for understanding of the differences between the minute and hour hands—their lengths, what they mean, and how they move. Ensure that children can translate from "half past 3" to the numeric version "3:30."

> **SMP Tip:** Encourage children to use precise language when stating the time and when discussing their mathematical reasoning related to time. Language should include terms such as: "hour," "half-hour," "about," "o'clock," "past," and "___-thirty." *(SMP 6)*

Hands-On Activity

Construct a digital clock face.

Materials For each child: cardstock, 28 toothpicks

- Have children draw a colon in the middle of the cardstock to create their own digital clock display.

- Ask children to make an "8" using exactly seven toothpicks. Demonstrate how to make the other digits (0–7, 9) by removing specific toothpicks from the 8. Allow time for children to practice.

- Have children divide their toothpicks into four groups of seven. Explain that each group of seven toothpicks will be used for one of the digits on their digital clock.

- Have children use toothpicks to form the numbers to display various times on their digital clocks.

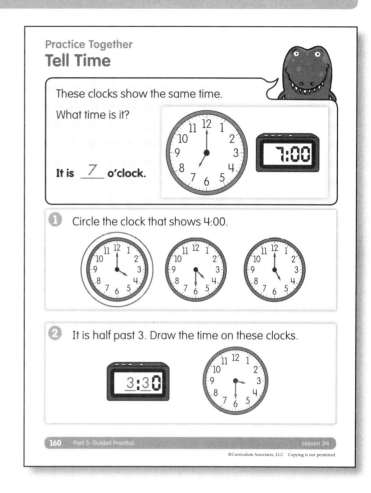

Mathematical Discourse

- *Boom drew half past 3 by pointing a small hand to the 6 and a long hand to the 3. Is this correct? Why or why not? How would you fix it?*

    Error Alert Children should recognize that Boom switched the hands. The long hand should be on the 6 and the short hand should be on the 3.

STEP BY STEP

- Before children work on this page, review the key concepts in the lesson.

- Read each problem aloud, then have children work independently to solve.

- For Problem 3, ensure that children are visually distinguishing the minute hand and hour hand. The hour hand should be between 12 and 1, not on the 12.

- In Problem 4, 11:00 and 1:00 are mirror images. Make sure that children do not get the two times confused.

- Problem 5 requires reading and modeling both digital and analog clocks. Check that children write the hour to the left of the colon and the minutes to the right.

> **SMP Tip:** Children use the structures inherent in the clock face and the digital time display when they tell time. They can use their knowledge of halves of a circle to help them read and write time to the half-hour. They recognize that the colon on the digital clock separates the hours and minutes, and use this information to correctly place the hour hand and minute hand. (*SMP 7*)

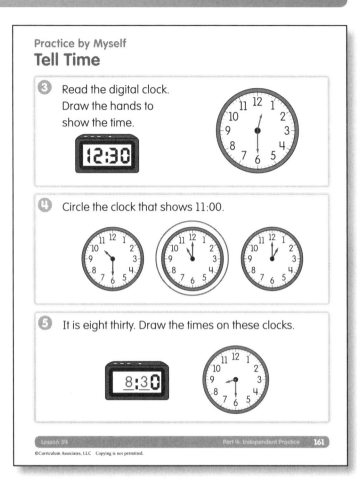

ELL Support

Discuss multiple English meanings of the words "hand" and "face."

- Children know what their face is and they have learned what a clock face is. Discuss similarities and differences.

- Children know what hands are. The fingers on their hands can point to things like the hands on a clock point to the numbers.

Mathematical Discourse

- *How would you explain to someone who can't tell time how to read these clocks [show a digital and analog clock]?*

  Listen for children's understanding of hours and minutes and how each kind of clock differentiates hours and minutes. Children should be able to discuss the colon on the digital clock and the size/shape of the hands on an analog clock as well as the different speeds at which the hands move. Some children might explain the meaning of ":30" and "half past". Others might tell how to read the hour from an analog clock, by the placement of the hour hand.

Assessment and Remediation

- Ask children to state the time for analog clocks showing 1:30, 3:00, 8:30.

- For children who are still struggling, use the chart below to guide remediation.

- After providing remediation, check children's understanding using the following problem: Draw the time shown on this digital clock (digital clock shows 6:00). [child draws an analog clock with the hour hand pointing to 6 and the minute hand pointing to 12]

If the error is . . .	Children may . . .	To remediate . . .
2:30 or 9:30	not understand that the hour is the one that has been passed, not the one that is upcoming.	Ask: *Where is the hour hand pointing?* [in between two numbers] Explain that the time doesn't say the "next" number until the hour hand points to it or passes it. Elicit that the time is "half past" 1 or "half past" 8, which is the same as 1:30 or 8:30.
3:30 instead of 3:00	not recognize the placement of the minute hand.	Cover up the clock face except for the area from 1 to 4. Have children identify where the hour hand points [directly at 3]. State that the hour hand points directly at the number at the start of the hour. Ask: *Where does the minute hand point at the start of an hour?* [straight up to 12] Reveal the whole clock.
other errors	be confused about minutes and hours.	Cover up the clock face except for the area around the hour hand. Guide children to determine the correct hour or the hour that the time is just past. Reveal the whole clock. Discuss the placement of the minute hand.

Hands-On Activity

Construct a clock face.

Materials For each child: yarn, cardstock, glue, sticky notes

- Give each child a piece of cardstock. Have them glue on a yarn circle. Then have them write the numbers 1 through 12 on sticky notes.

- Children discuss in small groups how to place the numbers onto their clock faces.

- When everyone has made their clock face, discuss how these are like and different than actual clocks. Have children draw hands on their analog clock faces to show a time (to an hour or half hour).

Challenge Activity

Solve simple time problems.

Materials For each child: individual clock models or paper clock templates

- Pose very simple problems, such as: *3 hours past 4:00* or *a half-hour past 1:00* or *a half-hour past 8:30.* Problems should involve only adding hours within 12, or adding a half-hour onto a given time.

- Have children respond to each prompt by moving the hands on their clock models to show the new time, or writing the numbers as if on a digital clock face.

- Ask children to explain how they determined the time.

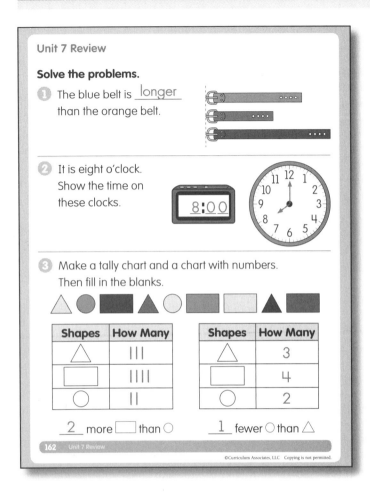

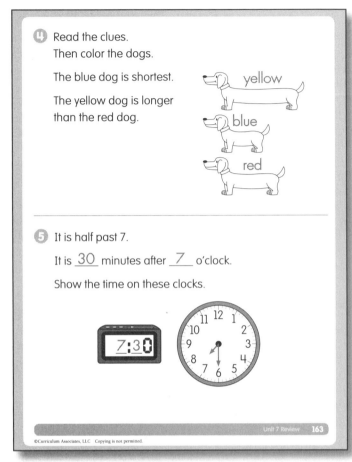

STEP BY STEP

- Have children solve the problems individually and show their work. Emphasize that children are free to use whatever way helps them solve the problems.

- Observe as children work. For Problem 1, ask children to explain how they know which belt is shorter and which is longer.

- For Problems 2 and 5, be alert for children who have difficulty distinguishing the hour hand and minute hand on the analog clock.

Materials For each child: Measuring Tools (Activity Sheet 39)

- For Problem 6, look for evidence that children understand the principles for using a reference unit to measure an object: line up the edge of the first unit with the edge of the object being measured and align the reference units so that they touch but do not overlap.

- If children struggle with Problem 8, ask questions such as:

Where will you start measuring?

How do you know how many squares or rectangles to count in order to find the length?

STEP BY STEP

Materials For each child: Measuring Tools (Activity Sheet 39)

- On this page, children compare the lengths of three objects. Then they use two different units to measure one of the objects. Distribute strips of squares and rectangles from the activity sheet.

- Direct children to complete the Put It Together on their own.

- Read the directions and task aloud. Make sure children understand what they need to do to complete the task.

- As children work on their own, observe their progress and understanding. Respond to their questions and provide additional support as needed.

- Have children share their measurements with the class. Ask them to explain why it takes more squares than rectangles to measure the pencil.

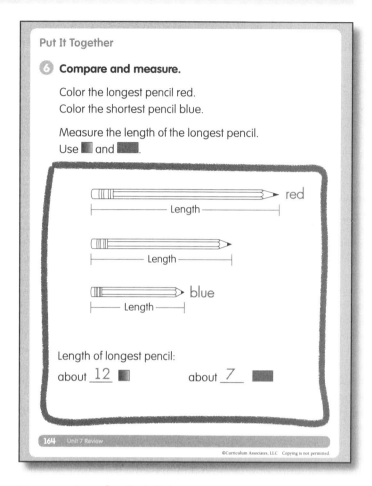

SCORING RUBRICS

Expectations for 4–3 Points

Points	Expectations
4	The child: • identifies the shortest and longest pencils. • accurately measures the longest pencil using both squares and rectangles.
3	The child: • identifies the shortest and longest pencils. • accurately measures the longest pencil with one of the units and is close with the second unit.

Expectations for 2–0 Points

Points	Expectations
2	The child: • identifies either the longest or shortest pencil correctly, but maybe not both. • accurately measures the longest pencil with one of the units but not both.
1	The child: • is unable to identify the shortest and longest pencils. • fills in length measurements, but both numbers are inaccurate.
0	The child: • does not attempt to complete the task.

Activity Sheets

These Activity Sheets are provided for use with the Opening Activity and Hands-On, Fluency, and Differentiated Instruction activities found in the **Ready®** Teacher's Resource Book. These activity masters may be photocopied for classroom use. Refer to the activities in the lessons for a full list of materials and instructions.

Number Paths

| 1 | 2 | 3 | 4 | 5 | 6 | 7 | 8 | 9 | 10 |

| 1 | 2 | 3 | 4 | 5 | 6 | 7 | 8 | 9 | 10 |

| 1 | 2 | 3 | 4 | 5 | 6 | 7 | 8 | 9 | 10 |

| 1 | 2 | 3 | 4 | 5 | 6 | 7 | 8 | 9 | 10 |

| 1 | 2 | 3 | 4 | 5 | 6 | 7 | 8 | 9 | 10 |

Number Bond Recording Sheet

Number Bond Mat

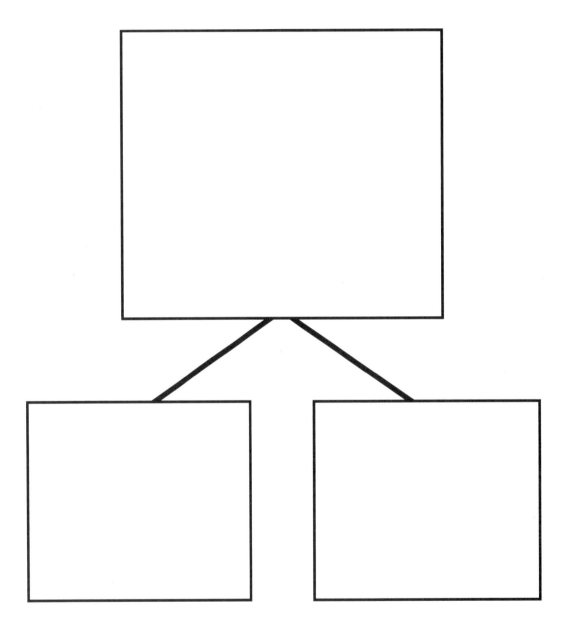

Number Bond Practice to 5

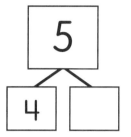

| 5 |
| 4 | |

| 5 |
| 3 | |

| 5 |
| | 1 |

| 5 |
| | 2 |

| 5 |
| 1 | |

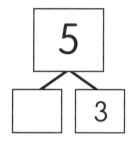

| 5 |
| | 3 |

| 5 |
| 4 | |

| 5 |
| 2 | |

| 5 |
| | 1 |

| 5 |
| 3 | |

| 5 |
| 1 | |

| 5 |
| | 2 |

| 5 |
| | 1 |

| 5 |
| 4 | |

| 5 |
| 3 | |

| 5 |
| 2 | |

| 5 |
| 4 | |

| 5 |
| | 3 |

| 5 |
| 1 | |

| 5 |
| | 2 |

| 5 |
| | 4 |

| 5 |
| | 3 |

| 5 |
| 3 | |

| 5 |
| | 2 |

| 5 |
| 1 | |

Addition Table 1

0 + 0 ____	0 + 1 ____	0 + 2 ____	0 + 3 ____	0 + 4 ____	0 + 5 ____
1 + 0 ____	1 + 1 ____	1 + 2 ____	1 + 3 ____	1 + 4 ____	1 + 5 ____
2 + 0 ____	2 + 1 ____	2 + 2 ____	2 + 3 ____	2 + 4 ____	2 + 5 ____
3 + 0 ____	3 + 1 ____	3 + 2 ____	3 + 3 ____	3 + 4 ____	3 + 5 ____
4 + 0 ____	4 + 1 ____	4 + 2 ____	4 + 3 ____	4 + 4 ____	4 + 5 ____
5 + 0 ____	5 + 1 ____	5 + 2 ____	5 + 3 ____	5 + 4 ____	5 + 5 ____

Partners for 6 Practice

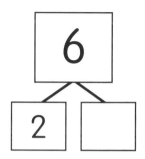

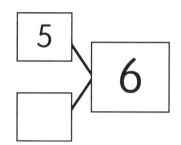

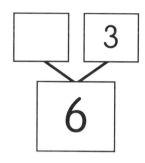

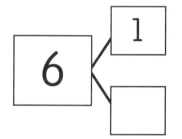

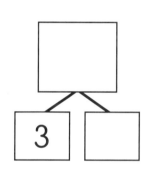

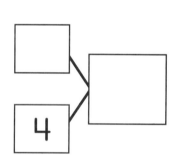

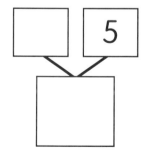

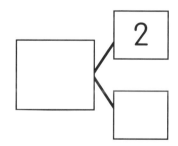

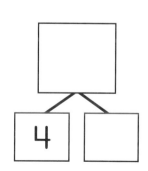

Partners for 7 Practice

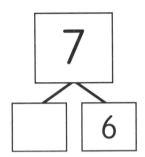
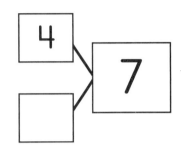
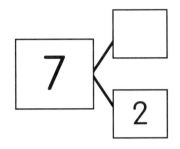

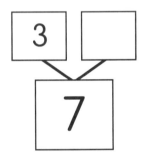
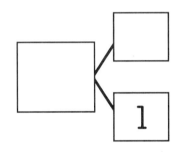
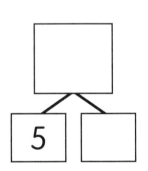

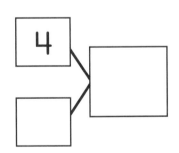
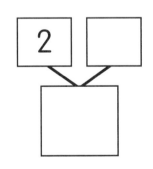
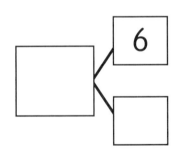

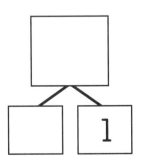
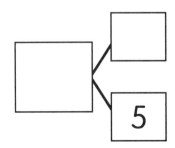
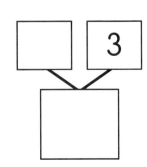

Grid Paper

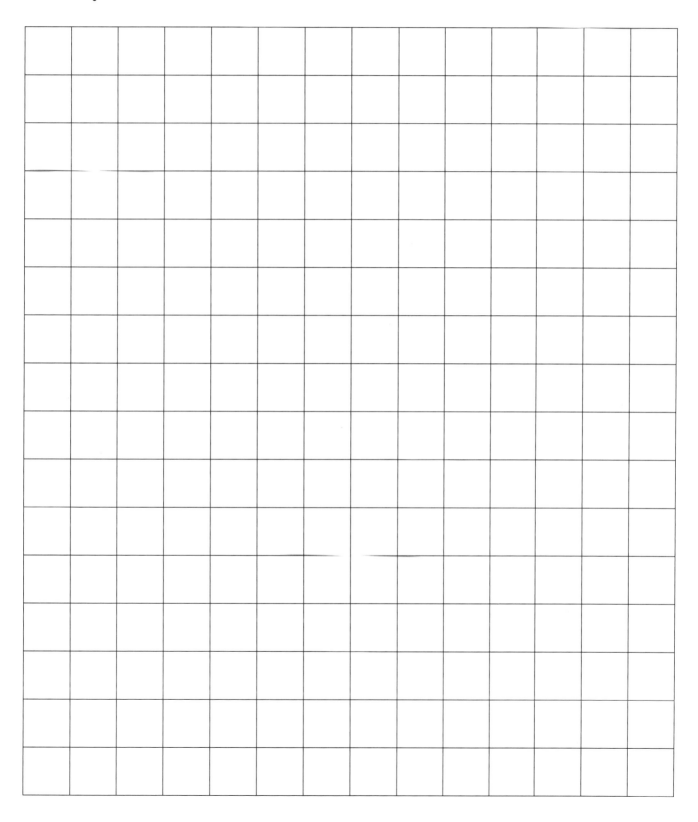

Partners for 8 Practice

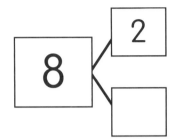

2 + ____ = 8

8 = ____ + 2

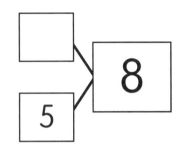

____ + 5 = 8

8 = 5 + ____

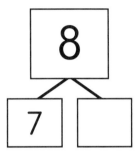

7 + ____ = 8

8 = ____ + 7

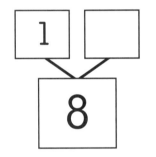

1 + ____ = 8

8 = ____ + 1

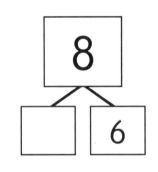

____ + 6 = 8

8 = 6 + ____

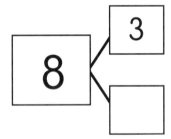

3 + ____ = 8

8 = ____ + 3

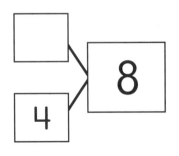

____ + 4 = 8

8 = 4 + ____

Partners for 9 Practice

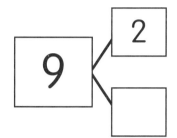

$2 +$ _____ $= 9$

$9 =$ _____ $+ 2$

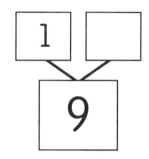

$1 +$ _____ $= 9$

$9 =$ _____ $+ 1$

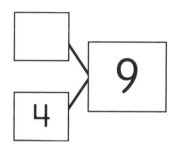

_____ $+ 4 = 9$

$9 = 4 +$ _____

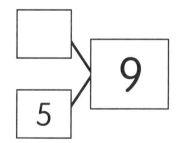

_____ $+ 5 = 9$

$9 = 5 +$ _____

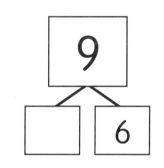

_____ $+ 6 = 9$

$9 = 6 +$ _____

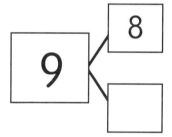

$8 +$ _____ $= 9$

$9 =$ _____ $+ 8$

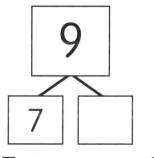

$7 +$ _____ $= 9$

$9 =$ _____ $+ 7$

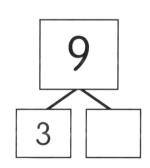

$3 +$ _____ $= 9$

$9 =$ _____ $+ 3$

10-Frame

Partners for 10 Practice

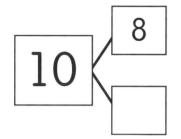

8 + ____ = 10

10 = ____ + 8

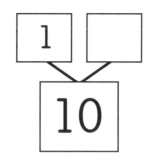

1 + ____ = 10

10 = ____ + 1

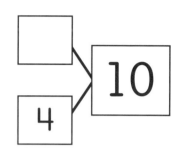

____ + 4 = 10

10 = 4 + ____

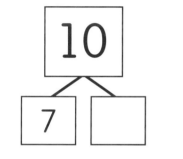

7 + ____ = 10

10 = ____ + 7

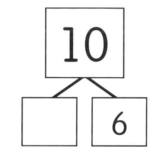

____ + 6 = 10

10 = 6 + ____

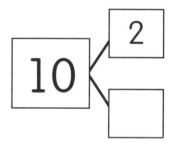

2 + ____ = 10

10 = ____ + 2

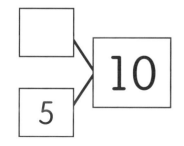

____ + 5 = 10

10 = 5 + ____

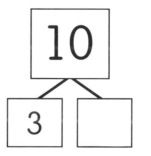

3 + ____ = 10

10 = ____ + 3

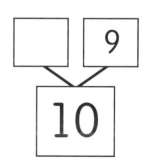

1 + ____ = 10

10 = ____ + 1

True and Untrue Number Sentences

_____ + _____ = _____ + _____

_____ + _____ = _____ + _____

Addition Table 2

1 + 1	1 + 2	1 + 3	1 + 4	1 + 5	1 + 6	1 + 7	1 + 8	1 + 9
2 + 1	2 + 2	2 + 3	2 + 4	2 + 5	2 + 6	2 + 7	2 + 8	
3 + 1	3 + 2	3 + 3	3 + 4	3 + 5	3 + 6	3 + 7		
4 + 1	4 + 2	4 + 3	4 + 4	4 + 5	4 + 6			
5 + 1	5 + 2	5 + 3	5 + 4	5 + 5				
6 + 1	6 + 2	6 + 3	6 + 4					
7 + 1	7 + 2	7 + 3						
8 + 1	8 + 2							
9 + 1								

Addition Table 3

1 + 1 2	1 + 2 3	1 + 3 4	1 + 4 5	1 + 5 6	1 + 6 7	1 + 7 8	1 + 8 9	1 + 9 10
2 + 1 3	2 + 2 4	2 + 3 5	2 + 4 6	2 + 5 7	2 + 6 8	2 + 7 9	2 + 8 10	
3 + 1 4	3 + 2 5	3 + 3 6	3 + 4 7	3 + 5 8	3 + 6 9	3 + 7 10		
4 + 1 5	4 + 2 6	4 + 3 7	4 + 4 8	4 + 5 9	4 + 6 10			
5 + 1 6	5 + 2 7	5 + 3 8	5 + 4 9	5 + 5 10				
6 + 1 7	6 + 2 8	6 + 3 9	6 + 4 10					
7 + 1 8	7 + 2 9	7 + 3 10						
8 + 1 9	8 + 2 10							
9 + 1 10								

Facts Practice 1

1 + ___ = 6	___ − 5 = 1	8 − ___ = 7	___ = 5 + 4
10 − 8 = ___	___ = 9 − 2	___ + 1 = 9	0 + ___ = 6
___ + 0 = 8	10 − ___ = 4	6 − 4 = ___	9 + ___ = 10
2 + ___ = 6	___ = 10 + 0	___ − 0 = 7	7 − 6 = ___
3 = 8 − ___	3 + 3 = ___	9 − ___ = 1	7 + 0 = ___
___ + 4 = 10	9 − ___ = 0	3 + 5 = ___	___ = 10 − 7
3 + ___ = 9	8 = 10 − ___	4 + ___ = 8	___ − 6 = 3
6 + ___ = 7	9 − 5 = ___	___ = 6 + 2	___ + 9 = 9
___ = 10 − 9	___ + 3 = 10	7 − 4 = ___	5 + ___ = 10

Facts Practice 2

___ = 4 + 2	9 − ___ = 10	___ + 2 = 9	8 − 7 = ___
___ − 1 = 9	7 + ___ = 8	___ = 1 + 6	9 − 3 = ___
8 − ___ = 4	___ + 10 = 10	0 + 8 = ___	___ = 6 − 2
5 + ___ = 6	___ − 3 = 4	___ = 3 + 4	10 − 4 = ___
___ = 1 + 8	8 − ___ = 6	___ + 2 = 7	0 + ___ = 7
7 − 1 = ___	___ + 6 = 8	7 = 6 − ___	___ = 4 + 5
___ + 7 = 10	5 = 10 − ___	9 + 0 = ___	___ − 5 = 2
6 − ___ = 9	2 + 8 = ___	9 = 2 + ___	___ − 0 = 6
___ = 5 + 3	10 − 3 = ___	9 − ___ = 5	4 + ___ = 10

Facts Practice 3

___ + 3 = 6	9 − ___ = 0	___ = 7 + 3	8 + ___ = 10
0 = ___ − 6	___ + 3 = 7	10 − 0 = ___	6 − ___ = 3
8 − 0 = ___	___ + 7 = 9	___ = 2 + 5	___ − 8 = 0
10 = ___ + 9	___ = 1 + 7	10 − ___ = 8	6 + ___ = 6
7 − 7 = ___	___ + 0 = 10	8 − ___ = 5	8 + ___ = 6
___ − 7 = 2	___ = 10 − 0	6 = 1 + ___	7 + ___ = 7
___ + 9 = 9	___ − 6 = 2	9 − ___ = 4	6 + 3 = ___
7 = 6 + ___	7 − 2 = ___	___ + 5 = 10	10 − ___ = 3
___ = 9 − 0	5 + 4 = ___	10 − ___ = 10	___ − 8 = 0

Hundreds Chart

1	2	3	4	5	6	7	8	9	10
11	12	13	14	15	16	17	18	19	20
21	22	23	24	25	26	27	28	29	30
31	32	33	34	35	36	37	38	39	40
41	42	43	44	45	46	47	48	49	50
51	52	53	54	55	56	57	58	59	60
61	62	63	64	65	66	67	68	69	70
71	72	73	74	75	76	77	78	79	80
81	82	83	84	85	86	87	88	89	90
91	92	93	94	95	96	97	98	99	100

Facts Practice 4

How many ways can you make 7?

___ + ___ = 7   ___ + ___ = 7

7 = ___ + ___   7 = ___ + ___

___ + ___ = 7   ___ + ___ = 7

How many ways can you make 8?

___ + ___ = 8   ___ + ___ = 8

8 = ___ + ___   8 = ___ + ___

___ + ___ = 8   ___ + ___ = 8

8 = ___ + ___

How many ways can you make 9?

___ + ___ = 9   ___ + ___ = 9

9 = ___ + ___   9 = ___ + ___

___ + ___ = 9   ___ + ___ = 9

9 = ___ + ___   9 = ___ + ___

Number Bond Practice for 10

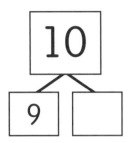 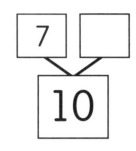 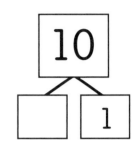

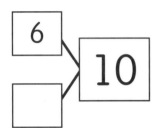 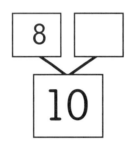

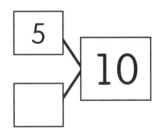 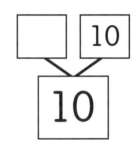 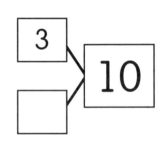

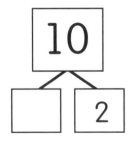 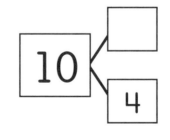 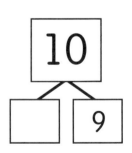

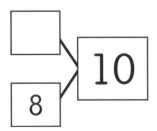 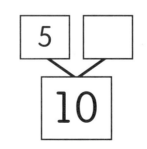 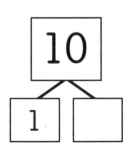

Teen Number Cards

	11	12	13
14	15	16	17
18	19	+	−
=	<	>	☐

120 Chart

1	2	3	4	5	6	7	8	9	10
11	12	13	14	15	16	17	18	19	20
21	22	23	24	25	26	27	28	29	30
31	32	33	34	35	36	37	38	39	40
41	42	43	44	45	46	47	48	49	50
51	52	53	54	55	56	57	58	59	60
61	62	63	64	65	66	67	68	69	70
71	72	73	74	75	76	77	78	79	80
81	82	83	84	85	86	87	88	89	90
91	92	93	94	95	96	97	98	99	100
101	102	103	104	105	106	107	108	109	110
111	112	113	114	115	116	117	118	119	120

Tens Cards

	10	20	30
40	50	60	70
80	90	+	−
=	<	>	☐

Digit Cards

0	1	2	3
4	5	6	7
8	9	+	−
=	<	>	☐

10 More, 10 Less

20 + 10 = _____	**40 − 10 = _____**
10 + 10 = _____	**20 − 10 = _____**
30 + 10 = _____	**60 − 10 = _____**
40 + 10 = _____	**30 − 10 = _____**
20 + 10 = _____	**70 − 10 = _____**
50 + 10 = _____	**50 − 10 = _____**
70 + 10 = _____	**80 − 10 = _____**
10 + 10 = _____	**90 − 10 = _____**
80 + 10 = _____	**40 − 10 = _____**
40 + 10 = _____	**70 − 10 = _____**
60 + 10 = _____	**20 − 10 = _____**
50 + 10 = _____	**60 − 10 = _____**
90 + 10 = _____	**50 − 10 = _____**
30 + 10 = _____	**90 − 10 = _____**
80 + 10 = _____	**30 − 10 = _____**

Place-Value Mat

Tens	Ones

Practice Adding Tens

	My Work
60 + 35 = ____	
____ = 27 + 20	
____ = 10 + 19	
16 + 40 = ____	
50 + 21 = ____	
____ = 44 + 30	
23 + 70 = ____	
____ = 10 + 72	
18 + 20 = ____	
10 + 52 = ____	

Practice Adding Tens and Ones

	My Work
14 + 22 = _____	
_____ = 74 + 14	
35 + 21 = _____	
43 + 24 = _____	
_____ = 85 + 12	
51 + 23 = _____	
21 + 25 = _____	
63 + 22 = _____	
_____ = 17 + 11	
31 + 42 = _____	

Practice Regrouping to Add

	My Work
18 + 38 = ____	
29 + 28 = ____	
36 + 47 = ____	
47 + 25 = ____	
58 + 36 = ____	
21 + 19 = ____	
38 + 27 = ____	
48 + 43 = ____	
29 + 29 = ____	

Name: _____

Shapes 1

rectangle	**triangle**	**hexagon**
 4 sides 4 square corners opposite sides equal	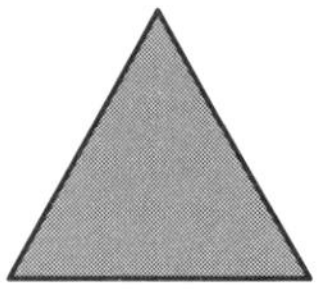 3 sides 3 corners	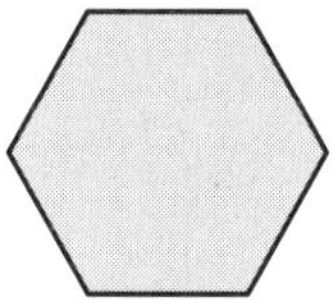 6 sides 6 corners
Any shape with 4 sides and 4 corners	**square** 4 equal sides 4 square corners	**rhombus** 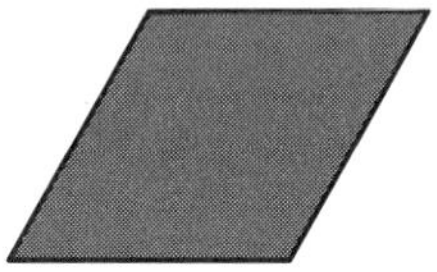 4 equal sides 4 corners
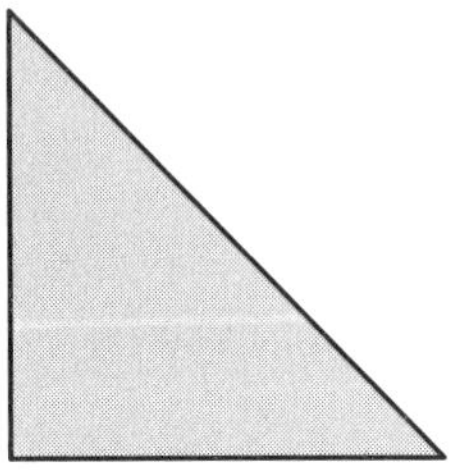	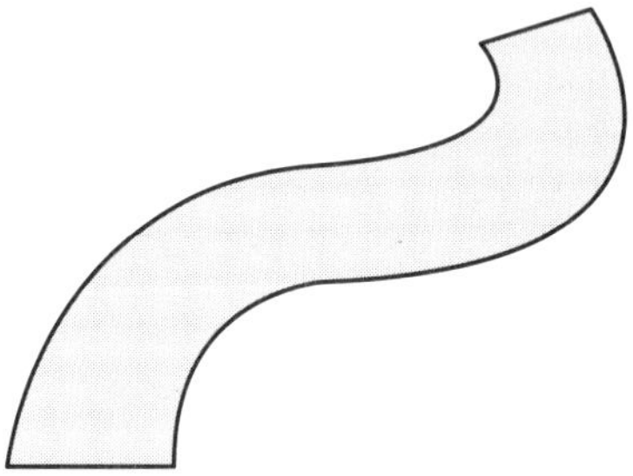	
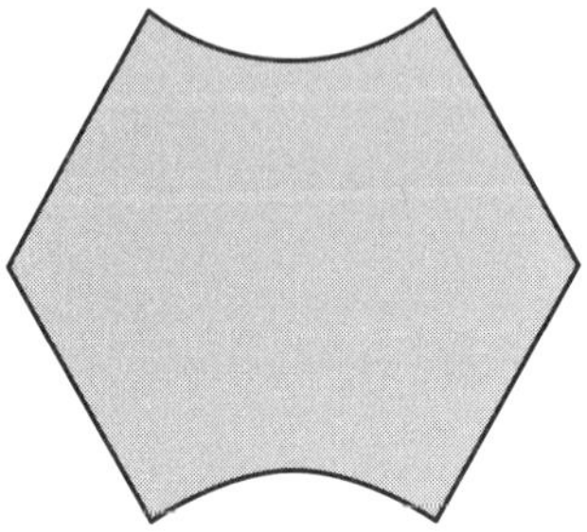	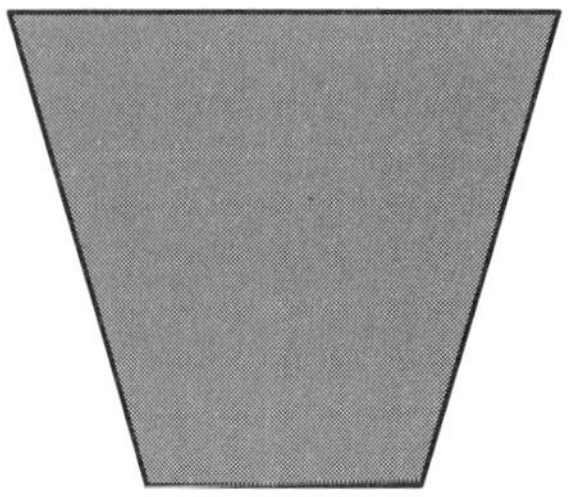	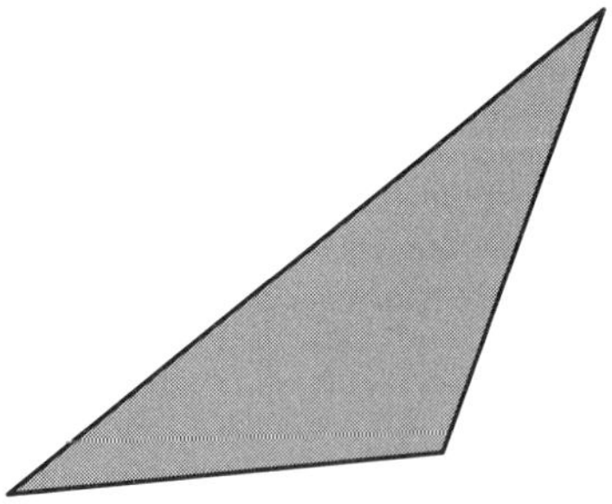

Name: _____

Shapes 1 (continued)

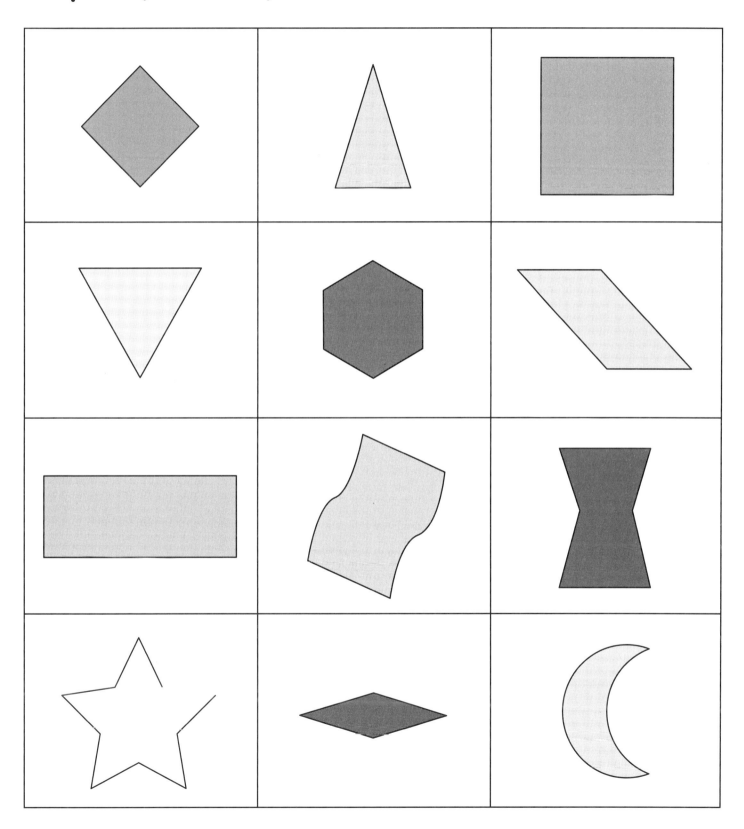

Shapes 2

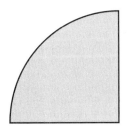  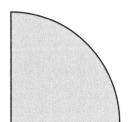 

 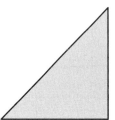 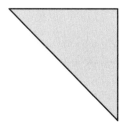 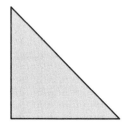

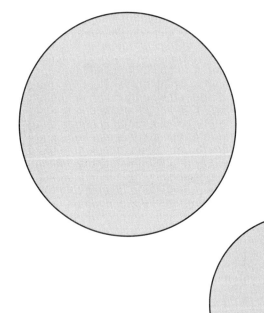 

Pattern Blocks

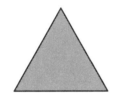
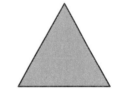

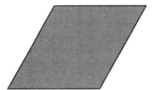

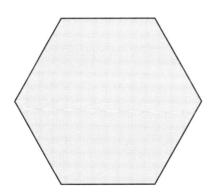
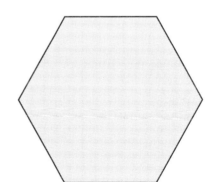

Name: _____

Data Cards

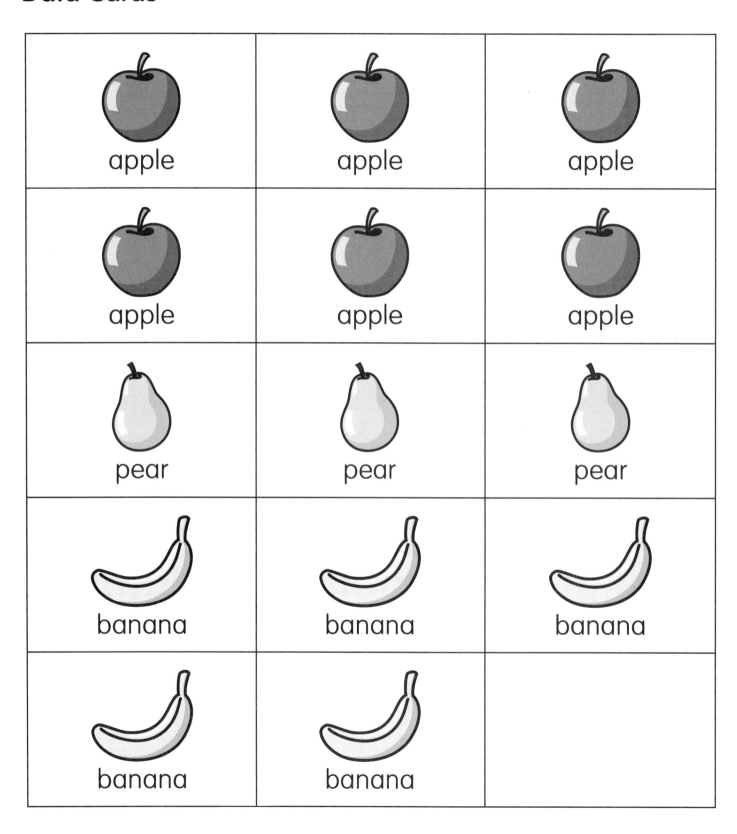

Chart Template

Practice Adding Three Numbers

	My Work
4 + 5 + 6 = ____	
8 + 4 + 2 = ____	
5 + 7 + 5 = ____	
3 + 9 + 7 = ____	
6 + 4 + 6 = ____	
9 + 7 + 1 = ____	
2 + 8 + 8 = ____	
5 + 3 + 5 = ____	
9 + 2 + 1 = ____	
7 + 7 + 6 = ____	

Practice Making a Ten to Add

Change each number sentence to have 10 as one addend.
Write the totals.

Example:
5 + **8** = _13_
_3_ + _10_ = _13_

---

9 + **6** = _____ ____ + ____ = _____	**7** + **9** = _____ ____ + ____ = _____
8 + **4** = _____ ____ + ____ = _____	**6** + **8** = _____ ____ + ____ = _____
9 + **9** = _____ ____ + ____ = _____	**8** + **7** = _____ ____ + ____ = _____
4 + **7** = _____ ____ + ____ = _____	**9** + **8** = _____ ____ + ____ = _____

Make Equal Facts

Write numbers in the boxes to make true number sentences.

Example:

13 = 13

$\boxed{6}$ + $\boxed{7}$ = $\boxed{8}$ + $\boxed{5}$

---

13 = 13

$\square$ + $\square$ = $\square$ + $\square$

12 = 12

$\square$ + $\square$ = $\square$ + $\square$

---

16 = 16

$\square$ + $\square$ = $\square$ + $\square$

10 = 10

$\square$ + $\square$ = $\square$ + $\square$

---

8 = 8

$\square$ + $\square$ = $\square$ + $\square$

6 = 6

$\square$ + $\square$ = $\square$ + $\square$

---

7 = 7

$\square$ + $\square$ = $\square$ + $\square$

9 = 9

$\square$ + $\square$ = $\square$ + $\square$

Name: _____

Measuring Tools

Clock Face

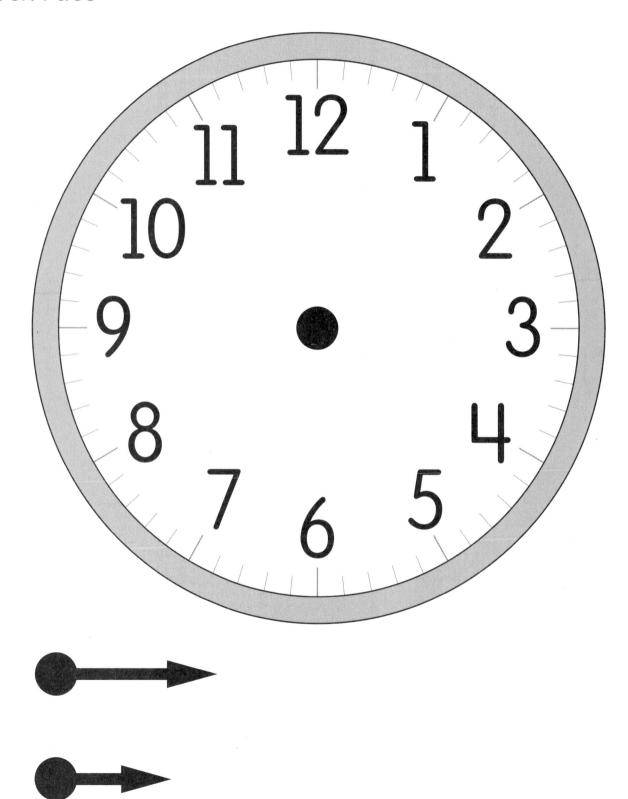